Praise for 7

"I will not be shy. I consider *Time Loops* to be the most significant intellectual work on a paranormal topic in the last fifty years, since Jacques Vallee's *Passport to Magonia* (1969), to be precise. Not only does Eric Wargo show us how strong the evidence for precognition really is—already a major accomplishment. He gives us scientific, psychological, and interpretive tools for thinking about these phenomena in strikingly original ways. In the process—the real stunner for me—he points us toward (or looks back from) the future of knowledge, a future in which the humanities are as crucial as the sciences. Buckle up tight and get ready for the roller coaster ride of your life. And why not? As Wargo shows us with astonishing rigor and humor, these 'time loops' may well *be* our lives."

— JEFFREY J. KRIPAL, AUTHOR OF *MUTANTS AND MYSTICS* AND *SECRET BODY* AND CO-AUTHOR OF *CHANGED IN A FLASH*

* * *

"Precognition is the genie that can't be put back in the bottle. Eric Wargo writes with epic breadth, keen observation, deep rigor, and—above all—great integrity on a topic of innate controversy. He succeeds gloriously in providing this century's first historical and analytic overview of precognition and its causes. You will be hearing much more about this field—and this writer."

— MITCH HOROWITZ, PEN AWARD-WINNING AUTHOR OF *OCCULT AMERICA* AND *THE MIRACLE CLUB*

* * *

"For those who wonder if experiences of precognition are real, or perhaps just coincidences or mistakes of memory, *Time Loops* provides a well written, balanced overview of the latest scientific interpretations of these mind-bending phenomena. Spoiler alert: Based on an increasing body of experimental evidence, yes, precognition is real."

— DEAN RADIN, AUTHOR OF *ENTANGLED MINDS* AND *REAL MAGIC*

* * *

"*Time Loops* is the definitive inquiry into cases of people who remember their future. Eric Wargo is the Sherlock Holmes of retrocausation."

— NICK HERBERT, AUTHOR OF *QUANTUM REALITY* AND *FASTER THAN LIGHT*

TIME LOOPS

Precognition, Retrocausation, and the Unconscious

Eric Wargo

ANOMALIST BOOKS
San Antonio * Charlottesville

An Original Publication of ANOMALIST BOOKS
**Time Loops: Precognition, Retrocausation,
and the Unconscious**
Copyright 2018 by Eric Wargo
ISBN: 978-1938398926
Second Edition

Cover Art: lvcandy/iStock
Book Design: Seale Studios

For information about the publisher, go to AnomalistBooks.com,
or write to:
Anomalist Books, 5150 Broadway #108, San Antonio, TX 78209

Acknowledgments xi

Introduction: Beyond Folk Causality
(or, One Damn Thing *Before* Another) 1

PART ONE: WELCOME TO THE NOT YET

1. The Size of the Impossible—Disasters, Prophecy,
   and Hindsight 17

2. "If I Were You, I'd Stay on the Ground for a Couple
   of Days"—Victor Goddard, J. W. Dunne,
   and the Block Universe 43

3. Postcards from Your Future Self—Scientific Evidence
   for Precognition 63

4. The Psi Reflex—Presentiment and the Future-
   Influencing-Present Effect 79

PART TWO: "HOW CAN THIS BE?"

5. Catching Precognitive Butterflies—Chaos, Memory,
   and *Premory* in the Thermodynamic Universe 99

6. *Destination: Pong* (or, How to Build a Quantum™
   Future Detector) 121

7. A New Era of Hyperthought—From Precognitive
   Bacteria to Our Tesseract Brain 147

PART THREE: TIME'S TABOOS

8. Sometimes a Causal Arrow Isn't Just a Causal Arrow—
   Oedipus, Freud, and the Repression of Prophecy   175

9. Wyrd and Wishes—Metabolizing the Future in Dreams   201

10. Prophetic *Jouissance*—Trauma, Survival, and the
    Precognitive Sublime   233

PART FOUR: LIVES OF THE PRECOGS

11. A Precognitive Seduction—Maggy Quarles van Ufford,
    Carl Jung, and the Scarab   255

12. Fate, Free Will, and *Futility*—Morgan Robertson's
    Tiresias Complex   279

13. "P.S. What Scares Me Most, Claudia, Is That I Can Often
    Recall *the Future*"—The Memetic Prophecies of
    Philip K. Dick   295

14. The Arrival of Meaning and the Creation of the Past 317

    Postscript: A Ruin from the Future   335

    Notes   345

    References   395

    Index   421

For Laura and Emily

Surely you don't disbelieve the prophecies,
because you had a hand in bringing them about yourself?
— J. R. R. Tolkien, *The Hobbit* (1937)

ACKNOWLEDGMENTS

My thinking on time, causation, and precognition has been shaped and honed by many discussions over the past several years with friends and readers of my blog *The Nightshirt*, some of whom have shared stunning, sometimes funny, sometimes heartbreaking personal experiences of their own. Most will remain anonymous, but I must single out for thanks a few friends and e-friends who have especially helped me by pointing me to ideas or writings I didn't know about, by posing keen questions, and sometimes by needed opposition and push-back: Adam Elenbaas, Walter Johnson, Chris Savia, Alex van Oss, and "Vortex." Nick Herbert also provided valuable feedback on a draft of this book and pointed me to some physics material I had missed, for which I am deeply grateful.

I also thank Jeffrey Kripal for his encouragement of my work, for his comments on my manuscript, and for our ongoing dialogue about things paranormal. History will look very kindly on Jeff for bringing these subjects into the light of serious, sympathetic, scholarly inquiry. The more I research anomalous phenomena and "time loops," the more I am actually pained by the arrogant, condescending, sometimes hostile dismissal of these subjects by cultural authorities—a predictable reaction that has contributed to a long climate of silence and embarrassment around a fascinating dimension of human experience. Jeff's work is changing the conversation, creating what I hope (and believe) is a real shift toward greater openness and acceptance.

I especially thank Patrick Huyghe, my editor at Anomalist Books, who has been a strong advocate for my ideas since the start and who has long encouraged me to write a book. Our many conversations over the past few years have hugely helped me clarify what I wanted to say. He also came up with the title.

The biggest thank-you goes to my wife, Laura, and our daughter, Emily, for their long suffering and putting up with my need for quiet solitude in the evenings and on weekends, when we could have been "doing something fun."

Beyond Folk Causality
(or, One Damn Thing *Before* Another)

*Our element is eternal immaturity. The things that we
think, feel, and say today will necessarily seem foolish to
our grandchildren; so it would surely be better to forestall
this now, and treat them as if they were foolish already...*

— Witold Gombrowicz, *Ferdydurke* (1937)

Thiotimoline is an aromatic compound extracted from the bark of
the shrub *Rosacea Karlsbadensis rufo*. First isolated and described by
Russian botanists in the 1930s, its properties baffled Soviet and American
scientists for well over a decade. The extract, a whitish crystalline
powder, dissolved so fast when water was added to it that they had to
devise a new measuring instrument to measure its solubility accurately.
What they found was stunning, and at first, totally unbelievable: Thiotimoline
dissolves 1.12 seconds *before* water touches it.

The question chemists always asked about thiotimoline effectively
personified or anthropomorphized the substance: How did it "know"
when, or if, water was going to be added?

Thiotimoline's ultrafast solubility, dubbed "endochronicity" by the
Russians, met with so much initial skepticism in the chemical community

that very little further investigation was done on this compound until the early 1950s, when the reasons for its extraordinary behavior were finally discovered through a technique called crystallography.

Thiotimoline is an organic molecule, which means that it contains a carbon atom bonded to other atoms. Carbon forms four such *valence bonds*, positioned at each point of a tetrahedron. What the Soviet chemists discovered was that the carbon atom in thiotimoline is somewhat different than other carbon atoms: Two of its carbon valence bonds extend across the *temporal dimension*, not a spatial dimension. It means that one of its bonds is slightly in the molecule's past, and another is in the molecule's *future*. This accounts for thiotimoline's curious property of dissolving slightly before water touches it.

Eventually the "endochronometer" devised to measure the rate of thiotimoline's dissolution became more interesting than the plant extract by itself, due to the many possible real-world applications of performing measurements on a four-dimensional molecule. Think about it: If the adding versus not adding of water to a lump of chemical could somehow be tied to an outcome having real-world relevance—the weather, the winner of a horse race, the success of a satellite launch, or the attacks of an enemy in war—then a genuine predictor of future events was within grasp. Although 1.12 seconds is not much forewarning of an event, chaining together a lot of endochronometers (each with their little lumps of thiotimoline) would greatly enlarge that narrow window and create the world's first precognitive circuit—what researchers called a "telechronic battery."

Unfortunately, human nature being what it is, it did not take long to figure out that such a device could be turned into a very destructive weapon. Interceding to *prevent* contact with water after the thiotimoline in a telechronic battery dissolved caused an Atlantic hurricane to suddenly change course and obliterate the lab and the battery, fulfilling its chemical prophecy and ensuring that no paradox (or what one researcher called "Heisenberg Failure") occurred.

Thiotimoline is fictional, of course—an ingenious hoax perpetrated by Isaac Asimov in a series of faux-journal articles, beginning with "The Endochronic Properties of Resublimated Thiotimoline" in the March 1948 issue of *Astounding Science Fiction*.[1] The young writer was then a graduate student in chemistry and wanted to give himself practice writing for his dissertation by doing a story in the utterly humorless style of a journal article. He followed up his tour de force with his 1953 "The

Micropsychiatric Applications of Thiotimoline" and then "Thiotimoline and the Space Age" in 1960.

It made for a fun thought experiment. But it was also remarkably prescient of real discoveries in physics that have been made over just the last decade. In 2009, for example, a research team at the University of Rochester used a high-precision sensor to measure how much a mirror was deflected by the photons in a laser beam, and then measured a portion of the photons a second time. The photons subjected to a second measurement were found to have deflected the mirror *previously* much more than the portion that didn't get the second measurement.[2] It suggested that that second measurement amplified those photons *in their past*.

There should really be a row of about twenty exclamation marks following that last sentence.

For over three centuries, our expectations about cause and effect have been dominated by the way objects like elementary particles "hit" other particles and deflect them, in sequence—the mechanical billiard-ball "action and reaction" that Isaac Newton codified in 1687 as his Laws of Motion. Objects move through space, carrying a certain amount of energy with them, and imparting that energy to other objects they interact with. It's an assumption that works well for predicting most of the things we encounter in our daily lives, like bodies and billiard balls, icebergs and ocean liners, and for creating machines. And it is why the natural-science worldview that arose in the Enlightenment was called *mechanism*, seeing the world as a big machine.

But it has long been known that the machine view doesn't hold in all situations, or at the smallest scales. On the scale of atoms and photons, a frustrating unpredictability was found to reign. For instance, while you can predict when half the atoms in a lump of radioactive material like uranium-235 will decay (i.e., its half-life), you cannot predict when a single uranium-235 atom will decay; it is completely random. About a century ago it became the central dogma of the new field of quantum physics that this randomness imposed strict limits to how much an experimenter can know about a physical system. Any given fact about a particle, such as its position or its velocity, had to be regarded as *uncertain*, taking the form of a vague smear of probabilities, until someone actually performed an experiment and got a result. The dominant interpretation of quantum mechanics for most of the past century has been glossed by the term "Copenhagen Interpretation," a rough consensus some of the field's big names reached in the mid-1920s that a particle has no fixed, determinate reality unless and until it is observed.

But recently, an alternative, even more mind-bending but also more elegant interpretation is winning a growing number of converts. That's the idea that what looks to our human eyes random or uncertain (because we cannot predict it other than statistically) may actually reflect the effects of unseen influences of the future, acting "backward" on the present. For instance, the precise amount each photon deflected the mirror in the Rochester experiment seemed to be influenced by the *next* thing the photon interacted with after it bounced off the mirror. Experiments like this—we will learn about some others later in this book—are actually shaking the foundations of physics and vindicating Albert Einstein, who famously could not accept that God would be so unclassy as to turn His universe into a giant craps table. What seemed for all the world like randomness—blind chance—may really be the previously unseen influence of particles' *future histories* on their present behavior. *Retrocausation*, in other words.

We may be on the verge of a massive shift in how we view time, causality, and information. Classical causality, the one-thing-after-another billiard-ball world of Isaac Newton and his Enlightenment friends, is being revealed as *folk causality*, a cultural construct and a belief system, not the way things really are.

Could physics' new two-way perspective on the behavior of matter at a fundamental level have anything to teach us about human behavior?

Consider a highly publicized 2011 article by Cornell University psychologist Daryl Bem, called "Feeling the Future."[3] Unlike "The Endochronic Properties of Resublimated Thiotimoline," this was not a hoax or a fiction, but in many respects it was similar to Asimov's story, in that it described an apparently time-defying behavior, this time not of water-soluble organic molecules but of Cornell University undergraduates.

Turns out that if you put 100 Ivy League kids in front of a computer and ask them to guess which of two "curtains" on the screen hides a picture, they tend to be correct more often than chance would predict when the not-yet-shown picture is explicitly erotic—of "couples engaged in nonviolent but explicit consensual sexual acts" (according to the description they read prior to signing the consent form). The students' accuracy did not deviate from chance when the pictures were of boring romantic but nonsexual scenes, like couples kissing or a wedding. Unknown to the participants, the correct answer and the type of picture—erotic or neutral—were randomly selected by the computer *after* the students made their choice.

Bem's picture-guessing experiment was one of nine he had conducted during the first decade of this millennium, all of which reversed the causal direction in four basic paradigms in psychology, including *reinforcement* (what the above example was testing), *priming* (subliminal influences on behavior), *habituation* (the tendency of familiarity to breed disinterest), and *facilitation of recall* (or the reinforcing effects of repeated exposure on learning). Eight of his nine experiments produced statistically significant but "impossible" results from the standpoint of unilinear causality.[4] For example, students preferentially remembered words in a word-learning task that they were exposed to again *after* the test. (Again, picture a row of about 20 exclamation points.) But while it made headlines and even got Bem onto the *Colbert Report*, the paper sparked a flurry of hostility, embarrassment, and ridicule from across psychology and other scientific fields, and the ridicule continues to this day. Just Google "Daryl Bem" and you'll get a taste of it.

Bem's article was controversial not just because of what he purported to find—as we will see, he was only the latest in a long line of serious researchers to report time-defying psychological effects in carefully controlled laboratory studies—but because he had the poor taste of publishing his causally perverse results in one of the highest-ranking journals in psychology, the *Journal of Personality and Social Psychology*. Although his paper passed peer review, the ritual that traditionally sorts the scientific wheat from the chaff, and although Bem was a very well-respected experimental psychologist with a long track record of solid science in other areas like self-perception and attitude formation, the journal's editors felt compelled to publish an editorial comment addressing readers' inevitable concerns:

> We openly admit that the reported findings conflict with our own beliefs about causality and that we find them extremely puzzling. Yet, as editors we were guided by the conviction that this paper—as strange as the findings may be—should be evaluated just as any other manuscript on the basis of rigorous peer review. Our obligation as journal editors is not to endorse particular hypotheses but to advance and stimulate science through a rigorous review process.[5]

The editors' reference to "beliefs about causality" highlights an important point. Causality is part of our belief system, and beliefs have a cultural basis, not just an empirical one. Ours is the first and only society in history to not—at least not officially—make a place in its story of causality for sensing or knowing events in the future, and more generally for the *teleological* relevance of "final causes" in explaining human affairs. Yet ordinary people in all walks of life, in every culture on Earth (including our own) and throughout recorded history, have reported getting forewarnings of traumatic or threatening events, commonly called *premonitions*; and many religious traditions make a place for the ability of certain individuals to speak or even write about future events, commonly called *prophecy*. On top of that, many researchers besides Bem have accumulated masses of robust and compelling evidence for the human capacity to unconsciously sense or feel the future, or *presentiment*. The term *precognition*, which means knowing or perceiving future events in some fashion other than through normal inference, is an umbrella term that is often used to encompass the rest.

Packing to Leave

I'll warn you right now: Precognition, prophecy, premonition, presentiment—I will use these overlapping terms somewhat interchangeably although generally remaining consistent with their specific connotations—is a touchy subject. People can react unpredictably when things go "the wrong way." You've heard the woodsman's advice, don't get between a bear and her cubs? Well, don't get between a modern, science-literate person and their beliefs about causality. The result is liable to be condescension, ridicule, or worse. Again, just go on Google or Wikipedia and you will see what I mean: Like the filthy brown cloud around the Peanuts character Pigpen, a cloud of epithets like "baloney" and "hogwash" and "pseudoscience" attaches itself to ESP, precognition, and related subjects wherever they appear in polite society, along with the implication that people who believe in or experience these things are sadly self-deceived.[6] The subject of precognition is, as physicist Daniel P. Sheehan puts it, "beyond the pale of polite discussion."[7] The Dutch psychologist Eric-Jan Wagenmakers, upon reading Bem's article, reported that he had to keep putting it away: "Reading it made me physically unwell."[8]

Thus, while researching and writing this book, I did not tell very many people what I was working on.

But on several occasions, friends and acquaintances who learned of my interests were eager to tell their own experiences. I ended up, unexpectedly, with a not-unimpressive dataset of experiences from my social circle in Washington, DC, and from readers of my blog *The Nightshirt*, who shared stories with me in emails. My rule in this book has been to use only public, published sources and not, for instance, any of my own precognitive dreams (with one exception in the Postscript); and most of the "ethnographic" material I collected is too personal, or too sad in a couple cases, to share anyway. But it feels appropriate to tell a couple anecdotes here (with permission) to set the stage for our journey through the topic of precognition and the "loopy" ways it influences our lives.

A Washington, DC, software engineer and artist in her mid-30s, whom I will call Anne, told me in an interview about a series of experiences that had occurred in her late teens and twenties, specifically dreams in which, she said, "I knew something I couldn't possibly know—typically, that someone I knew had passed away."

One of these dreams occurred the first few weeks of her freshman year of college. Anne dreamed of encountering her ex-boyfriend's father on the steps of an academic building on her campus. "There was a big glass door, and he had just walked up the steps and was about to walk through the doors. He turned around and looked at me and looked down to where I was standing and said, 'Well, bye!' And he had his hands in his pockets and his glasses were on and he was really peaceful, and he walked through the glass door." As soon as she woke up, she said she knew that this had been a symbol somehow. She found out later that day that her ex's father had died. She knew that he had been a professor at a different university, and thus encountering him in her dream on her own campus made a kind of symbolic sense. She also knew that he had recently been diagnosed with a slow-growing cancer but that he was expected to live a few more years, so this death was not expected.

A few years later, after college, Anne recalled waking early one weekend morning to go to the bathroom and passing the open door of her roommate, who was busy packing his suitcase. She asked him what he was doing, and he said that he was going home to be with his family because his uncle had just died. Anne did not know her roommate's uncle, but did vaguely know, from something her roommate had mentioned months earlier, that his uncle was ill. She said she was terribly sorry and went back to bed.

She awoke what felt like maybe an hour later and found her room-mate still packing his bag, still on his bed, just as she'd seen him before. She was surprised that he had not already left to drive to his family's house.

She said, "I'm so sorry to hear about your uncle, again," and her roommate looked startled—he blanched—and said, "How did you know about that?"

She said, "You told me this morning, when I woke up earlier, that your uncle died."

"We didn't talk this morning," he said.

Anne realized at that moment that she had only dreamed of awakening the first time.

In her late twenties, Anne also had a series of dreams of seeing the home of a close childhood friend, from above, as though approaching it in a hot air balloon. She had lost contact with the friend about a year earlier but felt that these dreams somehow symbolized that something was wrong in that house—perhaps an illness or death in the family. She later learned that her friend had died of an opioid overdose. Anne did not know that her friend had started using drugs and had become addicted during the last two or three years of her life.

In the course of corresponding about precognition and this book-in-progress with Jeffrey Kripal, a Rice University historian of religion and a leading scholar of the paranormal, Jeff shared with me an experience of his own that was remarkably similar to Anne's dream about her room-mate, although in Jeff's case the context was more amusing than sad.

Jeff described how he had recently been compiling an archive at his university related to paranormal phenomena. In the course of this effort, he had received an envelope from a retired Pentagon employee who had accumulated a large library on UFOs and was planning to donate it to the archive.

Jeff wrote: "I opened it and saw that it was a brief essay he had written about his one and only paranormal experience. I did not have time to read the essay, so I tucked it into my schedule book."

Jeff was too busy to read the essay because he was about to leave on vacation. When he returned, he found the envelope. Except … it was still sealed. "It had never been opened. I looked and looked at each edge, expecting to find a scissor cut. Nothing. More puzzled, I cut it open and found what I 'remembered'—an essay on his one and only paranormal experience (a partial levitation). I was more puzzled by the memory than the levitation."

Examples like this, especially since they are so trivial, will readily be ignored or dismissed by skeptics as false memories, hindsight bias, or simple déjà vu, an erroneous signal of familiarity attached to a novel experience. (Those of a more paranoid disposition may instead suggest that Jeff really did open the letter, just as he remembered, but that the trickster-like forces that really run the show re-sealed the envelope afterward.) I will be arguing that skeptics' claims—about the biases that distort our perceptions, for instance—sometimes do not hold up against masses of compelling evidence, including laboratory evidence, that something about our cognition—or our consciousness, if you prefer that term—really transcends the present moment. Premonitory dreams, weird "memories" of things that haven't happened yet, and other odd experiences in which we seem to overtake ourselves in time may reflect that we genuinely *think across the fourth dimension*, not unlike Asimov's thiotimoline molecule.

Anomalous experiences frequently are reported in the context of stress. In the aftermath of Hurricane Harvey, which devastated coastal areas of Texas at the end of August, 2017, a Houston woman I will call Michele contacted me after reading an article I had written on precognition. She found my article when searching the internet for information that might illuminate something baffling she had experienced that day, as she and the rest of her city were trying to return to normal existence in the aftermath of the flooding that had ruined so many homes and lives.

Michele described how she had been feeling stressed and ungrounded when she went to run some errands, including a trip to the post office. The traffic was terrible, as a friend had even warned her before she left, but at the post office she found an empty parking space right in front of the building. But at that point, a voice inside her head said, "Don't park here. You might hit a car when you back out." She then had the thought, "Do I have my insurance card?"

Disregarding this warning voice, Michele parked in the spot anyway. Later, when she was backing out, she collided with another car that was doing the same thing. She then discovered that, indeed, she did not have her insurance card.

It was not the first time Michele had failed to heed her own driving-related premonitions. She told me about a similar, weirdly *fractal* experience in which she had been driving with a friend and in fact telling that friend about *another* friend's accurate premonition of a motorcycle accident, when she approached a red light. She had just finished telling the story, when her inner voice told her to run the red light. Although she safely could have done so, her "better judgment" censored the impulse to violate traffic safety rules, and she pulled to a stop ... at which point her car was rear-ended. "So, there I was telling a story about the importance of heeding precognitive warnings, and then I didn't heed my own! That is, assuming it was even possible for me to heed it."

These puzzling experiences, among others, led Michele to question deeply our culture's folk causality, and even the central dogma of free will: "I've been thinking that the future may affect the past or present and that perhaps free will is an illusion (or at least different than what we think)." Indeed, the collision in the post office parking lot led her to a conclusion very similar to what I will be arguing in this book: "What if the premonition of the accident was the direct result of the accident itself, especially the traumatic emotions I felt? In other words, if the accident never happened, then maybe I could not have been forewarned."

A favorite story genre in books on ESP are "catastrophes averted" because of some premonitory warning such as a dream.[9] We will see in this book that premonitions that go unheeded or are impossible to heed are just as (if not more) common and raise troubling questions in the minds of those who experience them. "What's the use of a premonition if it can't be used to prevent or avert a disaster?" is an obvious one. I will be arguing that precognition, premonition, prophecy may not be what we think they are, and that even when they seem to warn us of traumas, accidents, or catastrophes on the road ahead, and may even prepare us for them, they are really about our future *survival* of events that throw our lives, or at least our emotions, into upheaval. They may even orient us toward subtle emotional rewards that can occur in the context of those upheavals.

After Michele backed into another car in the parking lot of the Houston post office, she got out and faced the other driver. "At first, his look was hard, maybe anger, maybe anguish," she said. Even though she did not know who was at fault, Michele told him "I'm so sorry. There's just so much stress with all that's been happening."

She said the other driver's look softened. "Don't worry about it," he said. "This will all be taken care of. I just lost my house and everything in the flood."

"That's when I started crying and couldn't stop," she said, and she and the other driver held each other's arms—"a brief moment of loving acceptance. It was beautiful."

I suggested to Michele that the voice in her head before taking that parking spot may not have been trying to warn her against a course of action but could, in some weird way, have oriented her *toward* that rewarding moment of human connection in the context of the stress everyone in her city was feeling. After all, a car accident easily remedied through insurance is small potatoes when set against the devastation of homes, and the net gain in this event was a needed moment of meaningful human connection—and at least for Michele, a fascinating precognitive experience.

Although precognition often surfaces to awareness in the context of stress and trauma, even death in many cases, I will argue that it really orients us ultimately to life, and to a renewed, intensified awareness of being alive.

In Part One of this book, we will see numerous examples of precognition and what I am calling *time loops*: baffling, causally circular situations in which a precognitive experience partly contributes to the fulfillment of the precognized event—what is sometimes called a "self-fulfilling prophecy." In addition to anecdotal claims of precognition and a fascinating, semi-scientific investigation of the subject by a pioneer aeronautical engineer a century ago, we will also see how laboratory evidence strongly (in fact, overwhelmingly) lends support to the possible verity of the anecdotal claims: Information from our future somehow appears able to exert an influence over our behavior, albeit usually in oblique, non-obvious ways. That it so often seems to operate outside of conscious awareness suggests that precognition may be a very primitive, basic guidance system, one that could be shared widely in the animal kingdom.

In Part Two, we will examine the "how," the physics and biology that might make such a thing possible. Not only is retrocausation being demonstrated in physics experiments like the one mentioned earlier, but various lines of evidence from fields like quantum computing and quantum biology make it increasingly plausible that biological systems may, within limits, be able to "pre-spond" to future stimuli. Exactly how it works is still speculative, but precognition is no longer absurd from a materialist scientific standpoint, the way it was even just a decade or two ago. The brain may well turn out to be an organ that extracts meaning from an otherwise noisy, but constant, informational reflux from the *Not Yet*.

The Not Yet is a term I use for the unknown-but-soon-to-be-known future: something that is on its way, about to arrive, and that brings with it understanding—such as the meaning of a baffling dream, or the confirmation of a hunch. Precognition, I will argue, is about our strange relationship to the Not Yet, orienting us toward increased understanding and meaning coming down the pike.

Even if such a possibility is increasingly scientifically thinkable (if not fully explainable), anything that upsets the one-way folk-causal order of things is *really hard* to wrap our heads around. When it comes to matters of time and causality, we are all a bit like A. A. Milne's Winnie-the-Pooh—we are "bears of little brain." Besides being plain difficult, it is almost as if precognition has a force field around it, a dense and intimidating fog of *taboo*, tending to deflect even people who notice its operation in their own lives onto a course of denial or forgetfulness. When people experience dreams that relate uncannily to imminent experiences, for example, they will often grasp at other explanations—preferring even to think that they are just crazy or self-deceived—rather than actually cut through the thickets of illogic around these phenomena and try to understand them.

Because precognition is taboo, the perfect place to look for guidance in traversing the fog of unreason that surrounds it is the original science of unreason and taboos, psychoanalysis, the subject of Part Three. Since the psychoanalytic clinic is a context where real people's lives, dreams, and thoughts are subjected to close scrutiny and have sometimes been written down in great detail, the case studies of Sigmund Freud and other pioneers in this controversial realm of human inquiry provide a rich trove of data on precognition. And interestingly, Freud himself turns out to have been, without knowing or acknowledging it, a "precog" *par excellence*. His most famous dream, for example, turns out to have startlingly foreshadowed the illness that would claim his life decades later. Freud's own explicit denial of the possibility of precognition could even be seen as his tragic flaw, making his life a fascinating case study of a man haunted by time loops he could not or would not confront.

Precog was a term coined by the science-fiction writer Philip K. Dick, who wrote a lot about precognition because it seemed to be a constant and baffling feature in his own life. To really understand precognition, we have to place these experiences within the context of the individual's life story. Fortunately, both psychotherapeutic case studies and the world of letters provide countless examples of odd and interesting time loops caught in amber, enabling us in many cases to take a biographical approach to studying the phenomenon. Over the course of this book we will see several striking time loops from the lives of famous writers and other artists, and in Part Four, we will look closely at how precognitive experiences shaped the biographies of three people: Phil Dick, a turn-of-the-century sea adventure writer named Morgan Robertson, and a highly precognitive patient of Carl Jung named Maggy Quarles van Ufford (the until-recently anonymous woman at the center of the famous scarab story, the centerpiece of Jung's writings on synchronicity).

What the psychoanalytic and literary cases all strongly suggest is that precognition is not seeing or getting some glimpse of future events "out there" in objective reality. Rather, it is an engagement with personally meaningful realizations or learning experiences ahead in a person's own life. Sometimes those future realizations pertain directly to the circumstances in which a premonition or a dream first occurred, giving a genuinely loop-like structure to our lives and thoughts. I will even suggest that what since Freud's day has been described as the neurosis- and creativity-generating "unconscious mind" may really be our waking consciousness displaced in time.

I began with a story about a lump of dissolving crystalline powder, so I will conclude with another one. Early in the last century, the philosopher Henri Bergson wanted to awaken his readers to the unfolding of matter in time. He argued that when we imagine living things and inert objects as existing totally in the present moment, having only spatial characteristics, we cannot understand them fully. In his masterpiece *Creative Evolution*, he used a lump of sugar in a glass of water to illustrate an altered, *intuitive* perception of matter in its *durée*, or continuous unfolding. The way the sugar presents itself at any given moment to our senses, he argued, is just a shadow of its full glory; to fully apprehend it, Bergson wrote, "I must wait until the sugar melts."[10]

I must wait until the sugar melts. Another way of putting it is that the sugar is not just a lump of chemical. It *is* or *has* a story, and stories have beginnings, middles, and ends. Your understanding of the sugar's story can never be complete until you see how things turn out. When you do that, you apprehend the sugar's story in a more complete way ... and you may even detect that that dissolution of the sugar was already included in its prior dry, crystalline state. It might have even influenced that earlier state in some way. That is the possibility we are going to explore in this book—not for sugar, but for people.[11]

PART ONE

Welcome to the Not Yet

"I'm just one hundred and one, five months and a day."

"I can't believe that!" said Alice.

"Can't you?" the Queen said in a pitying tone. "Try again: draw a long breath, and shut your eyes."

Alice laughed. "There's no use trying," she said: "one can't believe impossible things."

"I daresay you haven't had much practice," said the Queen. "When I was your age, I always did it for half-an-hour a day. Why, sometimes I've believed as many as six impossible things before breakfast."

— Lewis Carroll, *Through the Looking-Glass* (1871)

The Size of the Impossible — Disasters, Prophecy, and Hindsight

[I]f we collect enough seemingly "anecdotal" or "anomalous" experiences from different times and places and place them together on a flat and fair comparative table, we can quickly see that these reports are neither anecdotal nor anomalous. We can see that they are actually common occurrences in the species.

— Jeffrey J. Kripal, *The Super Natural* (2015)

Thousands of years ago, in what is now called Greenland, a gentle snow fell on a vast silent white desert, a bitter cold, and totally uninhabited plain. The ice crystals from that snowfall left a thin layer on the landscape and merged with it. Hour by hour, day by day, year by year, century by century, subsequent snowfalls fused with the ones underneath (as they had done for hundreds of thousands of years), building up the ice to a thickness of two miles in places. The enormous weight of the ice pressing downward forced it to extrude sideways, through the gaps in the mountain range that rings the land. One of these ice rivers is called Jakobshavn Ice-Fjord, on Greenland's West coast, and it flows at a rate of about 65 feet a day, toward the cold gray arctic water of Baffin Bay.

Where Jakobshavn presses out into the sea, at low tide, the unsupported weight of the six-mile-wide, half-mile-thick glacier causes it to give birth—the process is called calving. Enormous mountains of ice crash into the roiling water, ponderously roll over, and then spend weeks, months, sometimes even years in a sort of traffic jam of their iceberg siblings before gradually drifting off into deeper waters.[1] They slowly melt as they follow the currents carrying them counterclockwise around Baffin Bay, up past Ellesmere and Devon Islands, then south past Baffin Island. The larger ones make it farther, dying in the relatively warm waters of the North Atlantic Gulf Stream.[2]

The year 1910 was a particularly good one for calving in Greenland because of a stretch of warm wet weather two years earlier. High snowfall in 1908, coupled with increased melting, weakened the glaciers structurally, leading to many more icebergs being birthed at the beginning of the century's second decade.[3] One of the many icebergs that crashed into the water during low tide one day in the spring of 1910—made of snow that may have fallen as long ago as when the boy king Tutankhamun was reigning in Egypt—was big enough to survive the journey around Baffin Bay and south past the coast of Labrador and the Grand Banks of Newfoundland over the next 18 months.

Its journey was slow and lonely. Ships avoid those waters and the icy perils they contain, so only a few hardy humans, hunters from the arctic and Norway, had gazed on it; it was seen mainly by whales and seals and seabirds. But then in April, 1912 this still-massive predator—a couple million tons, but much smaller than it had been at birth two years earlier—drifted at its leisurely pace into the shipping lanes that linked Great Britain and the United States. At this point, its original underbelly, blackened from millennia of scraping across Greenland soil, was now uppermost, jutting about 90 feet into the air in a high central peak flanked by two smaller ones, almost like a great bat. At 11:40 PM on the night of April 14, this big black bat loomed out of the darkness a mile ahead of the biggest ocean liner in history, making its maiden voyage from Southampton, England, to New York, via Cherbourg, France, with 2,224 souls aboard. The *Titanic* was then about 1,000 miles short of its destination, Manhattan.

The huge ship was moving fast, at an overly confident 22.5 knots, and when the lookout spotted the black shape dead ahead, the quartermaster was unable to swerve the ship's massive bulk to avoid a collision. The crew watched horrified as the iceberg scraped across the starboard side of the hull. The vessel was so massive that few passengers even felt the collision, and those on the bridge who knew what had happened were initially optimistic. Systems like automatic electrically powered seals that partitioned the damaged compartments from the rest would keep this "unsinkable" ship afloat. But six of the ship's sixteen compartments were rapidly filling with water, and gradually a grim reality set in: The ship was sinking. And due to a combination of hubris and just plain corner-cutting, the White Star Line, the company that had built this ship, had only provided enough lifeboats to save a third of the passengers.

The decorous pandemonium that ensued has been famously depicted in movies, from Roy Ward Baker's 1958 *A Night to Remember* to James Cameron's 1997 *Titanic*. The women and children who took to the available lifeboats, who watched the floating city up-end in the water and finally break in half, remembered vividly the screams of their husbands and fathers drowning in the water. What was more terrible was the sudden silence when the stern of the ship finally slid into the blackness, less than three hours after the collision, in the early morning hours of April 15.

You could hardly ask for a more definitive demonstration of Newtonian physics than the *Titanic*'s fatal encounter with that iceberg. Objects travel well-understood, predictable paths through space dictated by their own inertia; when they collide, both objects are changed by the energy they bring to the encounter. What happened to the *Titanic* after the collision has been described in countless books and stories and movies, and the wreckage can still be seen on the ocean floor. The iceberg did not come out unscathed either. It was seen and photographed in subsequent days by ships searching the area for survivors. How it was damaged below the waterline is unknown, but above, it sported a great red stripe along its side, which you could imagine was a scar from its battle with the steel leviathan, or blood of the *Titanic*'s passengers. Actually it was fresh red paint, applied in the Harland & Wolff shipyard of Belfast, Ireland, where the ship had been completed nearly a year earlier, and now carried off with the ice.

But those predictable paths through spacetime leading to that event were also predictably *un*predictable. The causal arrows leading to any event are, for practical purposes, infinite. In the vast cosmic ocean of causes and effects—particles intersecting with other particles and changing each other's course—what counts as an "event" at all is purely arbitrary. We could tell the story of any individual snowflake in that multimillion-ton iceberg, the vast majority of them oblivious to the metal object it struck, just as we could tell the story of any rivet in the ship, or any passenger, or the story of any molecule of paint that was transferred from the latter object to the former over the minute they were in contact. That inconceivable multitude of bits of matter, their countless vectors, makes it impossible for anyone besides God—and probably even God—to have predicted the event or precisely how it would unfold.

Quantum physicists, who live in a world of delicate measuring instruments and fundamental particles of matter, call every physical interaction a "measurement." You might say the *Titanic* performed a measurement of that iceberg. *The New York Times*' headline the next day, "TITANIC SINKS FOUR HOURS AFTER HITTING ICEBERG," was the printed, published result.

But almost as if to thumb its nose at physicists and their measurements, a dense fog of "impossible" coincidence hovers over that resolutely Newtonian disaster, making it a perennial object lesson in studies of paranormal or psychic phenomena. A psychiatrist and parapsychological researcher named Ian Stevenson compiled 20 accounts of such coincidences in the *Journal of the American Society for Psychical Research* in the early 1960s.[4] I will cite a handful of examples.

Ten days prior to the *Titanic*'s departure from Southampton, an English businessman who had booked passage on it, Mr. J. Connon Middleton, slipped into a depression. Ordinarily he was not a person who remembered his dreams at all, but he awoke on the morning of March 30 and related to his wife a distressing dream that the ship he was going to be sailing on in ten days' time was "floating on the sea, keel upwards and her passengers and crew swimming around her." His mood darkened further when he had the exact same dream the following night. Not one to change his plans because of a dream or two, no matter how distressing, he simply allowed the matter to gnaw at him. So imagine his relief when he received a cable from his American associates suggesting he postpone his trip. It gave him the excuse he needed to cancel his booking … and saved his life. Friends testified later that he had told them of his dreams and his relief at not traveling on the *Titanic*, prior to the disaster.[5]

In the early evening of April 14, the night of the collision, a Methodist minister in Winnipeg, Manitoba, Reverend Charles Morgan, was making a list of hymns to be sung at his service that night. He nodded off momentarily, and in the hypnagogic half-awake, half-dreaming state that, history shows, produces a remarkable number of creative epiphanies as well as perhaps glimpses of the future, the minister saw the number of a hymn from the hymnal in front of his eyes. The number, and the hymn, were unfamiliar to him, but he took it as a sign and added it to his list. Later, reading from their hymnals, the congregants sang "Hear, Father, While We Pray to Thee, for Those in Peril on the Sea." They had no way of knowing that, at roughly the same time, thousands of miles away in the North Atlantic, passengers in the *Titanic*'s second-class dining room were also singing this same hymn begging God's protection for the souls of seafarers, at the request of one of the passengers, Reverend Ernest Carter. It was a weirdly portentous choice for both ministers, as this was still two hours *before* the *Titanic*'s collision with the iceberg.[6]

Later that same night, a Massachusetts woman named Clara Cook Potter awoke her husband, Baptist Minister Charles Francis Potter, to tell him of a vivid, terrifying dream. "I saw what seemed to be a high structure," she said, "something like an elevated railroad. There were people hanging on the outside of it as if they were holding on by their hands to the top rail of a guard fence. Many of them were in their night-clothes, and they were gradually losing their hold and slipping down the inclined sides of this structure. I felt they were dropping to certain death." The terror they felt, she said, was enough to jolt her awake. Days later, after news of the *Titanic*'s sinking flooded the press and artists reconstructed the scene of the ship's terrified passengers clinging to its tilting rails, Mrs. Potter reported that these depictions where exactly like what she had seen in her dream.[7]

An anonymous member of a traveling acting troupe performing a comedy in a small Northern Illinois town reported to the American Society for Psychical Research (ASPR) that the troupe's manager, Mr. Black, could only be roused from sleep with great difficulty on the morning of April 15. After his worried companions applied towels soaked in cold water to his face, he finally woke "with a wild look in his eyes," and announced: "Folks, something terrible has happened! I saw a large ship sinking and hundreds of people being drowned. You will find it is true because I saw the San Francisco earthquake and fire this same way at the time it happened." When the group arrived at the train depot to depart to their next town, the station agent said, "Folks, I just received word over the telegraph that the big ship *Titanic*, on her maiden voyage, hit an iceberg and sank, drowning hundreds of people." Mr. Black reportedly told his troupe "I told you so," but the witness said none of them ever mentioned another word to each other of the strange affair. (If the account is accurate, the station agent was misreporting the news or had mis-heard it. On the morning of the 15th, it was being reported in the press only that the ship had hit an iceberg. Some reports even said it was being towed to Halifax, Nova Scotia.)[8]

Some people reported peculiar visions related to relatives who had been working or traveling on the *Titanic*. A Vancouver woman, Mrs. Henderson, reported a strange waking dream two days after the *Titanic*'s loss: a vision of her sister-in-law and niece, the wife and daughter of her brother Willie Simpson, who (she then thought) was working on another White Star liner. In a letter to her sister on April 19, she wrote: "I saw Bessie and Nina crying and clinging to one another. I seemed to be in a kind of dream and yet I was wide awake and had not even been thinking of them." Henderson had no way of knowing when she wrote her letter that her brother Willie had been offered and accepted a job on the *Titanic* just before its departure and had perished. She only learned her brother's fate (and the impact of the news on his family) after she sent her letter.[9]

Several seeming prophecies centered on and/or issued from the pen of a distinguished English journalist and avid spiritualist, W. T. Stead, who unlike Mr. Middleton did not cancel his booking on the *Titanic*'s maiden voyage despite several forewarnings. In the 1880s, as editor of *The Pall Mall Gazette*, Stead printed a fictional article about the death of many passengers of a doomed ocean liner, along with his editorial warning: "This is exactly what might take place, and what will take place, if liners are sent to sea short of boats." It certainly could be chalked up to ordinary safety concerns; although in 1892, he wrote another story describing the fatal collision of an ocean liner with an iceberg, after which a sole passenger (the narrator) is rescued by another ship, the real White Star liner *Majestic*, captained by its real captain, Edward J. Smith.[10] Stead turned this story into a novel, *From the Old World to the New*, which was published the following year, in 1893.[11] The real Captain Smith, nearly two decades later, became captain of the *Titanic*, and, of course, went down with his ship. In 1900, Stead also described a premonitory vision of his own death that may have corresponded to the reality in the early morning hours of April 15, 12 years later: "I had a vision of a mob, and this had made me feel that I shall not die in a way common to the most of us, but by violence, and one of many in a throng."[12] Two psychics Stead had been fond of consulting also reported to him premonitions of death or disaster at sea, although he ignored them.[13] (After Stead's death, fellow spiritualists reported communicating with the dead journalist; his spirit allegedly informed one of them that he had asked the ship's orchestra to play "Nearer My God to Thee," but it is known that that tune was not played. It makes a nice story, though.)

Stead was not alone in writing about an ocean liner tragedy involving an iceberg. The most famous *Titanic* "prophecy" by far was a short novel published 14 years earlier, in 1898, by a then-popular sea adventure and science-fiction writer named Morgan Robertson. His novel *Futility* depicts the collision of a remarkably similar luxury liner called *Titan* with an iceberg. Robertson's *Titan* was also making a run between England and New York (returning to England from New York, in the *Titan*'s case), also striking an iceberg on its starboard side, around midnight on an April night in the North Atlantic, and with great loss of life due to an insufficiency of lifeboats. Like the *Titanic*, Robertson's *Titan* had three propellers and two masts and was the largest ocean liner ever built. Whereas 1,520 people perished on the *Titanic*, all but 13 of the *Titan*'s 3,000 passengers perished in Robertson's story. Apart from their names and passenger capacities (the *Titanic* too could hold about 3,000 people), numerous details between the real and fictitious ships align closely:

	RMS *Titanic*	"*Titan*"[14]
Length	882.5 feet	800 feet
Water-tight compartments	16	19
Displacement	66,000 tons	45,000 tons
Gross tonnage	45,000	46,328
Horsepower	46,000	40,000
Lifeboats	20	24
Speed at impact	22.5 knots	25 knots

Because of its closeness in so many particulars, Robertson's *Futility* is the best known of all disaster prophecies, and thus naturally the most debated. One writer, Jack W. Hannah, an Evangelical Christian attempting to prove that Robertson's novel was "a piece of literature that contains a word of God," calculated that the odds were one in four billion that the coincidences between Robertson's story and the *Titanic* disaster could be due to chance. Revisiting the case in the early 1980s, psychiatrist Jule Eisenbud basically agreed that some sort of "paranormal foreknowledge" was likely involved but found enough flaws with

Hannah's statistics and reasoning that he lowered the odds to a more modest one in 1,024.[15] Skeptic Martin Gardner on the other hand, in a book compiling many uncanny predictions of the *Titanic* disaster in order to debunk ESP claims, argued that "There is no way to estimate, even crudely, the relevant probabilities."[16]

Gardner is right. There is no way of objectively calculating the likelihood or unlikelihood of a correspondence between a novel—or a dream, or a vision, or some other premonitory inkling—and a later historical event. Rare events are commonplace, and human beings are terrible at grasping this, runs the refrain of professional statisticians and psychologists in the face of paranormal claims.[17] Because of the "law of large numbers," an impossible, once-in-a-lifetime event is probably happening to someone somewhere at any given time, and will likely happen to you too. And anything can be sliced and diced to yield startling coincidences. Gardner points out the following, by way of comparison to the *Futility-Titanic* case:

> It seems incredible … that in Psalm 46 of the Bible the forty-sixth word is "shake" and the forty-sixth word from the end is "spear," and that Shakespeare was 46 when the King James translation was completed. Taken in isolation, such coincidences seem paranormal. But we must realize that in a book as vast as the Bible the probability is high that *some* astounding word coincidences would occur. It is like finding a long run of consecutive digits in the endless decimal expansion of pi.[18]

In addition to being unable to calculate the odds of oddities, we are also swayed in a million different directions by our biases. There are lots of them. The psychologists' bias bestiary grows more massive by the year; at the time of this writing, Wikipedia's "List of Cognitive Biases" page listed over 180.[19] Thus every claim of the paranormal is met with an eye-roll and a named bias to explain why your perception of the situation has been distorted by expectation or wishful thinking (*confirmation bias*) or failure to take some factor into account in your reasoning. One of the most interesting and perilous, and one I shall be returning to again and again throughout this book, is hindsight bias— the distortion of our memory by later events, making past events seem predictable when they really weren't. It has a close cousin, *selection bias*, or what is known in science as the "file drawer effect"—the tendency to discard data that don't conform to our desires or expectations. These are related because hindsight is itself a kind of selection, a narrowing of the frame in which we view the past.

An event like the *Titanic*'s sinking gives us new frames of reference, and after it happens, individual and cultural memory will suddenly discern specific chains of ordinary causation leading up to it that would otherwise have remained invisible or drowned out by noise—causal arrows emerging from the clouds of chaos. In this process of selection, hindsight will inevitably turn up some *apparent* anomalies, like sharks and dolphins caught in a tuna fisherman's nets. According to the law of large numbers, in a universe of thousands of novels and stories, one or a few of them are bound to match the sinking of an ocean liner closely enough to seem "prophetic"—particularly when we extend our allowable timeframe out by years and decades, as we must in the case of Robertson's *Futility* or especially W. T. Stead's *From the Old World to the New*.

Gardner also shows that when you put the prophecies in context, at least some of the impossibility of the coincidence between Robertson's novel and the *Titanic* disaster dwindles. The size, passenger complement, speed, etc. of the ship, for instance, were predictable. Any writer who knew anything about ocean liners would have extrapolated realistically from the existing ships of the White Star Line and other shipping firms of the day and arrived at a "biggest-ever ocean liner" more or less matching the Titanic's stats. As we saw with journalist Stead, the fear of fatally hitting icebergs in the North Atlantic was a very real one at the time and for decades beforehand, having claimed countless smaller ships, and thus it was natural fodder for writers of sea yarns. Several novels and stories from the years prior to the *Titanic*'s sinking used such collisions as plot devices.[20] Those collisions commonly happened in the spring, so it was natural for Robertson to sink his *Titan* in April. And any writer wanting to inject the dramatic elements of hubris and corporate negligence into such a story might naturally give his ocean liner too few lifeboats. Here again, Robertson was not the only one to use this plot device. For Gardner, the fact that Robertson was not alone in writing a story with this premise weakened, rather than strengthened, the case for prophecy.

The coincidence of names, too, Gardner found less than compelling. He called attention to an obscure science-fiction novel called *A 20th Century Cinderella or $20,000 Reward*, written just a couple years after

Robertson's *Futility* by an otherwise unknown writer named William Young Winthrop and set in the year 1920; the novel makes reference to an ocean liner called the *Titanic*, built (like the real *Titanic*) by the White Star Line. It was published in 1902. "It seems to me entirely possible," Gardner wrote, "that the White Star company, as early as 1898, when Robertson wrote his novel, had announced plans to construct the world's largest ocean liner and to call it the *Titanic*."[21] Gardner could provide no evidence for this notion, although he cited an 1892 news item from *The New York Times* about the White Star Line's plan to build a huge ocean liner—similar in stature to the eventual *Titanic*—called the *Gigantic* (which was never actually built). "It seems clear now what happened," Gardner wrote:

> Knowing of plans for the *Gigantic*, Robertson modeled his ship on this proposed mammoth liner. After the use of such names as *Oceanic, Teutonic, Majestic*, and *Gigantic*, what appropriate name is left for such a giant liner except *Titanic*? Not wishing to identify his doomed *Titan* with the White Star line, Robertson dripped the "ic" from the name. The White Star's later choice of *Titanic* for its 1910 ship was almost inevitable. The company was surely aware of Robertson's *Titan*, but perhaps did not mind adopting a similar name because it was firmly persuaded that its *Titanic* was absolutely unsinkable.[22]

This scenario makes a fine "just so" story to explain why Robertson *might* have named his fictional ocean liner *Titan*, but it is not actually based on any evidence, only an assemblage of individually plausible might-have-beens. Some degree of supposition is unavoidable when trying to make sense of the past—we never have all the data we'd like, so the available facts are always supplemented with "frog DNA" in our reconstructions of events (to use a metaphor from the movie *Jurassic Park*, where cloning dinosaurs from fragmentary genetic material was made possible using DNA of living animals). I too will be resorting to a little supposition in this book. But while sometimes fraudulent mediums, fortune tellers, and psychics have been exposed by detection of cheating, most "debunking" of alleged psychic or paranormal experiences reported by ordinary people *only* amounts to supplying some alternative explanation, one that typically invokes the fallibility of human perception, memory, and reasoning. It is up to the reader to assess whose story is really more reasonable or believable, the psychic claimant's or the debunker's.

Questions of precognition and other "paranormal" occurrences are certainly a quagmire—Gardner is absolutely right in this. If you don't like quagmires, don't read farther, because with the whole topic of precognition you are stepping in a very big one. But the skeptics are as easily made to look foolish flailing in this quagmire as the true believers are.

We will return to Morgan Robertson and *Futility* later in this book. There are more potentially precognitive dimensions to the novel than Gardner admitted and that even proponents of its "prophecy" have realized.

Touching the Slab

On the other hand, coincidences that may look outrageously uncanny at first glance do frequently have a way of evaporating on closer examination. Readers of my blog, *The Nightshirt*, shared with me a number of coincidences around the events of 9/11—an event with an even bigger halo of alleged paranormal events and premonitions than the *Titanic* disaster. One that stood out to me initially for its strangeness concerned the Millenium Hilton, a 55-story slab of dark glass built in 1992 immediately adjacent to the World Trade Center. It appears to have been consciously modeled by the architect Eli Attia on the enigmatic slab in Stanley Kubrick's 1968 film *2001: A Space Odyssey*. In the film, the slab first appears among starving man-apes on a savannah, subtly—psychically—giving them the idea of killing and enabling their evolutionary uplift. Millions of years later, on the way to the Moon, Haywood Floyd stops at the iconic double-ringed space station in orbit, which features a Hilton hotel, and then proceeds to the Moon, where he is shown a slab that has just been excavated in Tycho Crater. After the World Trade Center towers fell to the violent attack, photographs of the site, with the stark black slab-like Hilton Hotel now exposed in the background by the vast pit being cleared of rubble in the foreground, looked a lot like the second slab in the movie, rising from the lunar dust where it had been excavated, surrounded by floodlights.

This coincidence seemed "synchronistic" to some—as though some archetypal pattern having to do with violence and cosmic transitions imprinted itself on historical events. But zooming in on this case, the strangeness and even the coincidence quotient dwindles. The real year 2001 fast approaching naturally would have invited thoughts of Kubrick's film to supply some design idea for the first hotel to be named for the millennium.[23] And while the slab in the film is associated with violence (among other things), there is hardly anything unique about that—indeed, the violence committed by the hijackers on 9/11 was not really the kind of violence shown at the beginning of *2001: A Space Odyssey*, killing with some brand-new technology as part of our species' cultural evolution or uplift. Moreover, violence of all kinds, literal and metaphorical, occurs on the streets of Manhattan, and in the offices above, all the time.

Pictures of the Millenium Hilton (the developer intentionally misspelled it with one *n* to make it more distinctive) looming above the ruins of the World Trade Center are still fun to look at side-by-side with stills from *2001*, but the more you pick this "synchronicity" apart, the more it mainly boils down to the coincidence of the year 2001 and a suggestive photo-op. Selecting a framing of a scene or an event to make it meaningful is precisely what photography—and cinema—is all about, after all. From an almost infinite number of angles, pictures of the Hilton after 9/11 do not seem meaningfully coincidental in the slightest. Photographers may even have been unconsciously or consciously guided by iconic images like those in *2001* when photographing the building with the rubble in the foreground. In short, what at first seems strangely coincidental quickly loses much of its uncanny grandeur, the "size of the impossible" when examined with a critical eye.

But the fact that in the infinite universe there will be myriad coincidences that only seem impossible, or meaningful, from a certain point of view is no kind of argument that our commonsense understanding of causality is complete, or that there aren't real "synchronicities." Who are skeptics to say that people might not sometimes be right when they detect the operation in their own lives, or in history, of some principle that has not yet been given mainstream psychology's stamp of legitimacy, such as premonitions of future events? We know our understanding of physical reality is not complete—physicists are clear on that—and we will see in Part Two that new advances at the intersection of physics and biology are radically revising our understanding of living systems too. Among other things, they raise the possibility that the brain may have properties that could even be time-defying. Given the certainty that science is not finished and that new revolutions await us, is it reasonable to insist that there are no undiscovered realms of human capacity awaiting to be catalogued and investigated?

Consider another coincidence related to 9/11: a bronze 1999 sculpture by Jamaican-American artist Michael Richards, called *Tar Baby vs St. Sebastian*. It is one of a series of sculptures Richards created in the late 1990s in which he depicted himself as one of the Tuskegee Airmen—the African American aviators who distinguished themselves during and after World War II yet were still subject to segregation and racism. In *Tar Baby*, Richards depicts himself in bronze, standing rigidly erect (one might say tower-like) in an aviator's suit and helmet, being pierced by numerous planes—similar to how the early Christian martyr St. Sebastian is depicted in countless Renaissance paintings, as a pincushion of arrows. The eerie detail here is that Richards died on 9/11 in his studio, which was on the 92nd floor of the North Tower of the World Trade Center, where he had spent the night.

Much has been made of this one seemingly prophetic sculpture. Does it add to the case for prophecy, or subtract from it, that aviation-related destruction and martyrdom were themes that had come to obsess the artist during the five years leading up to his death? His sculptures include many objects being impaled by planes, planes hitting bullseyes, and planes crashing to the ground.[24] Two of his final pieces, according to friends who had visited his studio in the days before the disaster, were also of himself being impaled by planes, surrounded by fire and meteors.[25] Another was of himself as a Tuskegee airman riding a meteor.[26]

The arguments of skeptics can be anticipated: *Tar Baby vs St. Sebastian* is one of billions of artworks created by Americans in the years leading up to 9/11, and one of perhaps thousands created in those years just by people who were killed in or who survived the disaster. Among them, we know of only one work in which a person (the artist) is "martyred" specifically by planes impaling his body. Thus (the argument would run), our focus on this one apparent correspondence to the terror attacks ignores the vast denominator, all the other artworks that never even entered into our calculations because they don't seem relevant. Our desire to make sense of the traumatic event on 9/11 causes us to find meaning in this one uncanny and heartbreaking case and see Richards' sculpture as somehow prophetic in hindsight.

But such arguments contain biases of their own, and in a way are just as arbitrary. No two people respond exactly alike to the same stimulus, and in fact many people around the world did produce artworks or write stories that seem uncannily prophetic in light of the events of

9/11. Issue #596 of *The Adventures of Superman*, released on September 12, 2001 (but obviously drawn and written sometime in the weeks preceding the disaster), shows the twin "LexCorp" towers smoldering after being attacked in a superhero conflict. The issue was promptly recalled by the publisher, DC Comics, making it now something of a collector's item.[27] In June, 2001, Oakland, California, hip hop artists The Coup created a cover for their upcoming CD *Party Music* showing the towers exploding; after 9/11, the CD release was delayed until the band could create a new cover.[28] On March 4, 2001, the pilot episode of a spinoff of the *X-Files* called *The Lone Gunmen* centered on a government plot to hijack a jetliner by remote control and fly it into the World Trade Center. This seemingly too-prescient-to-be-coincidence episode supplied fodder for conspiracy theorists claiming that the government had foreknowledge of or planned the attacks.[29] A quick Google search turns up many more artworks and pieces of cultural ephemera that seem to have anticipated 9/11 in one way or another.

And most people do not create art at all but respond to inspiration in different ways. For one thing, everybody engages in the nightly internal sculpture called dreaming. Dreams seemingly corresponding to some future event or upheaval in the dreamer's life are probably the most common paranormal experiences (reported by 17-38 percent of people in surveys[30]). And as might be expected, many people reported dreams and other premonitions of the 9/11 events. The Rhine Center in Durham, North Carolina, which collects disaster premonitions, received more calls about dreams and other premonitions of 9/11 than any other disaster.[31] Again, a quick Google search turns up pages and pages of stories, including stories of people who perished in the attacks and whose loved ones recalled their doomed visions in dreams in the days and weeks before.[32]

Skeptics are particularly dismissive of claims of premonitory dreams, noting that in the vast majority of such cases, the dream has been recalled and recorded after the event it supposedly predicted. They can point to the well-established fact that memory is a malleable thing, easily selecting among its vast and ever-shifting contents to create apparent coincidences in hindsight. Dream memories are vague and fleeting in the best of circumstances, so alleged prophetic dreams are particularly suspect. Psychologist Elizabeth Loftus, a pioneer of false-memory research, writes: "One person may swear that the details of a tragic accident were forecast in his dream. Later, after an accident does occur, he checks his dream diary, he may discover that the emotion of the dream was unpleasant but the details only had a vague resemblance to the accident." [33] He may, true enough; but in fact, the opposite is very often true.[34]

There is, for instance, the case of a retired art professor named David Mandell in the London suburb of Sudbury Hill. A 2003 British TV documentary profiled Mandell and his astonishing record of seemingly precognitive dreams, which he depicts the next morning in drawings or watercolors and then photographs under the calendar clock at his local bank to provide a time stamp and forestall accusations of fakery or faulty memory. On September 11, 1996—five years to the day before the attacks in Manhattan—he reported awakening from a terrifying dream and sketched his vision of two tall towers crashing down in a disaster that he said felt to him like an earthquake. Six months later, he had the dream again, and painted it in watercolor—the towers in his painting are flanked by a shorter building with a pyramidal top. Nine months after that dream, he sketched a third dream in which two twin-engine planes crashed into a pair of buildings, from opposite directions. Mandell recalled feeling terrible shock, "shuddering and shaking," on the day of the terror attacks in Manhattan when he saw the pictures on television, and how stunningly they matched his dreams. Revisiting his watercolor, it exactly matched the New York skyline with the burning towers flanked by the pyramid-topped American Express Building. Because of his method of date-stamping them with photographs at his bank, he was able to verify the coincidental date of the first dream as well.[35]

As common as they are, in our culture presentiments and premonitions are seldom shared publicly, because of those eye-rolling skeptics (and every family and workplace has one)—but they are the kinds of things people do sometimes share with partners or close friends. Private divulgences of such things in letters or journals are commonly uncovered by biographers, although as isolated occurrences they will carry little evidential weight. Recently, historian Jonathan W. White, researching a history of sleep, sleep deprivation, and dreams during the Civil War, stumbled on a rich trove: hundreds or thousands of premonitory dreams in letters between soldiers and their spouses, girlfriends, and mothers. While not having intended to write a book on psychic phenomena, White cites in his book *Midnight in America* numerous accurate (often sadly accurate) precognitive dreams by ordinary Americans during that incredibly uncertain and stressful period of American history.[36] Such dreams, White argues, provided ordinary Americans with meaning in the face of overwhelming loss and fear, often confirming their belief in God or providence.

It is precisely that fact—that "prophecy" might give meaning and consolation in the face of trauma and a heartless universe—that fuels skeptics' claims that people are simply biased; they *want* something like precognition to be real. That we are biased to find evidence for our preferred worldview is an argument that cuts both ways, though, as we will see. The fact that prophecies and premonitions are most often reported around traumas of one sort or another is no kind of argument against their existence. It only makes sense that some ability to pre-sense future events—if it exists—would orient us specifically toward meaningful upheavals, and experiences of death and loss are some of the most meaningful in our lives.[37]

Usually it takes some kind of public solicitation of premonitory dreams by researchers sympathetic to their mere possibility to elicit them in sufficient numbers that they can be examined as anything more than one-off occurrences. No modern discussion of the topic fails to consider the case of the tragedy that struck the small South Wales village of Aberfan on October 21, 1966. Just after the pupils at the village school had finished singing "All Things Bright and Beautiful" in the assembly hall and taken their seats in their respective classrooms, half a million tons of mine debris, piled on an adjacent mountainside and undermined by recent heavy rains, gave way and flowed into town, destroying the school. Rescuers were only able to pull out a handful of children alive. In all, 144 people were killed.[38]

Thinking that large numbers of people may have had premonitions of such a disaster, a paranormal investigator named John Barker solicited readers of the *Evening Standard* newspaper to report any dreams or visions they may have had before the event. The paper received 60 letters, most reporting premonitory dreams about trapped children, children being buried in coal, children dying in avalanches, and so on. One of the premonitions came (indirectly) from one of the victims of the disaster: The day before the event, a 10-year-old student at the school, Eryl Mai Jones, told her parents she dreamed that the school was gone because "something black had come down all over it." In all, 24 of the letters included some kind of evidence of the premonition being recorded or told to someone before the disaster and thus could not be readily explained away as simple memory distortion.

Skeptic Richard Wiseman, in his book *Paranormality: Why We See*

What Isn't There, devotes a chapter to debunking prophetic dreams, including the many dreams of the Aberfan disaster. For instance, he notes that for several years before the disaster, local authorities had been worried about the danger posed by the mine debris piled on the hillside. Three years before the event, a local engineer wrote that residents of the village shared this apprehension. So, Wiseman writes, "it is possible that the young girl's dream may have been reflecting these anxieties."[39] It is possible, certainly, but even if 10-year-old Eryl Jones was cognizant of the worries of grown-ups in her community, how would she have formed such a precise image of the mine debris destroying her school, specifically on the day before it did in fact happen? Unless the girl had similar dreams constantly—a possibility, certainly, but also a supposition—then Wiseman's suggestion is rather desperate-sounding, and hardly convincing that this was "just chance."

As for how so many people reported such dreams, Wiseman resorts to the law of large numbers argument. He estimates that, given 365 nights of dreaming, each year for an adult lifetime (15-75) of about 60 years, a given adult will experience 21,900 nights of dreams, and that he may dream of an event like the Aberfan disaster once in that time. Statistically, the chances of having that dream on the night before an event roughly matching it would be one in 22,000, he says. But given that there were 45 million people in Britain, all subject to the same odds, about 2,000 people in every generation would have the amazing experience of dreaming about an event like Aberfan closely before a real event like it. "To say that this group's dreams are accurate is like shooting an arrow into a field, drawing a target around it after it has landed and saying, 'wow, what are the chances of that!'"[40]

But the question of the likelihood versus unlikelihood of a coincidence between a dream or an artwork and a supposedly predicted event, as Gardner put it in his book on the *Titanic*, is "not well formed" and can never be, for precisely the same reasons that the event was unpredictable in the first place: How do you isolate the relevant causal factors behind any event, or any two events that seem to coincide? Any calculation depends on how you define an event, how you draw lines around pieces of data, how much weight you attach to which causal arrows, decisions that in the end must be arbitrary or guided by your particular interests and biases.[41] Also, it is just as impossible to estimate the "rarity" of motifs in dreams as it is to estimate the rarity of events in real life. As a result, it is just as easy to use the law of large numbers to make the opposite argument from that of Wiseman. Writer Anthony Peake, countering Wiseman's debunking of the Aberfan disaster dreams, offers the following calculation:

> [L]et us assume that there is a million-to-one chance that when a person has a dream about a plane crash a plane crash happens the next day. There are seven billion people on this planet. Now, according to a researcher called Hines, each human being has around 250 'themes' in any one night. ... So, by extrapolation, that is 1,750,000,000,000 dream themes every night. Assuming our one-in-a-million chance that somewhere in the world a plane will crash after a person dreams of a plane crash, then up to 1.75 million people may experience such a clairvoyant dream. This is 1.75 million for every disaster that takes place [and] a minimum of 547 million people every year will experience an absolutely stunning precognitive dream that will come true the very next day. Strange how quiet they all are! We can all play with this law of large numbers ...[42]

In cases like 9/11 or the *Titanic* or the Aberfan disaster, we must also remember that massive loss of life is in a sense its own file drawer, taking away a vast and highly relevant sample we can never consult. We'll never know how many victims of the *Titanic* or people who were working in the World Trade Center or children in that Welsh school had dreams or premonitions of the disaster that they failed to report to anybody (or heed as warnings). Consequently, the *n* we are left with may only be a fraction of the total. History does not have a control group.

There is also a more basic problem, and that is that all these calculations rest on the prior presumption that dream contents are random. That has been the preferred position of many scientists over the past century, who have been as hostile to psychoanalytic and other interpretive approaches to dreaming as they are toward alleged psychic phenomena. But the idea that dreams are simply meaningless, random productions of the overactive brain is no longer borne out by the evidence of mainstream dream research, as we will see later. Even leaving aside the question of precognition in dreams, many researchers now would agree that dream content relates to an individual's life experiences, possibly consisting of mnemonic associations to events in waking life.[43] Dreams are not random images, in this view, but are meaningfully linked to the dreamer's biography and priorities.

Consequently, any argued correspondence or non-correspondence of a dream motif to an actual rare event rests on establishing the rarity of that motif in the individual's own dream life, not its rarity in the world of possible (random) dreams. Without knowing a great deal about the former, there is no way to calculate the "odds" of a particular idea or image showing up in an individual's dreams, let alone in the dreams of any large sample of people. Wiseman estimates that people will dream of an event like Aberfan once in a lifetime; there is no basis to make such a claim. Some people dream of disasters nightly. But people being people, they are unlikely to keep extensive databases of their dreams.[44] Even when dreamers do keep computer-searchable records, since dream elements are drawn from an individual's life history, subjective judgment plays a huge role in any interpretation of dream content or any assessment of dreams' correspondence to events, whether in the past or future; thus such assessments stand little chance of swaying someone who will only listen to a claim that can be supported with statistics. It is this fact—that the dreamer is an n of 1 and that dream significance cannot readily be quantified and replicated—that has hindered the experimental study of dream content for decades and has biased many researchers against meaning-centered dream theories of whatever sort.

Dreams lie on the unstable fault line between the objective and subjective. On one hand they are natural phenomena, probably reducible to physical processes in the brain; on the other hand, they have to do with meaning, which is ultimately the unique value of some image or symbol *to* an individual, based on his or her unique life experience. There may be no objective meaning in dreams, or objective way to assess their meaning. Thus, even if dreaming is every bit as natural and as biological as the process of digestion and its underlying processes can be studied scientifically, dream *interpretation* is largely beyond the pale of the methods used in science. It ought to be obvious that both approaches might be necessary and may even complement each other. Yet as we will see later, dream scientists have often been intolerant of hermeneutic approaches, to the detriment of making much progress toward understanding an extremely interesting, probably functionally crucial activity that humans spend about ten percent of their lives engaged in.

* * *

Time itself is another subject, not unrelated to dreams, whose notorious two-facedness has polarized thinkers for a century. On April 6, 1922, the physicist Albert Einstein, who insisted time was an objective, purely measurable, scientifically knowable framework, squared off at the Société française de philosophie in Paris with the philosopher Henri Bergson, who insisted that time was something rich in subjective meaning and could not be reduced to spatial terms (as Einstein's relativity theory implied).[45] The event left intellectuals across Europe and America profoundly divided. It would be silly, in hindsight, to say that only one of these geniuses was right and the other wrong. They simply approached a profound problem from two very different avenues, both of which may be equally valuable and important. A decade and a half after this debate, F. Scott Fitzgerald observed in *Esquire* magazine that "the test of a first-rate intelligence is the ability to hold two opposed ideas in the mind at the same time, and still retain the ability to function."[46] Some never seem to get Fitzgerald's memo, unfortunately.

Academic disciplines that find themselves straddling the fault line between objective science and interpretation because they study the meaning-oriented behavior of human beings historically face unique difficulties, and often end up divisively fractured as a result. Psychology, which has long been polarized between an experimental/scientific mindset and the intuitive clinical approaches originally pioneered in Victorian Europe, is the clearest example, but there are others. My own graduate training was in anthropology, a field similarly riven between a more objective and materialist orientation and a more interpretive/ hermeneutic pole. The most interesting thinkers in these fields—the "first-rate intelligences"—have been the ones best able to "flicker" between alternative perspectives on the same problem, paying attention to the objective and subjective while recognizing that neither can be collapsed into the other.

Precognition, as a time- and dream-bound phenomenon, firmly straddles the fault line between the objective and subjective. I will be arguing on one hand that it is probably a neurobiological function related to memory, and thus we can expect a physical, material explanation in years or decades to come (in Part Two, I sketch what such an explanation *might* look like in its broad contours). But like a person's memory, precognition is highly personal and centers on personally meaningful experiences. Thus, except for its defiance of the usual causal order, precognition is little different from anything else in a person's biography— it needs to be understood within a life context and is subject to the same hermeneutic methods that are familiar to psychoanalysts and literary critics and philosophers. The tools of both the sciences and the humanities must be brought to bear, and neither should be favored over the other. The best we can do is flicker from one perspective to the other.

Larger, Wilder, Stranger

Wiseman, like most skeptics, repeats the argument that people believe in precognitive dreams and premonitions because they want something like prophecy to be real, that it confirms some preferred view of the world. Here he is certainly right. But he omits mentioning that the same thing is true for skeptics. The playwright J. B. Priestley, in a 1964 book on precognition and related questions called *Man & Time*, acknowledges that we cannot help but be biased in one direction or the other: "either we want life to be tidy, clear, fully understood, contained within definite limits, or we long for it to seem larger, wilder, stranger. Faced with some odd incident, either we wish to cut it down or to build it up."[47] Many parapsychologists and other writers on the subject of precognition, who may likely fall in the "larger, wilder, stranger" camp, are susceptible to confirmation bias, but skeptics are just as commonly driven by conservatism bias, an unwillingness to consider new data. The bias-accusation game, like the "law of large numbers" game, is one that can be played by both sides.

And while it is easy for skeptics like Wiseman to shoot down any one amazing anecdote with a volley of familiar biases and errors, divide and conquer must be seen for what it is: A wish to cut the affront down to size by isolating individual cases and making them seem like one-offs.[48] The file-drawer effect, too, cuts both ways. Compelling but "impossible" coincidences, dreams, premonitions, and so on are experienced by many, many people around many life events, and those who actually report them publicly or tell them to researchers represent only a tiny fraction of a larger unknown N. Most do not feel safe to divulge such experiences, given the stigma against the impossible that persists in our culture.

The notion that people ought to be announcing their precognitive dreams from the rooftops whenever they have them, and that they must be the rare product of erroneous thinking since they are publicly disclosed so infrequently, runs exactly counter to the reality of human conformism. When most people in our culture do experience what they think could be a prophetic dream, they will tend to disbelieve it. Because social norms so powerfully inhibit sharing such dreams, there is no ready stock of public examples to validate one's individual experience, thus the denial and skepticism are self-perpetuating. Cognitive dissonance is likely to boot the anomalous datum right out of awareness or memory. Martin Gardner claims that "there is a curious type of person, anxious to gain recognition in a community"[49] by falsely claiming to have predicted some event like the *Titanic* in a dream. But the opposite "type," the conformist deeply fearful of being stigmatized as a kook and thus unlikely to notice let alone share anomalies, is surely far more prevalent.[50]

Priestley solicited viewers of a BBC television program called *Monitor* to send him their own accounts of precognition and premonition to be included in his book. He was overwhelmed at the response, writing that he stopped counting after 1,000; the total (according to a later researcher) was in the ballpark of 1,500[51] and included several hundred precognitive dream accounts. One thing that became clear from this enormous pile of correspondence was how taboo the whole subject was regarded, at least in mid-1960s Britain, and what barriers letter-writers had experienced against according their experience much, or any, validity. "Women especially, often mentioning scoffing 'down-to-earth' husbands, confessed their eagerness to write to somebody who might believe them."[52] The gender breakdown of acceptance versus non-acceptance of anomalous experience may have shifted slightly in the past half century, but the basic division between "down to earth" skepticism and open-mindedness on such questions probably has not.

Certain vocal skeptics notwithstanding, this invalidation is generally much subtler than even the kind of condescension Priestley's female letter-writers reported getting from their husbands. What he found even more interesting and significant than overt resistance to the idea of precognitive dreaming was the more common experience of what might be called "simple ignoral":

> in most instances, when a dream had been told to husbands or (less often) wives or other members of the family or friends or workmates, and this dream had come true, these other people might marvel for a little while but always left it at that. The prevailing notion of Time was not then challenged. Our contemporary idea of ourselves was not questioned. Something odd

had happened, that was all; it could not be fitted into the accepted pattern, so it was ignored. [53]

People who experience anomalies like a dream that "comes true" afterward will tend *not* to shout it from the rooftops; they will sweep the experience under the rug, just remain silent, or feel obliged to accept an alternative framing of their experience. Those alternative framings may come from skeptical authorities like no-nonsense spouses and doctors or from writers of books like *Why People Believe Weird Things*[54] (by skeptic Michael Shermer, who clearly never heard of the benefits of believing six impossible things before breakfast) or books with subtitles like *Why People See Things that Aren't There* (i.e., *Paranormality*, by Wiseman).[55] Science is not finished—it is never finished—so can we really consider what is and isn't there a settled matter?

Throughout history, there has been one diplomat who can shuttle across the divide between the objective science of causes and the subjective study of meanings and barter a truce between the disputants. That diplomat is *reason*—in the old-school sense, the kind of thing that pre-postmodern philosophers still debated but that seems somehow quaint in our day. Since even the most reasoned skeptics like Martin Gardner admit there is no way to even approach the problem solely with numbers and statistics, all sides in the debate must supplement their arguments with appeals to this arbiter. How reasonable is the "it's just coincidence" argument in any particular case, or the bulk of the cases, versus some other explanation more in line with the existence of something like precognition? This book will present many examples that will appear more or less persuasive, depending on your point of view. There are no smoking guns, but for very interesting reasons having to do with the nature of time and information, there *cannot be* smoking guns. This is why I find the topic so fascinating: Precognition operates in the shadow realm of uncertainty. Some things that look very much like precognition may indeed be just coincidence, and there is no way to know for sure. By the same token, I will show that many examples of likely bona fide precognition have been hiding in plain sight, for instance in psychoanalysts' clinical writings, yet have been overlooked because they have been given alternative, less causally offensive—but also less parsimonious and I think less believable—theoretical framings.

To provide reasonable (if not strictly scientific) proof of precognition's reality, one could do no better than cite a modern case recently brought to light by Rice University historian of religions Jeffrey J. Kripal. He has done more than perhaps any other scholar in our time to legitimize psychic phenomena and the paranormal (he prefers the less pejorative term "super natural"[56]) not only as valid topics for academic inquiry but also as things that are just plain real—even if we do not yet have an adequate understanding of how they work. His recent case is a Houston woman named Elizabeth Krohn, who began experiencing frequent and distressing dreams after surviving a lightning strike in the parking lot of her synagogue in 1988.[57] Often these dreams corresponded to imminent plane crashes or other disasters reported in the news, and she learned to authenticate them by recording them in emails to herself, providing a time and date stamp and a kind of electronic paper trail. For example, on January 15, 2009, at 2:57 PM, Israel time—this occurred during a trip to Jerusalem—Krohn awoke from an afternoon nap and emailed herself the following dream:

> MID-SIZE COMMERCIAL PASSENGER JET
> (80-150 PEOPLE) CRASHES IN NYC. MAYBE IN
> RIVER. NOT CONTINENTAL AIRLINES. NOT
> AMERICAN AIRLINES.
> IT IS AN AMERICAN CARRIER LIKE
> SOUTHWEST OR US AIRWAYS.[58]

Her husband, who had been napping by her side, remembered that she told him that the passengers seemed to be *standing on the wing of the plane*, even though this detail seemed absurd to both of them at the time. Six and a half hours later, at 8:57 Eastern time in the United States, US Airways Flight 1549 made an emergency landing in the Hudson River after it struck a flock of Canada geese and lost engine power. Thanks to the expert piloting of its captain, Chesley "Sully" Sullenberger, all 155 passengers survived. Memorable photos that appeared in the news around the world showed the plane floating in the water with its lucky passengers spread out along both wings, awaiting rescue by nearby boats.

On February 2, 2015, at 5:52:15 AM, Central time, Krohn emailed herself the following:

> PASSENGER PLANE WITH PROPELLERS.
> PLANE IS WHITE. FOREIGN AIRLINE—
> MAYBE ASIAN. CRASHES IN A BIG

METROPOLITAN CITY RIGHT AFTER
TAKEOFF. RIGHT WING OF PLANE IS
POINTED STRAIGHT UP RIGHT BEFORE
CRASHING. MOST ON BOARD KILLED, BUT
SOME SURVIVORS.

Sent from my iPad[59]

A day and a half later, on February 4, TransAsia Airways Flight 235 crashed in the Keelung River near Taipei, Taiwan, right after takeoff; 43 were killed but there were 15 survivors. Crucially, a driver's dashboard video camera captured the crash and shows the right wing of the plane, propeller prominently visible, pointed straight up as it crossed over the highway ahead of the car, exactly matching Krohn's description of her dream. Like the pictures of the survivors of the Hudson River emergency landing, the dashboard camera video of Flight 235 was widely shown in the media and went viral on the internet.

I will state my own position plainly (lest it is unclear): In both of Krohn's stunning dreams (and several others cited in the book she and Kripal co-wrote, *Changed in a Flash*), claims of "mere coincidence" or the kind of "law of large numbers" calculations a skeptic like Wiseman might supply simply fail most any test of reasonableness. These dreams, like those painted by Mandell, were not reported by random members of the public as once-in-a-lifetime occurrences. They were part of a pattern in the life of an individual who had begun to notice dreams corresponding to imminent news events and did her best to record and authenticate them, at least to allay her own doubts that something extraordinary and inexplicable was occurring in her life. Moreover, that pattern happens to perfectly support a coherent and counterintuitive theory about precognitive dreams and other prophetic phenomena that an aeronautical engineer named J. W. Dunne adumbrated in a remarkable 1927 book called *An Experiment with Time*, which we will examine in the next chapter.

The theory, briefly, is that precognition is not a matter of seeing or knowing objective events in some generalized future time but is the accessing of knowledge a person will acquire in his or her own future, often directly related to some rewarding or troubling learning experience ahead. Although Krohn's dreams will typically be described as "premonitions of plane crashes," she was, as Kripal points out, clearly dreaming about *her future experience of seeing news stories* about those crashes, not the events as such. It is a crucial distinction. In fact, the idea that dreams focus intimately, or one might even say "myopically," on our own future experiences and the thoughts and feelings they provoke—not on events per se—is one thing that helps move the topic of precognition out of the murky realm of the "occult" or "supernatural" and into the realm of physical plausibility. It very much suggests an embodied, brain-based origin for these phenomena; they seem to be linked to memory and to meaning-making processes that have been studied in psychology and related fields for well over a century.

Cognitive biases and human clumsiness with statistics do often make people see illusory faces in the clouds of causality—that much is undeniable. But it also must be underscored that no one has ever actually shown that biases explain purported precognitive dreams. Nor can such arguments disprove the existence of "prophetic" artworks such as Robertson's *Futility* or Richards' *Tar Baby vs. St. Sebastian*. In every case, skeptics can only cite the possibilities of bias and memory distortion as more or less plausible alternative explanations, easing the minds of those troubled by the idea of information flowing from the future to the past. In the end, reason must be the arbiter of any particular case. Did Morgan Robertson actually receive some kind of paranormal foreknowledge of the *Titanic* disaster and weave it into his novel *Futility* in 1898? Were Mr. Middleton's dreams of the *Titanic* sinking just coincidences, or false memories confabulated after the disaster? There is no way of knowing for sure. No one case can offer definitive proof, for reasons that will be addressed at length. But one of my hopes in the next few chapters is to show that that idea—that information from the future "refluxes" to influence us in the present—is actually a very reasonable one, having increasing scientific support and plausibility.

2

"If I Were You, I'd Stay on the Ground for a Couple of Days" — Victor Goddard, J. W. Dunne, and the Block Universe

Listen:
Billy Pilgrim has come unstuck in time.

— Kurt Vonnegut, *Slaughterhouse Five* (1969)

The evacuation of the British Expeditionary Force (BEF) from Dunkirk, France, by a flotilla of private boats at the end of May 1940 was a heroic underdog moment that emboldened the Brits for a long and bloody struggle against Germany. In a now-famous speech to the House of Commons afterward, Winston Churchill famously promised that Britain would fight to the end, "on the beaches ... with growing confidence in the air [and] in the streets," and "never surrender." It would not have happened without the personal intervention of a BEF air staff officer and pilot named Victor Goddard.

As the officer in charge of the air forces defending the Allied soldiers trapped on the French coast by Hitler's tanks, Goddard saw personally what a dire situation the men were in—a situation that the British government did not fully appreciate. So at great personal risk, in the early morning hours of May 27, he and a few companions commandeered a bullet-riddled plane with no working radio from an abandoned farm outside of Dunkirk and flew across the Channel so that Goddard could personally plead with the heads of the armed forces in London. There, he forced his way into a meeting of the Chiefs of Staff and begged, on behalf of his commander, BEF General Lord Gort, that the Navy order all available boats—fishing boats, yachts, "everything that can cross the Channel … even rowing boats!"[1]—to aid in the evacuation. The rest is history … and a stirring 2017 film by Christopher Nolan.

But oddly enough, it is not this exploit but some fascinating and time-bending brushes with the paranormal that Goddard is best known for.

In 1935, for example, on a day jaunt to play golf in Gullane, Scotland, Goddard flew his Hawker Hart over a long-abandoned WWI airstrip in a little village called Drem, near his destination. During his visit, he drove to the site by car to speak with the owner about landing his plane there in the future, but found it unusable, having been turned over to pasture. The hangars were totally run-down, unsuited to house a plane. The next day—he estimated 16 hours later—on his return flight, Goddard flew through a thunderstorm and emerged from the clouds over the very same old airfield and saw—or thought he saw—something astonishing and impossible. What had been a derelict set of empty buildings and a strip overgrown with weeds was now a busy air base bustling with RAF flight crews … but they were wearing blue overalls, not the usual brown. The crews were tending four yellow planes; one was a monoplane distinctly unlike anything flown by the RAF at that point. And most oddly, those busy crews didn't pay him any heed, even though he zoomed over them at the perilously low altitude of about 30 feet.

Seconds later he was plunged back into rain and lost sight of the airfield.

Four years later, the preparations for war with Germany had made Goddard's brief vision a reality. The airfield at Drem, Scotland was again in use, and Goddard knew that one of the new training planes being flown there was a monoplane just like the one he had "seen" four years earlier. Also, the RAF had by this time changed the uniform for its flight crews: They now wore blue.[2] Goddard's experience has been described as a kind of "time slip"—a rare but not unheard-of animal in the bestiary of paranormal experiences.[3]

Goddard only wrote about this experience decades later, after his retirement. During their careers, military men and pilots generally don't like to sully their reputations or have doubts cast on their sanity by reporting things like "coming unstuck in time" (to use Kurt Vonnegut's famous phrase).[4] But this wasn't even the strangest thing Goddard witnessed. He was to find himself at the center of another, even weirder, time-slipping—or really, *time looping*—experience shortly after the war's end.

A year after his exploit with the BEF, Goddard was sent to the Pacific to supervise Great Britain's air efforts there against the Japanese. As Commander of the Royal New Zealand Air Force, he led his pilots to victory, alongside other Allied forces, at the Battle of Guadalcanal and in the Solomon Islands campaigns. Then at the end of the War, he was posted to India, where he administered Admiral Mountbatten's South East Asia Command as the British Air Forces took back Burma and Malaya from the Japanese.

In January 1946, Goddard's duties mopping up the messes made by the Japanese in the South Pacific were finished, and he was ready to head home to England and then begin the next and final phase of his illustrious military career, representing the RAF in Washington, DC. Instead of flying home the direct route, through Asia, he wanted to fly via Tokyo and the Pacific, so that he could personally say "thank you and farewell" to the Americans he had fought alongside, and especially to pay his respects to General MacArthur, one of the few other Allied military commanders to have seen the entire Pacific campaign through from start to finish. For his journey, Mountbatten in Singapore let Goddard take one of their most comfortable, well-equipped transport planes, a Dakota—the British name for the American C-47, the military version of the DC-3, many of which were lend-leased to Britain during the War. The plane was named *Sister Ann*.[5]

Goddard's trip to Tokyo in *Sister Ann* took him through Hong Kong and Shanghai, and it was during the latter stopover, at a cocktail party in his honor, that, amid the chatter of many Americans and Brits he did not know, Goddard overheard news of his own death.

"I'm very glad this party is really on tonight!" he heard an Englishman behind him say. "Of course, old boy, but why shouldn't it be?" said another man. "Well, wasn't it laid on to welcome Air Marshal Goddard? We haven't met him. We never shall. He's dead!"

Goddard couldn't believe what he was hearing. Was the man crazy? Was he hearing things?

The voice behind him went on, with an authoritative tone that Goddard found increasingly unsettling: "Died last night in a crash—hell of a crash. Yes, he was killed—no doubt about that. Not a hope. Bad show!"

This was too much—Goddard turned to see who it was spouting this nonsense. It was a naval commander, who simultaneously turned and met his gaze, and started as though seeing a ghost: "My God! I'm terribly sorry! I mean I'm terribly glad—that is—how extraordinary and how appalling! I do apologize!"

"I may be a bit moribund, commander" Goddard said wryly, "but I'm not quite dead yet."

The Navy man was Gerald Gladstone, captain of a Royal Navy cruiser, HMS *Black Prince*, currently docked in Shanghai harbor.[6] When Goddard pressed him for why he was under the impression there had been a crash, Gladstone admitted he had seen it in a dream the night before—or else that very afternoon, he couldn't quite remember. Yet it had been extremely vivid and clear: Goddard had gone down in a transport plane, probably a Dakota, on a rocky beach in either China or Japan, after being caught in a snowstorm. "You'd been over the mountains in cloud. Up a long time," Gladstone said. "I watched it all happen. … If I were you, I'd stay on the ground for a couple of days."

One thing an aviator does not want to hear is a premonition like that. And Goddard was not inclined to just brush it off as nothing, given his own aviation-related visions that had come true. Also, Goddard had, years before, read a most fascinating book by a pioneer aeronautical engineer-turned-philosopher named John William Dunne, about the reality of precognitive dreams. Gladstone, they quickly ascertained, had just been reading the same book, *An Experiment with Time*, which accounted for his own confidence in discussing his dream as something that might have really come true. It didn't mean much to Goddard that Gladstone had "seen" him flying a Dakota, since that was a very common type of transport plane, but his description of the crash occurring on a beach in China or Japan was unsettling, considering he was going to be making a flight from Shanghai to Tokyo the following morning— the next leg of his journey to meet General MacArthur. So Goddard pressed the man for details of his dream: "Did your dream show you what sort of people I was traveling with?"

"Yes," Gladstone said slowly, "an ordinary service crew."

"Anybody else?" Goddard was curious whether Gladstone's dream showed that he had been carrying—although only as far as Shanghai— a civilian, Hon. Seymour Barry, who was in Asia as a journalist for *The Daily Telegraph*.

"Yes," Gladstone said definitely. "Three civilians. Two men and a woman. All English."

Goddard was relieved. "I'm carrying no one but a service crew. I did have one civilian aboard, but he's not going on."

The two men chatted a bit about Dunne's book—Goddard, who understood it better, found himself needing to clarify the author's argument for his new acquaintance. Gladstone, for his part, must have felt a good deal of embarrassment, first at having pronounced so confidently on the party honoree's death, and then at being corrected about the finer points of Dunne's book and the topic of precognitive dreams—which his recent dream now didn't seem to be an example of, after all. After their conversation, they moved apart, and Goddard never met Gladstone again.

If that were the whole story, of course, we would not know of it now. But as it happened, this deeply awkward, brief conversation between an Air Force hero and a somewhat befuddled Navy captain was just the beginning of a harrowing 24 hours in Goddard's life. He was no stranger to daring exploits in war, but he later described this episode in a lengthy 1951 *Saturday Evening Post* account as his favorite true adventure story.

Things began to get unsettling for the air marshal just minutes after he drifted off to join another conversation at the party. Mr. Barry, the journalist who had flown in *Sister Ann* as far as Shanghai, approached him and asked if he could, despite his previous intention to remain in China a few days, join Goddard as far as Tokyo instead. Without betraying his trepidation, Goddard agreed.

It only got worse later that evening, when Goddard joined the British Consul General George Alwyne Ogden and some other guests for dinner at Ogden's home. Midway through the meal, the Chinese butler handed Ogden a telegram: It was from the Foreign Office in London, saying it was imperative for the Consul General to visit the British high commissioner in Tokyo the next day. Ogden said to Goddard, "I am sorry to impose on you, but I wonder if you can possibly take me with you tomorrow?" There were now two civilians who wanted to fly with him. Goddard could of course say nothing about his worries, so again he agreed to this change in plans.

Then, before the dinner was over, Ogden received a second telegram. This time it was from the British representative in Tokyo, asking if they could bring along a stenographer. Goddard was sweating. Ogden asked Goddard if that was alright. "I can take him," Goddard said stoically, not betraying his trepidation, "… if he's a man."

"He's bound to be a girl, I'm afraid," Ogden replied.

Again, what could Goddard do but agree with this new passenger list, which now would match precisely what Gladstone said he had dreamed? The only stenographer available of course was a woman: a 20-year-old Englishwoman, Miss Dorita Breakspear. He wrote: "As an air marshal, how could I possibly say that I'd been warned supernaturally? Or by extrasensory perception, if that is the more fitting expression?"[7] Nevertheless, he felt he may be taking all of these passengers, including a young woman who had never flown before, to their deaths … all because of the dream of the odd Navy man he'd met earlier that evening.

As they took off the next morning, Goddard had to conceal his emotions.

> My depression was due to a foreboding that I was about to carry into mortal danger all who flew with me, and to the knowledge that I could not, for want of justification—or of moral courage—bid passengers other than myself remain behind. Here seemed a destiny which had to be risked, a destiny which could be averted not by delay, but only by a change which I could not force myself to make—a change of passengers.[8]

The story of the flight fills several big pages of the May 26, 1951, issue of *The Saturday Evening Post*, but the short version is this: *Sister Ann* departed Shanghai the next morning at 6:30 with her Air Force crew and three civilians. Despite good initial weather reports, the plane encountered a snowstorm over the Japanese coast, and after unsuccessfully trying to fly over the storm bank—the civilian passengers were not able to endure the thin oxygen at that altitude—and with too little fuel to reach an airstrip, Goddard's pilot was forced to crash-land the plane on a remote rocky beach on the West coast of Japan, 200 miles West of their intended destination of Tokyo.

The details of the incident were just as Gladstone had dreamed— with the exception that Goddard and all his passengers survived the ordeal. Their survival was largely thanks to the scrupulous preparedness of Goddard and his flight crew: removing the rear door of the plane while still in flight, so they wouldn't be trapped after the crash-landing, and padding the passengers in all available blankets and seat cushions to protect them on impact. Goddard refused to accept that his passengers, especially the civilians, would die in the "hell of a crash" his acquaintance had foreseen in his dream. Although the hard landing was harrowing, everyone was unhurt, and they were assisted afterward by friendly Japanese villagers. Thanks to the discovery of a Japanese-French dictionary at the local inn, they were able to communicate, in a limited way, with their hosts.

A skeptic might suggest that the crash was somehow a product of "suggestion"—that Goddard's superstitiousness about the dream influenced his own decisions and perhaps, via him, his crew. But Goddard did his utmost not to reveal Gladstone's dream, or his doubts, to his crew who were actually flying the plane.[9] Nor could suggestion account for how exactly Gladstone's dream matched the other details, such as the fact that the plane was carrying two civilian men and one woman.

Even a Stopped Clock Tells the Right Time Twice a Day

To make some sense of Victor Goddard's remarkable story, we must understand the discoveries and theories of J. W. Dunne, the English soldier-turned-engineer and philosopher whose book, *An Experiment with Time*, had persuaded both Goddard and Gladstone of the reality of precognitive dreams.

Dunne was born in Ireland in 1875, when his father, a British army general, was stationed in that country. During a long illness as a child, which kept him confined to bed, he did a lot of reading and thinking, even forming the beginnings of a new theory of time that, decades later, he would call Serialism.[10] He also read the novels of Jules Verne, which instilled in him a fascination he would later pursue as a career: aeronautical engineering. He reported several ecstatic religious experiences as a child, and brushes with "prophecy" as a teenager, but his interest in precognitive dreams dates mainly to the year 1899, when the 24-year-old Dunne was asleep in a hotel room in Sussex, England, dreaming he was having an argument with one of the waiters at the hotel about the time of day.[11]

Dunne's dream-self insisted it was half past four o'clock in the afternoon, but the stubborn waiter held firm that it was in fact half past four in the morning. Dunne began to wonder, in the dream, if his watch had stopped and whether he was the one in error, so he pulled it from his pocket to check—finding that indeed, its hands were motionless, frozen at half past four. With typical dream illogic, he concluded that he was radically confused about whether it was day or night simply because of his stopped watch. Also, as the image of the frozen watch in his hands faded, Dunne became aware of a din of a multitude of voices shouting in unison, "Look! ... Look! ... Look!" He awoke with these voices ringing in his head,[12] and obediently lit a match to have a look at his watch. It was not by his bedside, where he usually placed it before retiring; he had to rise and go looking through his things. He found it on a chest of drawers across the room from his bed ... and it *had* stopped, the hands frozen at half past four.

No answer for this coincidence of finding his watch stopped at 4:30 just after having dreamed of it came to Dunne's skeptical mind. Since his only timepiece had stopped, Dunne had no way of knowing the real time, of course, so he simply rewound it and went back to sleep, waiting to reset it against the hotel's clock the next morning.

When he descended to the hotel lobby for breakfast, he was surprised to find that his watch was only a couple minutes behind the hotel's clock. It suggested either that the watch had stopped right when he had his dream—perhaps the dream was stimulated when his sleeping brain ceased hearing the watch's faint ticking—or that it had stopped exactly 12 hours earlier but had (quite improbably) gone unnoticed by him the whole evening.[13] In either case, he was perplexed: How had his sleeping self been able to know exactly what time it was? Nearly three decades later, he wrote in his famous book on precognitive dreams, *An Experiment with Time*:

> If anyone else had told me such a tale I should probably have replied that he had dreamed the whole episode, from beginning to end, including the getting up and rewinding. But that was an answer I could not give to myself. I *knew* that I had been awake when I had risen and looked at the watch lying on the chest of drawers. Yet, what was the alternative? 'Clairvoyance'—seeing across space through darkness and closed eyelids? Even supposing that there existed unknown rays which could effect that sort of penetration, and then produce vision—which I did not believe—the watch had been lying at a level above that of my eyes. What sort of rays could these be which bent around corners?[14]

Alone, it is a mundane dream, presaging an event as trivial as the sinking of the *Titanic* or 9/11 were momentous. But it proved to be the first of many seemingly precognitive dreams Dunne experienced and recorded over the subsequent years.

Soon after his watch dream, Dunne enlisted as a soldier in Britain's war with the Dutch-speaking Boers in southern Africa, where he himself had lived for a period during his teens. Two of his most striking precognitive dreams occurred during and after his two stints fighting in this conflict. In January 1901, he had been invalided with typhoid fever. While recovering on the Italian Riviera, Dunne dreamed he was in a town on the Nile near Khartoum in the Sudan, where he met three white men, faces burned almost black from the sun, dressed in khakis he associated with his treks in South Africa. How had they gotten all the way to North Africa from South Africa, his dream-self wondered? The next morning, he read in *The Daily Telegraph* of precisely such an expedition arriving in Khartoum—a newsworthy event, as it was the first time the "Dark Continent" had been traversed by white men on foot.[15]

Then in 1902, while camped out with his regiment in Orange Free State during his second stint in the African conflict, Dunne had what he described as "an unusually vivid and unpleasant dream"[16] of being on a volcanic island about to erupt: Steam issued from vents in the ground, reminding him (in the dream) of the Krakatoa eruption. In that eruption, he knew, seawater had seeped into the lava chamber, creating superheated steam that acted as a bomb to destroy that island. Something similar was clearly about to happen in this dream, and the dreamer also knew that 4,000 people living on the island were going to perish in the explosion. The dream scene changed (as they often do), and the next part was a maddening bureaucratic nightmare set on a neighboring island, in which he went from office to office, trying unsuccessfully to convince French authorities of the peril so that the threatened 4,000 people could be rescued by boat. He noted that the "4,000" figure was repeated again and again.

When the next batch of mail arrived at his camp, it included a copy of *The Daily Telegraph*, in which Dunne read of the catastrophic eruption of Mont Pelée on the French island of Martinique in the Caribbean, with (it said) "probable loss of over 40,000 lives." An eyewitness at sea reported seeing the mountain literally split apart and explode. And it was reported that ships were busy trying to remove survivors to neighboring islands. It seemed to be another stunning confirmation of an event experienced in a dream. When reading the article, Dunne mis-read the figure as "4,000," and he records that he even kept re-peating that erroneous figure to people in conversation for a long time afterward. It was only 15 years later, he says, when copying the news story, that he caught his mistake (that in his reading, and his dream, he had been "out by a nought").[17]

Even though the Wright Brothers' historic flight at Kitty Hawk was still a year away and his own career as an aeronautical engineer was just a glimmer in his eye at this point, Dunne already possessed a keen engineer's mind, which he applied scrupulously to the problem of figuring out just what these dreams were. A crucial piece of evidence, in this and several other cases, came from the ways his dreams *deviated* from the real-life event he had dreamed about.

The final death toll in the Mont Pelée eruption turned out to be in the neighborhood of 30,000 people,[18] "nothing in common with the arrangement of fours and noughts I had dreamed of, and gathered from the first report."[19] The more Dunne reflected on this dream, as well as the previous one about the expedition to Khartoum, the clearer it became that they were both somehow triggered by his reading experiences, not by the events being reported: "[I]n each case, the dream had been precisely the sort of thing I might have expected to have experienced after reading the printed report—a perfectly ordinary dream based upon the personal experience of reading." "For *whence*, in the dream, had I got that idea of 4,000? Clearly it must have come into my mind *because of the newspaper paragraph*."[20]

This raised a fresh doubt in his mind: "How, then, could I be sure that those dreams had not been *false memories* engendered by the act of reading?"[21]—in other words, the skeptical position most often voiced in response to claims of "prophetic" dreams. The only way to answer that was, from then on, to record his dreams immediately upon waking, or tell them to another person, to establish that retroactive memory distortion—or what was at the time called "identifying paramnesia"—was not the explanation.

After Dunne was diagnosed with heart disease in 1903, his military career effectively ended and he devoted himself in earnest to studying his true passion, aeronautical engineering. He was a bold experimenter, designing several innovative tailless biplanes, including recognizable precursors to later "flying wing" designs. His own planes did not end up being used in the First World War or after, but as a manufacturer with military connections and a member of an industry delegation to Parliament, Dunne played an important behind-the-scenes role in winning military support for the young British aerospace industry.[22]

When he was not designing and building bizarre aerial contraptions, Dunne turned his interest in dreams into a more rigorous experiment—recording or telling his dreams after he had them, and comparing them systematically to events in his life that followed. He was soon rewarded with data points that helped him reject the less causally problematic notion that he had simply invented dream memories after the fact of reading interesting news stories. His new data from his "experiment with time" also helped further clarify the nature of this astonishing phenomenon of precognitive dreaming, and the way information from his own future intermingled with, or in some cases was represented by, material from ordinary memory.

In 1904, for example, he had a nightmare of people choking on suffocating smoke behind a railing and a kind of moving "lath" visible dimly through the smoke. The latter image he recognized upon waking as something he had seen in an early motion picture: the jet of water from a fire engine. He carefully reflected on the dream and its details before reading any newspapers. There was nothing similar to this in the morning paper, but the afternoon news brought a story of a fire at a rubber factory in Paris that suffocated a large number of female workers with thick smoke even after many had retreated outside to a balcony, where they were all pressed together—exactly the terrible scene he had witnessed in his dream.[23]

A few months later, on a fly-fishing trip to Austria with his brother, Dunne had a nightmare of a horse behaving crazily behind a fence, which initially alarmed him until he realized the animal could not get out from its confinement. He walked away, but then turned and saw the horse had somehow gotten out and was barreling toward him. The next day, while fishing with his brother, he saw nearly the exact scene—a horse behaving crazily—across the river, along with some other details such as a wooden walkway that he had distortedly seen in his dream. This prompted him to begin telling his dream to his brother—pausing midway in his story to make sure there was no gap or gate where the animal really could escape.

> Satisfied, I said, 'At any rate, *this* horse cannot get out', and recommenced fishing. But my brother interrupted me by calling 'Look out!' Glancing up again, I saw that there was no dodging fate. The beast *had*, inexplicably, just as in the dream, got out (probably

it had jumped the fence), and, just as in the dream, it was thundering down the path toward the wooden steps. It swerved past these and plunged into the river, coming straight towards us. We both picked up stones, ran thirty yards or so back from the bank, and faced about. The end was tame, for, on emerging from the water on our side, the animal merely looked at us, snorted, and galloped off down a road.[24]

Dunne noted that all these dreams were exactly like one might expect of dreams triggered by events of the day before, containing the same mix of real events and distortions. "No, there was nothing unusual in any of these dreams as dreams. They were merely *displaced in time*."[25]

Dunne's 1899 dream of the stopped pocket watch was not his first brush with "prophecy." As a teenager he had spent some time living as a student on a South African farm, and like many angsty teens, his emotions sometimes got the better of him. At 17, disappointed and angry at a choirmaster who persisted in making him sing alto long after his voice had deepened, and just generally outraged at the unfairness of it all, he ceased believing in God and deliberately started acting out in ways he was loath to specify even near the end of his life, when he wrote of this period. "How I cursed that master, and how I longed to curse the God in whom I no longer believed."[26] Alarmed at the "strange bouts of savagery" this otherwise decent chap found himself capable of (whatever they were), he decided that there were two "diametrically different" personalities in him, one good, one evil, vying for control of his body, and that he may have no choice but to take the latter path in life: "Goodness was nonsense: there was neither good nor evil: my so-called 'evil' personality was by far the freer of the two, and there were no limits to what it might achieve. Reason said: give it rein."[27]

No sooner had the teenager made this awesome decision to follow the dark side than he rode his horse to the closest town, Stellenbosch, to exchange his library book for a new one. This lover of adventures had already exhausted everything they had of that nature, unfortunately, including most of the titles by one of his favorites, Robert Louis Stevenson ... except one: *Dr. Jekyll and Mr. Hyde*. Dunne knew nothing about it, but the fact that it was by Stevenson bode well, so he took the book home with him.

Picture me at ten o'clock that night, reading by the light of a single candle, my hair standing on end. God! What I had escaped! My evil self, I saw clearly, would never have remained the Superman I had pictured it. Like Hyde, it would have sunk lower and lower as it threw off the trammels of its Jekyll.

But (I thought) what a marvellous coincidence! At the very moment when I have decided to give my Hyde the mastery, I pick up the grimmest story ever written—the story of a man who did that very thing.[28]

He decided it could be no coincidence, as the chances were a million to one. "There *was* a God! And He had intervened in the promptest and most effective way possible."[29] This prompted in the young rebel a provocation and challenge to God that proved unwise. Capping his disappointments up to that point, a short story he had submitted to a Cape Town periodical two months earlier—his first attempt at writing for publication—had not gotten him a response and, he presumed, had been rejected outright. So he made a promise:

I promised that, if the despaired-of letter would arrive by the next post, I would believe 'the whole thing', by which words I meant 'Pauline Christianity'. And next morning that letter arrived! My story was accepted! And ... I found, a little later, that I *could not* believe what I had promised to believe.[30]

His rational mind balked at literal belief in the Gospels, and the fact that he'd made a promise to a God to believe in a dogma that he couldn't rationally countenance put him in a kind of Catch-22 that dominated the next ten years of his life. In fact, it was his new theory of time, Serialism, for which his later precognitive experiences provided evidence, that helped resolve his dilemmas about God and the rest.[31]

Right at the time Dunne was fighting in the Boer War, Einstein was formulating his revolutionary theory of relativity, based on thought experiments about observers, light beams, and trains on parallel tracks moving at different speeds or in different directions. Dunne's dreams seemed to him evidence for what Einstein and other physicists and mathematicians were just beginning to assert: that since the present moment depends entirely on where you stand in relation to events—what might be in the past for one observer may still be in the future for another observer, and vice versa—then the future must in some sense *already exist*.

Einstein's theory of relativity suggested that time was a dimension like space. To help visualize this, his teacher, Hermann Minkowski, pictured "spacetime" as a four-dimensional block. For the purposes of this book, let's make it a *glass* block so we can see what is happening inside it. One's life, and the "life" of any single object or atom in the universe, is really a line—a "world line"—snaking spaghetti-like through that glass block. The solid three-dimensional "you" that you experience at any moment is really just a slice or cross section of a four-dimensional clump of spaghetti-like atoms that started some decades ago as a zygote, gradually expanded in size by incorporating many more spaghetti-strand atoms, and then, after several decades of coherence (as a literal "flying spaghetti monster") will dissipate into a multitude of little spaghetti atoms going their separate ways after your death. (They will recoalesce in different combinations with other spaghetti-strand atoms to make other objects and other spaghetti beings, again and again and again, until the end of the universe.) What we perceive at any given moment as the present state of affairs is just a narrow slice or cross-section of that block as our consciousness traverses our world-line from beginning to end. (If it helps envision this, the comic artist, occult magician, and novelist Alan Moore has recently revised the "block" to a football—one tip being the big bang, the other the "big crunch" proposed in some cosmological models.[32] I will stick with the term "glass block" since I am not a football fan and "glass football" sounds odd.)

Precognitive dreams, Dunne argued, show that at night, as well as other times when the brain is in a relaxed state, our consciousness can wriggle free of the present moment and scan ahead (as well as behind) on our personal world-line, like a flashlight at night illuminating a spot on the path ahead. This ability to be both rooted mentally in our body, with its rich sensory "now," and the possibility of coming unstuck in time (as Vonnegut put it) suggested to Dunne that human consciousness was dual. We not only possess an "individual mind" that adheres to the brain at any given time point, but we also are part of a larger, "Universal Mind," that transcends the now and that spaghetti-clump body. The Universal Mind, he argued, is ultimately shared—a consciousness-in-common—that is equivalent to what has always been called "God." Universal Mind is immortal. The body-bound individual mind is, in some sense, a "child of God and Man."[33]

Thus, by wrestling with the problem of time and mind, Dunne managed to bring himself around to belief, just as he promised. But the belief was radically different from straightforward Pauline Christianity, and his promise had been made, he realized, not to some deity outside of and separate from himself—it was a promise to the immortal Universal Mind that he was as much a part of as everyone and everything else.

Throughout history, many mystics have arrived at more or less this same conclusion Dunne did, although surely few mystical writings in history are supported by as many graphs and equations—and are as difficult to follow—as Dunne's writings on Serialism. (He followed up *An Experiment with Time* with four more books elaborating his theory with new metaphors and diagrams.) Equations or no, his view of consciousness as something transcendent of the body, shared by all creatures and actually "filling all space," is one that has met with considerable agreement in New Age metaphysics. It has even become a popular explanation for psychic phenomena among some parapsychologists, who use updated quantum mechanics metaphors like "entanglement" and "nonlocality" to explain the mind's connectedness to (or unity with) the rest of the universe. "Transcendent mind,"[34] "entangled minds,"[35] "One Mind,"[36] and so on are all terms widely used in the interesting margins where science meets philosophy and spirituality.

But for all his proofs and logic, many of Dunne's readers, and even many of his admirers, have not been altogether convinced by his reasoning about time in its relation to consciousness. Ultimately, Dunne's spiritual aim was to convince us of our immortality, of an undying God-like Universal Mind, but his theory of precognition does not actually support his own theory, based as it is on what appears very much like a kind of mirror of physical memory, rooted in an embodied experiencer. All of the precognitive experiences Dunne recorded centered on events his flesh-and-blood self, his "individual mind," directly experienced or learned about during his lifetime. The only real difference between these phenomena and ordinary memories was that they defied the usual causal sequence. He seemed to "remember" certain experiences *before* they occurred.

In fact, it is this basic observation—that precognition is about our personal experiences, not about other people's experiences or events in objective reality—that made Dunne's experiment with time so distinctive and valuable in moving us closer to an understanding of how precognition may actually work. He was really the first thinker about precognitive phenomena to draw a strict distinction between *foreknowledge of events in some generalized future time* (i.e., "the future") and *previews of future personal experiences*—the latter including learning experiences like reading about a major world event or disaster in the media. This distinction enabled him to discount most of the theories or models of psychical phenomena that prevailed at the time he was writing, including the notion of *clairvoyance* (seeing distant locales or hidden objects) and the Theosophical idea of "astral wandering" (the notion that consciousness can travel free of the body and witness distant events). Discrepancies between some real event and the way it was reported, such as the discrepancy of death tolls in the Mont Pelée example, served Dunne as what we might now call "tracers," showing that a direct, clairvoyant connection to the distant event did not account for his dream. Nor did astral wandering. Even if, in the dream, he felt like he was at the location where it all was happening, those tracers revealed that his dreaming brain had just created its own images to dramatize facts he would soon read in a newspaper article.

Also inadequate as an explanation for his dreams was the popular, highly intuitive notion of *telepathy*, the English psychologist Frederic W. H. Myers' theory of mental connection between people who share some emotional or familial bond. By the time Dunne was conducting his experiment, Myers' Society for Psychical Research (SPR) and its American counterpart the ASPR had for two decades been collecting accounts of psychic dreams, premonitions, and other phenomena such as "crisis apparitions" or "phantasms of the living," in which a person would see or encounter a relative or friend who was actually in trouble far away. People often reported having dreams of people they knew, finding out later that the subjects of their dreams had died or were undergoing some trauma at about the time they had the vision.[37]

The quite natural assumption underlying telepathy was that the consciousness of the human being in crisis can reach across distances in space (and even, to some limited extent, time) and make contact with loved ones and friends. Metaphorically modeled on the telegraph and related technologies of the day, telepathy was believed to be "powered" by strong emotion, especially strong negative emotion.[38] Although a large percentage of Dunne's dreams had an emotional component or centered on disasters of some sort, as predicted by Myers' trauma theory, the emotion carrying the mysterious signal, when he really scrutinized it, seemed to be *his own* emotions in the future, not those of distant people in trouble.

The clearest proof of this came from a dream Dunne had in 1912 about a plane crash involving a test-pilot friend whom he referred to as "Lieutenant B." Dunne was in Paris, inspecting an airplane being constructed there to one of his designs, and one morning he dreamed of his friend crashing a monoplane (rare in those days) in a meadow. In the dream, B. walked toward him out of the crash, unscathed, and explained that the crash had to do with the "beastly engine." Two days later, Dunne read a bulletin that B. had in fact died the morning he had his dream, and at about the same time, along with another man Dunne did not know, when a test plane they were flying crashed in a meadow near Oxford.

Since Dunne often had aviation-related nightmares at around 7 or 8 in the morning when loud traffic was in the streets, he could not assign any significance to the coincidence of time. But more importantly, when he himself later investigated the cause of the crash of B's plane— here note Dunne's forensic detective mind on display—he found that the engine had nothing to do with his friend's death: "the accident was due to the uncoupling of a quick-release gadget in one of the main 'lift' wires, and the consequent breaking upward of one wing."[39] The point of this detail is, "there would have been no doubt in B's mind that his wing had broken." Had it actually been B's "phantasm" visiting him upon his demise, that phantasm would not have attributed the crash to the plane's engine. Thus, however seductive the notion of crisis telepathy, or the more familiar spiritualist notion of visitation from "the other side," Dunne was able to readily falsify these explanations for his dream.

The timing of events is the critical thing: Dunne only investigated the crash and determined its true cause later on—this information was not yet known to him and was not contained in the paragraph in which he read of the incident. He thus determined that, *at the time he read and reacted to the news,* all his imagination would have had to go on was a comment the now-deceased pilot had actually made to Dunne's sister some days earlier—and that his sister would have relayed to him—*that he was worried about the engine in his plane.* Thus, the dream could not have been "of" the crash itself, nor of B's death per se, but "was associated with the personal experience of reading the paragraph."[40] As in the volcano dream, it was a dream of *his own future reaction to a personally affecting reading experience.* What that reading experience could not answer, his dreaming mind filled in using other information in his memory ("frog DNA" again), even if those details proved false. And it presented this ensemble of true and false knowledge in a dramatic frame that was also very much an invention of his imagination. "The dreaming mind," Dunne observed, "is a master-hand at tacking false interpretations on to everything it perceives."[41]

"I hope you won't blame Dunne for what didn't happen!"

So, if precognitive dreams really are "of" learning experiences and not "of" events as such, as Dunne argued, what exactly was the source of Captain Gladstone's dream about Goddard's plane crash on a rocky beach?

Gladstone, who was disguised with the pseudonym "Commander Dewing" in Goddard's *Saturday Evening Post* article, shipped out in HMS *Black Prince* the same morning Goddard took off for Tokyo in *Sister Ann*, so he could not have learned of the crash when he was in Shanghai, and it was not reported in the press ... until Goddard's article in 1951. But when Goddard arrived in Tokyo, he felt duty-bound to write a long letter to his acquaintance describing the ordeal. Goddard closes his story with Gladstone's reply, received months later:

> I am horrified to hear about your crash, and so long after the event. I went off to the Med. in a roundabout way the day you left, and have only just got your letter.
> I remember our meeting—you bet!—and I do vaguely remember that dream. But only very vaguely. You know what dreams are! No, I can't say that I actually saw you dead, but I certainly thought the crash was a killer. Glad it wasn't. And I hope you won't blame Dunne for what didn't happen![42]

Whether or not the crash itself was somehow influenced by Goddard's state of mind (that is, whether Gladstone "doomed" the flight with his careless divulgence of his dream), Gladstone found out about the crash—and thus would have had his precognitive dream—*because of Goddard's letter.*

So far, so good—it could indeed have been a full-on "Dunne dream," stimulated by a later reading experience rather than by the crash-landing per se.

But here is where the Dunne theory, and in fact practically any theory of precognition, may for many readers run aground—or perhaps

crash land—on the rocky beach of illogic: Goddard only sent that letter to Gladstone because of Gladstone's dream, and indeed that dream
is the only reason they met in the first place, and the only thing that
made the crash uncanny. The dream caused the letter, which caused the
dream. It was—if the precognition explanation be believed—a causal
loop, or what for convenience I call a time loop. The more familiar expression is "self-fulfilling prophecy," but whereas that usually is used in
a somewhat figurative sense, here it is meant quite literally.

Readers of science fiction may assume that such a causal tautology
is somehow related to the "grandfather paradox" that attaches to time
travel: The idea that if you went back in time, you could potentially kill
your own grandfather, which would prevent you from ever having been
born ... so that you couldn't go back in time and kill your grandfather
(more on which later). That assumption would be incorrect. Although
they often appear close to each other in pedants' bestiaries of common
faults of expression and logic, tautologies are not the same thing as
paradoxes.[43] If the universe allows information to travel backward in
time from an individual's future in such a way that it actually leads
the individual to "fulfill" a foreseen outcome (rather than thwart it),
then such loops would have to be the rule when it comes to precognition, and not the exception. We will see later that this is precisely how
"prophecy" works—it is *always* self-fulfilling.

I do not use the expression "time loop" to mean that the fabric
of spacetime itself is literally somehow warped, as in cosmological exotica like black holes or wormholes. Many people who have prophetic
dreams and "time slips" feel tempted to devise new theories of time
that, they think, are necessary to account for their experiences, including notions like temporal spirals, additional temporal dimensions, and
so on.[44] As I will argue in Part Two of this book, it may not be necessary
to know exactly what time is, or even what consciousness is, to solve
the problem of prophecy and precognition ... other than to suggest
what a number of mindblowing experiments in physics are now revealing: that information from the future does "travel backwards" to
influence the present. The only "new" mental model we really need to
help us navigate this weird territory of time loops is that (glass) block
supplied by Minkowski more than a century ago. But its implications
really are mind-bending and have only rarely been explored, either by
philosophers or by parapsychologists who (at least in principle) accept
the possibility of precognition.

To describe Gladstone's dream, for instance, as simply "a prophetic dream about a plane crash" misses the really head-scratching, "impossible," looping dimension of it. Gladstone didn't dream randomly about some plane crash somewhere; he dreamed about a plane crash involving a man he was going to have a personal interaction with the next day *because of his dream* and then get a very startling letter from a few months later, describing the crash ... and again, his dream was in all likelihood really *caused by* that letter, not the crash itself.

If we don't dismiss this whole affair as a case of faulty memory or random happenstance, or chalk it up to the vague "acausal" fog of synchronicity offered as a compromise by Carl Jung, the only explanation is a complex causal loop involving a man precognizing his own future reactions to a learning experience about a (future) acquaintance. *Gladstone's encounter with Goddard only occurred because of his dream; he only got Goddard's letter because of their encounter at the party; and his dream only occurred because of the letter.* And as we will see later in Part Three, when we delve into precognitive dreams and how they work, there may be additional psychodynamic wrinkles to this time loop. It was a dream after all—what would Sigmund Freud have to say about this one?

3

Postcards from Your Future Self —
Scientific Evidence for Precognition

"It's a poor sort of memory that only works backwards," the Queen remarked.

"What sort of things do you remember best?" Alice ventured to ask.

"Oh, things that happened the week after next," the Queen replied in a careless tone. "For instance ... there's the King's Messenger. He's in prison now, being punished: and the trial doesn't even begin till next Wednesday: and of course the crime comes last of all."

"Suppose he never commits the crime?" said Alice.

"That would be all the better, wouldn't it?" the Queen said ...

— Lewis Carroll, *Through the Looking-Glass* (1871)

K urt Vonnegut frequently hinted in his fiction that he believed in some kind of psychic connection between people. It is a premise in his novel *Cat's Cradle*, for instance, that we are linked to each other through networks of meaningful coincidences. When a writer on ESP phenomena named Alan Vaughan probed Vonnegut about whether these motifs sprang from anything in his own experience, the novelist volunteered an amazing, sad story of "telepathy or whatever" that occurred in 1958 and that happened to center on one of the most decisive turning points in his and his family's life.

Vonnegut described how in the mid-morning of September 15 that year, he suddenly left his study and walked across his Massachusetts house to the kitchen, where for no reason—just a funny feeling—he placed a long-distance call to the office of his brother-in-law, James Carmalt Adams, in New Jersey. "I had never telephoned him before, had no reason to call then." Adams wasn't at the office, and he would never arrive. At 10:30, the first two engines and three passenger cars of a commuter train went off an open drawbridge over Newark Bay, drowning Adams and 47 other passengers.

> There was a news flash over the radio about the railroad accident, without any details. I knew my brother-in-law had been on the train, though he had never taken the train before. I was on a plane within an hour, and had taken charge of his home and four children before the sun went down. My sister was a terminal cancer patient in a hospital at the time. She died the next day. My wife and I have since adopted and raised their children.[1]

Kurt was not the only Vonnegut to sense this looming upheaval in their lives—"my wife got the signals too." He told Vaughan that starting about two weeks before the tragedy, Jane Vonnegut "kept coming up with the odd notion: 'The refugees are coming, the refugees are coming.'"[2] And indeed, adding four newly orphaned boys to their own three children must have felt to the Vonneguts like running a refugee camp. Years later, in her own memoir about the aftermath of the tragedy, Jane remembered how even "allowing for some fantastic Einsteinian time warp, that was close enough to simultaneous for me to think that something really weird had been going on here. I had not yet heard of Jung's word *synchronicity*."[3] (Put a mental asterisk by that last word.

One of several ready go-tos in our culture's grab-bag of explanations for anomalous happenings is Carl Jung's "acausal connecting principle"; we'll be examining that concept with a critical eye later in this book.)

Vonnegut's out-of-nowhere urge to call his brother-in-law—and perhaps even his 1972 correspondence with Vaughan about the event—was undoubtedly in the back of his mind when he penned his 1973 novel *Breakfast of Champions*. In that book, the death of a 108-year-old woman sparks an odd, fleeting thought in the head of a man nine miles away, whose family she had cleaned laundry for when he was a little boy:

> Like all Earthlings at the point of death, Mary Young sent faint reminders of herself to those who had known her. She released a small cloud of telepathic butterflies, and one of these brushed the cheek of Dwayne Hoover, nine miles away.
>
> Dwayne heard a tired voice from somewhere behind his head, even though no one was back there. It said this to Dwayne: "Oh my, oh my."[4]

For half a century, the study of psychic experience was dominated by the concept of telepathy, the term first coined by psychologist Frederic W. H. Myers in 1882. Again, it meant a kind of communication between minds that could even, at least in a limited way, transcend time, and that manifested most often in times of crisis or trauma. The Victorian era was a time of growing cultural backlash against the reductive mechanism of Enlightenment science, which the sociologist Max Weber accused of having "disenchanted" the world and stripped human life of higher meaning and hope (Nietzsche's "death of God," etc.).[5] Among other things, the Newtonian, mechanistic, billiard-ball universe hadn't made room for any kind of knowing that could not be explained by some measurable energy carrying information across space (e.g., as light or sound waves). Information was physical, just as mind was physical, and if it could not be explained by physical principles, it was supernatural—and thus belief in it, no matter how widespread, amounted to superstition. Myers, like many thinkers of the time, challenged this Enlightenment view, but his theory of telepathy was still very much rooted in ideas and metaphors drawn from the science and technology of his day, especially then-new advances in telecommunications (the telegraph) and physics (radiation). His work—and his brilliant, "sciencey" neologism—was a strategic effort to rescue a vast domain of common human experience, "the psychical" (or what we would now call the paranormal), from the Enlightenment's dustbin of rejected, delegitimized human experiences.[6]

Besides collecting accounts of spontaneous cases of psychical phenomena and studying spiritualist mediums at work, SPR researchers also conducted telepathy experiments, for instance having participants make guesses about drawings or objects being viewed and "sent" by a partner nearby or at another location. But while such experiments often yielded interesting results, the subjective way results were assessed made them fall short of the standards being established in the relatively young field of scientific psychology.

In the early 1930s, two botanists at Duke University, Joseph Banks Rhine and his wife Louisa E. Rhine, began studying psychical phenomena with a new degree of experimental rigor, initially under the guidance of psychologist William McDougall. The Rhines' aim was to turn the study of psychical functioning, whatever it was, however it worked, into a real, quantitative science. As part of their overhaul-slash-facelift of psychical research, the Rhines renamed the field *parapsychology*; and to dispel the musty taint of Victorian drawing room séances, they gave a shiny new scientific name to their object of study: *extrasensory perception*, or ESP. The Rhines' initial research results were promising enough that in 1935 the Duke Parapsychology Laboratory was founded under J. B. Rhine's leadership.

To facilitate quantification and replication, Rhine used Zener cards in his experiments—decks of 25 cards, each showing one of five different symbols: a circle, a square, a star, a plus sign, or a group of three wavy lines. A typical protocol would involve one of a pair of student participants, the "sender," looking one by one at cards that had been drawn from shuffled decks, while another participant behind a screen or in another room would attempt to state which of the symbols had been drawn. (These are known as "forced choice" tasks—in contrast to the "free response" tasks involving drawings or verbal descriptions.) It was quickly discovered that some of the best test subjects performed just as well at "card guessing" when the target cards had not already been seen by anyone else. Ever rigorous about terms, the Rhines were careful to distinguish this separate skill of *clairvoyance*, or seeing things that were hidden or at a distance in space, from telepathy as such, although confusion over the boundaries between these two forms of ESP persisted in parapsychology for decades and is still the norm among laypeople.

Participants in the Rhines' lab tended to correctly guess more than the 20 percent that chance would dictate, but not by much, and participants' scores tended to drop as they became bored with the tasks—a widely seen phenomenon in parapsychology experiments known as the "decline effect." But over time, and after hundreds of experiments with large numbers of subjects, the support for telepathy and clairvoyance became substantial, at least statistically speaking. Nowadays we would say that the *significance* was high, while the *effect size* was low—an important distinction in all experimental research.

Initially it did not occur to the Rhines to study precognition—for instance by staggering the "sender's" looking at the card and the "receiver's" response in time. The mental model of thoughts being transmitted through space implied the same sort of simultaneity that would govern communication by telegraph or radio. Nevertheless, the Rhines and other researchers studying telepathy and clairvoyance found that participants in their experiments were sometimes able to guess cards or other targets *before* they were selected, without any apparent possibility of the subject predicting the result through ordinary inference. In this way, precognition emerged as a potentially separate, even more causally outrageous, third member of the ESP trinity.[7]

An Anomalous Anomaly

A serendipitous early experimental display of seeming precognition occurred in the context of a series of experiments conducted in 1939 by an English psychologist named Whately Carington. Carington wished to depart from the boring Zener card tasks that were yielding significant but unexciting results in the Rhines' protocols. Instead he reverted to an older method in telepathy research, using drawings as targets, but devised a scoring system that used independent judges and greater quantitative rigor than earlier drawing experiments had used.

On ten successive nights, Carington or his wife made a drawing of the first object named on a randomly selected page of a dictionary and hung the picture overnight on the wall of his office, which was curtained and closed to view by anyone outside. Meanwhile, from the comfort of their homes, 250 participants made drawings, on each night, of what they thought he had hung on the wall and then mailed their dated drawings to Carington. He repeated this ten-day experiment four more times, with some variations, for a total of 50 separate target drawings. Independent judges then scored the subjects' drawings—2,200 in all—based on how closely they resembled the target on display when the response was made.

The results were perplexing. For any given trial, the number of "hits" did not rise much above chance—which would be expected by anyone skeptical of the whole enterprise. Yet surprisingly, many of the drawings did match target drawings in the larger 10-target set for a given experiment. People seemed to be making "displaced hits" either into the past or, more impossibly, into the future.[8]

This seemed interesting, yet skeptical alarm bells will go off for any scientist, and Carington's immediate thought was that this could simply reflect coincidence, the law of large numbers at work. It is never kosher to adjust your hypothesis after the experiment, and talking about "displaced hits" sounds like shifting the goalposts to produce a positive result. So Carington ran an additional experiment to compare with the results of the first series: He created a separate set of 50 drawings of randomly produced nouns, the same way he had created the original targets, and used this new set of drawings as a control group in a new analysis of the original results with a brand-new, naïve set of judges.

The new judges found no more matches between the subjects' drawings in the five original experiments and *any* of the control drawings than would be expected by chance. These results seemed to confirm Carington's sense that some kind of ESP had indeed been operative in the original experiments. It really seemed as though the test subjects had been affected or influenced by the set of target drawings in their particular experiment, but in some cases even before the target drawing had been made or the noun selected from the dictionary. It suggested that (as Louisa Rhine later put it in her discussion of Carington's work) "to ESP, time is not the barrier it is in the world of sense perception."[9]

For Carington in 1940, when he reported on his drawing experiments in the *Proceedings of the Society for Psychical Research*, precognition was an anomalous anomaly, but it was not anomalous enough to challenge the prevailing model, inherited from the Victorians, that somehow information traveled through *space* and could somehow be received by individuals outside the ordinary sensory channels. Gradually, however, parapsychological researchers got more comfortable with the time- and mind-bending possibility that people can somehow gain information about future events, and designed experiments specifically to explore this bizarre realm of human psychology.

For instance in the 1960s, as part of a research program studying sleepers' ability to obtain dream impressions of paintings being viewed concurrently by another subject in a separate room ("dream telepathy"), psychologist Stanley Krippner, psychiatrist Montague Ullman, and parapsychologist Charles Honorton at Maimonides Medical Center in New York City ran two experiments with an experienced psychic "sensitive" to test whether he could dream of situations based on pictures randomly generated *after* the dream. In one of the experiments, over a series of eight nights, the subject scored five (of the possible eight) direct hits, again according to independent judges. It was experimental support (however modest) for Dunnean dream precognition.[10]

Then, beginning in the early 1970s, two laser physicists at Stanford Research Institute (SRI), Harold Puthoff and Russell Targ, conducted a government-funded research program into "remote viewing"—a less occult-sounding version of clairvoyance. In the early experiments, a psychic would be asked to describe or draw the scene at some randomly selected geographical location that was unknown to him or her, right as it was being visited by one of the experimenters; the psychic then would be taken to the site afterward as a form of feedback. On one notable early trial, star psychic subject Pat Price provided a detailed, accurate description of the Redwood City Marina several minutes before the experimenters (Puthoff and another associate) actually arrived at the location.[11] Targ and Puthoff then ran a series of experiments with another remote viewer, Hella Hammid, in which the target was selected and then visited by an experimenter *after* the subject had completed her viewing of the site; each of her four transcribed descriptions was matched correctly against the actual target by three independent (blind) judges.[12]

Beginning in the mid-1970s, a modified version of remote viewing that used geographical coordinates as targets was deployed as an intelligence-gathering tool, first by SRI psychics under the supervision of the CIA and later in the Defense Department–funded Star Gate program. The latter boasted a number of stunning successes including locating lost planes and providing intelligence on new weapons developments in the Soviet Union. These have now been described in several excellent histories and memoirs of the program, so I will not attempt to summarize this interesting chapter in ESP research.[13] But in some notable cases, Star Gate psychics were able to accurately describe an event in advance of its occurrence, again suggesting that remote viewing could be precognitive.[14] For instance during a Friday afternoon remote viewing session at Fort Meade, Maryland, in May 1987, a Star Gate remote viewer named Paul Smith elaborately described what seemed like an "accidental on purpose" missile strike on a warship somewhere near a desert country. His impressions made no sense given what he and the assigning officer knew of then-current geopolitics, and the notes from the session were filed away. The following Monday, newspaper headlines carried stories of the deadly "accidental" Iraqi missile attack on the USS *Stark* in the Persian Gulf.[15] The looseness about chronology in remote viewing was similar to what had been observed in earlier telepathy and clairvoyance experiments, leading to much speculation about how remote viewing might really work and its relationship, if any, to time.[16]

Over the span of two decades, from the mid 1970s until the mid 1990s, remote viewing experiments at SRI and at Science Applications International Corporation (SAIC, which took over the SRI research program in 1989) produced substantial support for psychic functioning.[17] University of California-Davis statistician Jessica Utts assessed the results of this research in a report commissioned by Congress. She argued that they greatly exceeded what would be expected by chance and could not be accounted for by methodological problems or fraud.[18] Utts has continued to defend these findings and the scientific study of ESP more generally. In her Presidential Address to the 2016 annual meeting of the American Statistical Association, Utts stated: "The data in support of precognition and possibly other related phenomena are quite strong statistically, and would be widely accepted if they pertained to something more mundane. Yet, most scientists reject the possible reality of these abilities without looking at the data!"[19]

Between 1976 and 1999, another laboratory, the Princeton Engineering Anomalies Research (PEAR) laboratory, conducted a large research program investigating "precognitive remote perception," involving subjects recording their impressions of geographical targets that would later be visited by an experimenter or in some cases had been visited in the past. The researchers, Brenda Dunne and PEAR Director Robert Jahn, conducted 653 trials of this type with 72 individuals. All the trials were labeled "precognitive" because the target for a given trial was always selected at random *after* the trial ended even if the target had already been visited. Over a third of the trials were "hits," as determined by independent judges, and the odds against chance of this success rate were determined to be 33 million to one. Participants were equally accurate no matter how far into the future (or past) they "viewed"—ranging from hours to weeks.[20]

In 1989, Charles Honorton and Diane C. Ferrari conducted a meta-analysis of 309 precognition experiments that had used forced-choice (e.g., Zener card) tasks by 62 investigators, involving over 50,000 participants, that had been conducted between 1935 and 1987.[21] They determined that 30 percent of the studies reached statistical significance, which may not sound like much, but only five percent would be expected from chance alone. With such a large number of experiments and trials (over two million), the overall significance of the meta-analysis was astronomical: on the order of ten septillion (10^{25}) to one. For the "file drawer effect" (leaving negative results unpublished) to negate that significance, there would have had to be 46 unpublished negative studies for *each* published study.[22] Those who cite this study often point out that while the overall effect size was small, it was comparable to or greater than major decisive studies in medicine, such as the study leading to the recommendation of using aspirin to help prevent heart attacks.[23]

There's a big problem, though. Despite years of searching, no researcher has ever detected any electromagnetic energy carrying ESP information across space, such as between participants in a Zener card telepathy task or between a remote viewer and some distant site or target object. Researchers in the U.S. and the U.S.S.R. often used Faraday cages, which shield against most forms of electromagnetic radiation, and also conducted tests between land and submarines (since seawater also shields against such radiation) and found that psychic abilities did not diminish as a function either of distance or of shielding—suggesting strongly that whatever is happening to produce the consistent positive experimental results, there is no physical transmission of information, at least not as we ordinarily understand it.[24] And as we will see later, even the evocative quantum-physical concept of *entanglement*, often indexed in popular books on ESP, cannot explain a transmission of information across space that would be necessary to explain telepathy or clairvoyance. As far as anyone knows, there is no meaningful quantum entanglement between separate individuals' bodies, or between a person's brain and a distant object or a picture in an envelope. This lack of an obvious physical mechanism has been one of the major impediments to making *psi* (the Rhines' neutral term for the principle underlying ESP) believable or even palatable to scientists outside the small field of parapsychology: Despite what the data purport to show, there is no physical way it ought to be possible.

Or is there? There is one thing that is very hard to "shield" against, and that is the psychic getting some form of feedback later in his or her life. Experiments testing alleged telepathy or clairvoyance/remote viewing in laboratory contexts frequently include some form of direct feedback to the participants immediately following a session, letting them know how well they did. Even when there is no feedback given as part of the experiment, it may often be possible to find out "the right answer" later. If precognition is real, then any kind of confirmation available later could theoretically be the origin of what only *seemed* to have been information gained via some other, easier-to-comprehend ESP modality.

This argument has been floated cautiously again and again in the literature on ESP.[25] It is essentially the conclusion reached by J. W. Dunne based on his forensic scrutiny of his own dreams, for instance. However much it seemed on the surface like clairvoyance or some other psychic modality, information that "came true" in his dreams could always be traced to his own future experiences, including reading experiences about distant events like a volcano eruption. Yet his Serialism theory, with its multiple levels of consciousness and the implication that our highest consciousness transcends the physical body, tended to distract from the more materialist conclusion his data pointed to: that precognition was, as it were, "all in his head"—his brain communicating with itself across time.

In 1974, Columbia University physicist and futurist Gerald Feinberg proposed a brain-based theory of precognition at a meeting of quantum physicists and parapsychologists in Geneva, Switzerland. If precognition exists, he argued, it is most likely a neurobiological phenomenon related to memory, but in reverse—or what he called "memory of things future."[26] He speculated, given the small effects seen in laboratory ESP research, that this faculty may be linked only to short-term memory, and thus works mainly for near-future experiences, and that in any case it could only bring information on events occurring or learned about during an individual's lifetime. He also suggested, tentatively, that many, perhaps all, other kinds of ESP "can be explained in terms of ordinary perception combined with precognition."[27] Feinberg was a bit of a maverick, who had made waves in physics circles as well as the popular science press in the late 1960s with his hypothesized particles called *tachyons*, which travel faster than light and thus backward in time.[28] Tachyons have never been found and are today no longer believed to exist. But as I will be arguing later, his suggestion about precognition and its relation to memory may have been highly prescient.

More recently, physicist Edwin May, who directed the ESP research at SRI after 1986 and then headed the program researching "anomalous cognition" (May's preferred term) after it was transferred to SAIC, and psychologist Sonali Bhatt Marwaha have also argued that all forms of ESP are likely precognition misinterpreted or misidentified.[29] Unlike Feinberg, they do not assume precognition is solely an "inside the head" phenomenon[30]; but reducing anomalous cognition to precognition is a bold step that may move the field of parapsychology forward by, as they say, "collaps[ing] the problem space"[31] of these phenomena. What has always seemed like several small piles of interesting but perhaps not overwhelming data supporting various diverse forms of psi or anomalous cognition may really be a single, impressively large pile of evidence for the much more singular, astonishing, and as I hope to show, physically plausible ability of people to access information arriving from their own future.

In Part Two, where I address the possible "nuts and bolts" of this ability, I will be making a case for precognition being something close to Feinberg's "memory of things future"—an all-in-the-head information storage and retrieval process, but one that is not limited to short-term memory. Evidence from life and laboratory suggests it may be possible, within limits, to "premember" experiences days, months, and years in our future, albeit dimly and obliquely, in a manner not all that different from how we remember experiences in our past. The main qualitative difference would be that, unlike memory for past experiences, we have no *context* for recognizing information from our future, let alone interpreting or evaluating it, and thus will seldom even notice its existence. We would also have little ability to directly search our memory for things future, the way we can rummage in our mental attic for information we know we acquired earlier in life. Yet things we will learn in our future may "inform" us in many non-conscious ways, and this information may be accessed in dreams and art and tasks like ESP experiments that draw on ill-defined intuitive abilities.

It is a hypothesis that remains to be explored and tested, but it could elegantly explain not only many anecdotal claims of precognition but also many experimental findings across ESP research, such as Whately Carington's "displaced hits."

* * *

Again, precognition was still a new and poorly-thought-out idea in 1940, and Carington did not know how to grapple with the implications of his results, so the possibility that participants might have been precognizing later feedback or information they might acquire through normal sensory channels *after* the experiment never occurred to him. Nor did it occur to later commentators like Louisa Rhine. But what we now need to realize, in light of the strong evidence supporting precognition, is that whether or not Carington actually hung the drawings up on his wall may have made no difference. In fact, he might not have needed to make drawings at all, *but only say he did* … in his published results.

If precognition is the influence on an individual's behavior of information that will be conventionally acquired later, including interesting future reading experiences as Dunne observed with his dreams—and by extension, even *false or erroneous reading experiences taken as true*—then any experiment participant who read Carington's article, "Experiments on the Paranormal Cognition of Drawings" in *Proceedings of the Society for Psychical Research* in 1940, would have had higher-than-chance odds of making drawings that matched some of the targets during the experiment a year before, in 1939. In his article, Carington explicitly lists the 10 targets for each of the five experiments—"bracket, buffalo, hand," and so on. The article was effectively what May and Marwaha call an "answer book."[32] Psychics and remote viewers may be people who intuitively know how to cheat by peeking at this book when making responses to questions they couldn't conventionally already know the answers to.

The precognitive hypothesis could account not only for the higher-than-chance correspondence between the participants' drawings and Carington's drawing sets for each experiment but also for the displacement factor. Even though all five experiments were written up in the same article, the lists of ten target objects for each group were listed separately, distinctly identified by their dates, as was identifying information for each group of subjects (e.g., "students in Dr. Thouless's lecture class" or "members of Mr. O. L. Zangwill's Workers Educational Association psychology class," etc.). Readers curious about how well they had done in the experiment a year earlier would have been quickly able to find their own experiment and the list of drawings. Getting the exact day right would have been unlikely, however—it would mean "pre-membering" exactly on which night you drew which picture, a tall order at a year's remove even for memory going the usual direction.[33]

A further detail also supports this interpretation. The published article gives verbal labels for the targets (the nouns extracted randomly from the dictionary) rather than reproducing the target drawings that Carington and his wife made of them. As might be expected if participants were making their drawings informed by future reading of his article, Carington noted that the "hits" seemed as if the subject had responded to the verbal label for the object (e.g., the word "hand") rather than to the picture:

> There is virtually no indication that subjects in any sense 'see' and copy the original. On the contrary, everything seems to happen much more as if those who scored hits had been told, 'Draw a Hand,' for example, than 'Copy this drawing of a Hand'. It is, so to say, the 'idea' or 'content', or 'meaning' of the original that gets over, not the form.[34]

Interestingly enough, this is nearly opposite the pattern reported in other early drawing experiments and in remote viewing experiments at SRI when feedback was available, which usually consisted of being taken to the site after the remote viewing session or being shown the object or picture visually. In those cases, subjects reported getting sketchy visual impressions during the task, with no sense of the identity or meaning of the object/location.[35] This has always been interpreted as a function of the distinctly nonverbal, non-analytical, "right-brained" nature of ESP.[36] Could it instead simply reflect the format (visual versus verbal) in which the feedback will be later received?

As an explanation for Carington's results, the precognitive hypothesis can be only that, a hypothesis. There is at this distance no way of knowing the identity of the individual participants or what their subsequent reading habits consisted of, including which ones went on to read his article later in their lives or otherwise may have received feedback directly from Carington. "Participants' Life and Learning Experiences Subsequent to the Experiment" are never included in published results of ESP experiments (or any psychology experiments), and it is obviously impossible to know, when you publish an article, who is destined to read the article later. Interestingly, Carington noted that a group of participants at Rhine's lab across the Atlantic at Duke University participated in the fourth and fifth experiments and scored exceptionally well. One possibility is that, having prior interest and experience in the field of telepathy research, as well as ready access to the *Proceedings of the Society for Psychical Research*, this group may have been more likely than the other participants to peruse Carington's article a year later.[37]

Attempts to experimentally assess the role feedback may be playing in ESP performance have produced inconsistent and unclear results. The SRI researchers considered feedback important to ESP performance, but they generally interpreted its role as psychological—the importance of feedback in learning a new skill, as well as bringing closure to a trial before moving on to the next one.[38] Later, Edwin May and two colleagues conducted studies of anomalous cognition at various intensities of feedback flashed on a tachistoscope, including a complete absence of feedback in certain trials. They reported that the two most experienced participants (of four) scored well at describing or drawing unseen, randomly selected target images both when the images were flashed after the session and in trials when they did not see this feedback, leading the researchers to conclude that feedback is not necessary.[39]

On the other hand, Marwaha and May reported an interesting experiment in which participants remote viewed randomly selected photos of sites around the Bay Area; the photos had been taken months earlier, but feedback consisted of being taken to the actual site after the remote viewing session. Participants' drawings and descriptions tended to match the sites as they existed when visited, in some cases differing significantly from the photographs (e.g., ponds had dried in the interim, or there was new construction). In other words, psychics' responses conformed to the feedback, not the intended "target."[40] In their meta-analysis of precognition studies, Honorton and Ferrari found a difference between studies that included feedback to the participants and those that did not. The strongest results were from experiments that included participants who had done well in previous experiments, were tested individually, and received feedback after each trial.[41] Performance in precognition tasks seems to correlate with the availability of confirming information in the participant's (near) future, yet the reason why is still debated.

The "precognition only" argument is not widely held among parapsychologists or remote viewers, who often report a subjective conviction that some part of their consciousness has left their body and is actually present at the location they are "viewing." But the most storied and successful living remote viewer, Joseph McMoneagle, concluded that his successes were not a function of mentally traveling across space but of receiving information from his future self. McMoneagle distinguished himself (and even earned a Legion of Merit award) for a series of stunning psychic exploits during his years on the Star Gate program. For instance, in late 1979, he was shown a photograph of a large building near a body of water and asked to describe what was going on inside it; he was told only that the building was somewhere in Russia. Over the course of a few sessions, he described and drew in detail a huge double-hulled submarine being constructed inside the building. Unknown to him, the building was adjacent to the White Sea, near the Arctic Circle, yet construction of a submarine at that location seemed impossible, given that there was no access to the ocean from the building. Authorities at the National Security Council who reviewed his notes and drawings thought what he had "seen" was absurd. But early the following year, his report was confirmed by satellite images showing a new deep trench that had been dug from building to the water, and a new enormous "Typhoon" class sub (the vessel featured in Tom Clancy's novel *The Hunt for Red October*) with numerous specific details matching his description.[42] When asked over a decade later how he thought remote viewing works, McMoneagle put it plainly:

> Simply put, I think that I am sending myself information from the future. In other words, at some point in the future I will come to know the answer to whatever question has been put to me in the past. Therefore, *whenever* the information is passed to me in its accurate form, that is when I send it back to myself in the past.[43]

According to such a logic, many if not all anecdotal accounts of spontaneous "telepathy" experiences could also be precognition in disguise. Notoriously, for example, some twins report telepathic connection, being able to feel each other's injuries or knowing of crises happening to each other even when living far away. But you cannot know for sure your twin sister broke her arm until you call her on the phone and find out about it—some physical, real-world confirmation is the only way to verify a "psychic" intuition. That phone call (or letter, or email) may in many or even all cases be the real source of that psi-acquired knowledge. (We will see later why it would be very easy to misattribute the source of anomalous insights gained via precognition.)

Whether and to what extent precognition can account for all ostensible forms of ESP—a still-open question—it is reasonable to suppose that precognition, not telepathy (or some cosmic alignment of archetypes a la Jung's synchronicity), was at work in the Vonneguts' case too. The butterflies that brushed Kurt's cheek did not fly all the way from his drowning brother-in-law James Adams in New Jersey; they flew from himself in his own future, when he was informed that Adams had been on the ill-fated train—a tragic piece of news with huge implications for his own future and that of his family. They were precognitive, not telepathic, butterflies.

4

The Psi Reflex — Presentiment and the Future-Influencing-Present Effect

Nor will it be possible in the future to dismiss as negligible the phenomenon of precognition, whether in dreams or in a state of wakefulness. Thus, exceeding the bounds of "official psychology," the American Atomic Energy Commission proposed in 1958 that "clairvoyants" should be employed in an attempt to foresee where Russian bombs would fall in the event of war. (31ˢᵗ August, 1958, Report of the Rand Commission.)

— Louis Pauwels and Jacques Bergier,
The Morning of the Magicians (1960)

Although countless science-fiction stories and movies have explored precognition, without doubt the most interesting "serious" literary exploration of the topic is Thomas Pynchon's unfinished 1973 novel *Gravity's Rainbow*. That sprawling menagerie of wild conspiracies and crazy characters, set during and after WWII in Europe, centers on the fate of an American army lieutenant, Tyrone Slothrop, whose amorous conquests around London during the Blitz infallibly predict V2 rocket strikes in an otherwise random distribution throughout the city. Slothrop's weird ability puts him under the scrutiny of "Psi Section," a division of military intelligence, who link his strange gift to Pavlovian conditioning he experienced as an infant. The hope of the various shadowy figures observing and pursuing Slothrop through much of the 760-page novel is somehow to exploit his ability ... but first, they have to simply understand it.[1]

It is hinted in the story that two decades earlier, a mad genius experimenter named Dr. Lazslo Jamf had used the infant Slothrop's erections as the "target reflex" tied to an unspecified conditioned stimulus "X." Classical Pavlovian conditioning, the basis of many human learning mechanisms and most familiar to nonscientists in the form of animal training, involves pairing an arbitrary event, called the "conditioned stimulus," with an animal's or person's instinctive response to a natural reward. Pavlov's model for this was his famous dogs: By repeatedly pairing the sound of a bell with a dog's natural response of salivating at the smell of food, he conditioned the animals to salivate at the sound of the bell even when there was no food present. The implication, in the novel, is that Dr. Jamf had paired the infant Slothrop's erections to some entropic stimulus, which somehow resulted, much later, in his adult habit of having sex right where one of Hitler's rocket-bombs would fall the next day.

The secret of Slothrop's condition(ing)—the mysterious X to which his infantile sexual response was paired—remains unanswered all the way through to an increasingly uncertain outcome, in which Slothrop descends into madness and even the circumstances of his childhood (including the very existence of Dr. Jamf) are called into question. I call *Gravity's Rainbow* "unfinished" because most readers do not get this far, detecting at some point about midway through that answers, and resolution, may not be forthcoming. But this has not prevented *Gravity's Rainbow* from being regarded as one of the masterpieces of 20th century literature, along with other unfinished works like *A Remembrance of Things Past* (readers of which usually don't get very far "past" the eating of the madeleine) or *Finnegan's Wake*.[2]

The difficulty of completion notwithstanding, Slothrop's gift is one of 20th century literature's most memorable MacGuffins. And as crazy and comical as it seems, his unique take on psychic phenomena proved to be uncannily prescient of parapsychological research of the decades that followed the novel's publication. These included not only the weaponizing of psi abilities, the purpose of the government-funded ESP research mentioned in the last chapter, but also subsequent research tying some kind of precognitive ability to people's involuntary reflexes.

The most interesting body of parapsychological research in the past two decades centers on detecting and responding to future stimuli outside of conscious awareness, the ability sometimes called *presentiment,* or "feeling the future."

From early on, parapsychologists had realized that ESP, whatever it is and however it works, largely seems to operate unconsciously and is often accessed best in the context of physical tasks that do not require deliberation or analysis.[3] In the 1990s, an electrical engineer then at the University of Nevada named Dean Radin designed experiments that used subjects' autonomic responses as a possible index of their ability to sense future events. In one 1997 study, he measured the skin conductance, heart rate, and blood flow to the fingertips of students and other adult volunteers while they viewed a series of randomly selected photographs—either calm landscapes and nature scenes or erotic photos or autopsies expected to elicit an emotional response. In addition to the expected high degree of arousal after seeing the emotional pictures, there was a smaller but distinct increase in arousal—what he called an "orienting pre-sponse"—peaking a second *before* the arousing (erotic or violent) images but not neutral pictures.[4] He conducted other similar experiments measuring eye movements and brainwave activity and found similar presponses to imminent stimuli.

Inspired by Radin's work, several other researchers have pursued presentiment studies, with similar success. Neuropsychologist James Spottiswoode and physicist Edwin May reported skin-conductance changes in advance of noise bursts.[5] At the University of Amsterdam, psychologist Dick Bierman and neuroscientist H. Steven Scholte reported increased activity in the visual cortex and amygdala (measured using fMRI) prior to randomly presented emotional pictures but not neutral pictures; men showed an anticipatory response to erotic pictures only, whereas women showed an anticipatory response to both erotic and violent pictures.[6] Neuroscientist Julia Mossbridge and colleagues at Northwestern University measured skin conductance in a picture-guessing task, finding that male participants' arousal increased significantly up to 10 seconds prior to a correct "hit," but not women's—possibly pointing to the greater reward males feel at being right.[7] A meta-analysis of 26 presentiment studies found high significance for this body of research; 87 negative unpublished studies would be needed to nullify their statistical significance.[8] A critical analysis of research in presentiment—also known as "predictive anticipatory activity"—by a team that included Jessica Utts (the statistician mentioned earlier) found it highly unlikely that statistical manipulations (sometimes called "*p*-hacking") could account for the positive results seen in these experiments.[9]

The most widely reported and controversial research on the unconscious influence of future stimuli on behavior—indeed possibly the most scandalous ESP research ever—was the series of studies mentioned in the Introduction by Cornell University psychologist Daryl Bem. Over the course of several years, Bem conducted a series of nine large experiments, involving over 1,000 student participants, in which he reversed the causal direction in four basic psychological paradigms: *reinforcement, priming, habituation,* and *facilitation of recall.*[10] In all four types of experiment, he found astonishing, seemingly time-defying effects. (Since Bem's experiments measured task performance rather than physiological responses, they are sometimes distinguished as tests of "implicit precognition,"[11] but for simplicity I will consider them under the "presentiment" rubric.)

Reinforcement is the tendency to respond positively to reward and negatively to punishment—the basis of operant conditioning, somewhat different from classical Pavlovian conditioning but involving similar brain mechanisms. In Bem's inversions of the usual temporal sequence, student participants tried to pick which "curtain" on a computer screen concealed a picture, clicking on the selected curtain to reveal if they were right. Some of the pictures were erotic (positive reinforcement), while others were neutral. Participants' accuracy at picking the right curtain did not deviate from chance when the picture was neutral, but they were significantly more accurate when the picture was erotic. Unknown to the participants, the correct answers were randomly selected *after* they made their choices, so it was distinctly a test of precognition, not clairvoyance—there were no pictures "already there" behind the curtains.

Priming, the ability of brief, subtle, or subliminal stimuli to affect our behavior, is commonly used in psychology to measure the influence of unconscious processing. In a standard priming study, participants' reaction time is measured when they press buttons on a keyboard to indicate a choice in response to some stimulus, but a few seconds beforehand they are very briefly exposed to a picture or word that they do not consciously register but that may make one or the other choice response faster or more likely. In Bem's priming studies, he reversed the usual order, placing the prime *after* the choice, not before. Participants indicated whether they found a picture on the screen pleasant or unpleasant, after which a word like "ugly" or "beautiful" would be flashed over one of the pictures quickly enough that it would not be detected consciously but might subliminally be registered. The data suggested that primes received after the button press influenced the rapidity of participants' responses—another seemingly impossible finding from the standpoint of ordinary linear causality.

Habituation is the tendency of both positive and negative reactions to stimuli to diminish with repeated exposure. For example, if subjects are subliminally primed with an appealing picture, when they are later asked to choose whether they prefer it or another picture, they will tend to choose the other one because the appeal of the one they've already glimpsed has diminished. Vice versa for negative or unappealing pictures. In Bem's studies, the "habituation" took place after the students were presented with the options and made their choices. Again, significant deviations from chance in the results showed evidence that participants were biased by their *subsequent* exposure to certain stimuli.

And lastly, inspired by the White Queen in Lewis Carroll's *Through the Looking Glass*, who explains to Alice that memory can go in both directions, Bem also conducted experiments in which participants were tested on words they had previously seen in a learning session, with the twist that some of the words were shown again *after* their test in a subsequent "practice phase." In keeping with his other results, participants tended to recall better the words that they were shown after the test. The take-home point of this and the rest of Bem's studies is that our behavior seems to be conditioned not only by what we have learned or been exposed to in the past but also, to some small but significant extent, by what we will learn or be exposed to in the future.

Besides ridicule, Bem's article prompted a great deal of soul-searching by psychologists concerned that his impossible findings were a symptom of a rot in the heart of their science. It led to an avalanche of efforts to replicate other findings whose significance was now in doubt because the researchers had used the same standard statistical procedures Bem had relied on. A large-scale effort to replicate 100 findings in three top-tier psychological science journals was only successful in 36 percent of the studies, revealing that possibly the majority of what was getting published in the field was subpar science.[12] Meanwhile though, smugly dismissive claims that Bem's "feeling the future" findings could not be replicated, which appeared quickly on the paper's heels, proved premature: A 2016 meta-analysis of 90 replications of his studies, 79 by researchers in other laboratories, supported his conclusion that future stimuli can affect people's behavior.[13] Statistical analysis of the results placed the significance level in the highest category for Bayesian statistical analysis, "decisive evidence," even when Bem's own replications were excluded. Over 500 experiments with negative results would have had to be left in file drawers to nullify this level of significance.

The psychical researchers of Frederic Myers' generation had viewed psychical ability as reflecting our higher consciousness, a dim adumbration of the next phase in our evolution,[14] and there is a long tradition, dating back two millennia to the Hindu yogi Patanjali, of viewing psychic abilities as "superpowers" (*siddhis*) attained through rigorous mental exercise.[15] In contrast, the presentiment research of Radin, Bem, and others is a natural outgrowth of the modern evolutionary assumption that whatever the nature of our future-feeling or future-sensing faculty, its expression must have a basic survival function for the organism and thus may actually reflect our "lower" functions and our evolutionary past, not our future. ESP has not been as extensively studied in animals as in humans, but suggestive research has supported something like ESP in animals. One series of experiments by maverick biologist Rupert Sheldrake, for example, supported the idea that animal companions have a sixth sense about imminent rewards such as the return of their owners.[16] At least one recent study also suggests that planarian worms—the simplest animals with a nervous system—may be able to orient away from future aversive stimuli as much as a minute in advance.[17]

For humans, an ability to orient toward social rewards would be highly adaptive, and this may be what we see in familiar experiences like the famous "sense of being stared at." Psychologists dismiss such a sense as a mistaken product of selection bias: Instances where you turned your head and didn't find another person looking back at you get left in your mental file drawer. On the other hand, experiments by Sheldrake have substantiated the existence of the phenomenon.[18] If presentiment serves a social orienting function, orienting us to another's looks is precisely the kind of experience it might be expected to give rise to.

That something like presentiment may be a basic adaptive trait is an argument made forcefully by James Carpenter, a clinician and parapsychological researcher at the Rhine Center in North Carolina. Synthesizing a vast array of findings across parapsychology into a single theoretical framework, he argues that ESP manifests constantly in our lives as part of an always-unconscious faculty he calls "first sight." [19] It is, he argues, the "leading edge" in our perception, preparing us for action, and even the ground of our efficacy in the world—"not an occasional ability but … an unconscious feature of each person's ongoing engagement with reality."[20] Carpenter does not limit first sight to our ability to sense the future—he includes other abilities classically distinguished from precognition, like telepathy and clairvoyance, as well as *psychokinesis* (PK) or mind-over-matter abilities. Whatever its scope, his basic argument, that first sight is "always at work, but always out of sight,"[21] is an important corrective to the common assumption that, if something like ESP exists, it must be a rare occurrence. We should not confuse how difficult we find imagining a thing with how difficult nature finds accomplishing it. If it exists at all, then first sight would not be some rare exception to nature's rules. It must be part of nature, and it would probably be ubiquitous—indeed fundamental—even if we don't yet understand how it works.

The Spy Downstairs

If first sight is a basic, adaptive trait, an aspect of our "lower" animal nature, we might expect it to manifest most strongly when our higher executive functions are off-line or taking a back seat. Precognition has often been linked to altered states of consciousness—not only dreams but also trance, meditation,[22] hypnagogic/hypnopompic states,[23] out-of-body experiences,[24] and the effects of hallucinogens.[25] Perhaps most importantly, it is also linked to "flow states" in which we engage in highly practiced creative as well as physically enjoyable or thrilling activities with high stakes. Michael Murphy, a pioneer in the human potential movement and co-founder of the Esalen retreat in Big Sur, California, wrote of transcendental and psychic experience manifesting in sports and martial arts, for example.[26] Some form of sixth sense guiding and protecting particularly intuitive soldiers has long been reported in war, and the Office of Naval Research reported in 2014 that it is actively pursuing research into how "Spidey sense" may work.[27] Mountain climbers and others in stressful or extreme situations report a dissociative, possibly precognitive state to which they often attribute their survival.[28]

One skilled, high-stakes physical activity with notorious links to precognition (as well as other paranormal phenomena) is aviation. As in combat or mountain climbing, piloting an aircraft requires senses attuned and alert, and puts the pilot in a thrilling, highly connected state of flow. Victor Goddard's precognitive "time slip" experience while flying over an abandoned air base in Drem, Scotland, was just one of several psychic phenomena he claimed to experience in his life;[29] notably, this one occurred as he was trying to navigate safely through a storm, necessitating heightened attention and adrenaline. Arctic explorer and aviator Sir George Hubert Wilkins reported a kind of psychic intuition he called "provenance" protecting him in his adventures.[30] Pioneer female aviator Jacqueline Cochran, a close friend of Amelia Earhart, reported in her memoir a facility with ESP, including several instances in which she psychically located missing aircraft.[31] WWII bomber pilot-turned-writer Martin Caidin reported a facility with psychic abilities and may have prophesied the real-life Apollo 13 space disaster in one of his novels.[32] (He also chronicled psychic and paranormal experiences in other pilots.[33]) One of the more naturally gifted psychics studied as part of the ESP research program at SRI was Richard Bach, pilot and author of the 1970 bestseller *Jonathan Livingston Seagull*.[34]

Acting, singing, playing a musical instrument, and other kinds of performance, when engaged in with skill and complete immersion, may also be conducive to precognition.[35] In the ancient world, prophecy manifested in song. I have argued elsewhere that mediumship may also be a form of disguised precognition, and it too is a performance, demanding physical engagement and a suppression of the critical intellect (to such a degree, in fact, that many mediums have no conscious memory of their trances afterward).[36] The performative dimension could also account for the oft-observed (and confusing) link between apparently genuine ESP phenomena and stage magic, another skilled and semi-high-stakes activity that takes the performer's critical faculties off-line temporarily. Russell Targ, one of the physicists in charge of the remote viewing research program at SRI, reported to Jeffrey Kripal that he received what he thought was real telepathic information while performing stage magic as a young man.[37] "Mixed mediumship" is the term for the oft-noted admixture of possibly real psi phenomena with stage trickery among magicians and mediums.[38]

And then there are fiction writers. Historians of psychic phenomena are fortunate to have a particularly rich record of precognitive experiences in the lives of writers. This is partly a natural file-drawer effect: Reports of anomalous experiences in the lives of athletes and soldiers, for example, would be relatively rare simply because sports and combat do not leave as rich a paper trail as writing. But additionally, because writing is (for some writers at least) precisely an enjoyable flow activity that engages an individual's intuitive and creative juices, the very act of recording ideas and inspirations may induce an "altered state" conducive to channeling information from a writer's future.[39] It is like attaching a printer directly to the phenomenon of interest. In memoirs and interviews, writers often describe their creative frenzies as a kind of trance in which ideas come unbidden; some report feeling that the thoughts of some other entity or higher self are being transcribed or channeled. In the last part of this book, we will examine two writer-precogs, Morgan Robertson and Philip K. Dick, who both described feeling possessed by a feminine muse when they wrote. Is "inspiration"—which originally meant possession by a divine spirit—simply a psychologically neutral term for drawing precognitively or presentimentally on a writer's own future?

One striking example of possible literary presentiment is that of Norman Mailer. Mailer had become famous at age 25 for his debut novel *The Naked and the Dead* (1947), but he struggled mightily with his second, *Barbary Shore* (1951), about a writer who rents a room in a Brooklyn Heights rooming house in order to write a novel. The writer character finds that his artist neighbors are an interesting mix, including a middle-aged Communist who is hounded by an FBI agent and turns out to have been a spy for the KGB. Mailer told an interviewer years later that he was plagued by a sense of disbelief in what he was writing—it seemed unrealistic to him: "The greatest single difficulty with the book was that my common sense thought it was impossible to have all these agents and impossible heroes congregating in a rooming house in Brooklyn Heights."[40] But like many artists, Mailer felt he had to honor and follow his inspiration wherever it led. He had to force himself to complete the book, and when it was panned by critics, he said, he resigned himself to forever being a second-rate writer.

Six years, a third novel, and a stint in Hollywood after *Barbary Shore*'s publication and savage reviews, Mailer found himself actually working in a studio in Brooklyn Heights, and one summer day (August 8, 1957) he was shocked to read a stunning *New York Times* cover story: "RUSSIAN COLONEL IS INDICTED HERE AS TOP SPY IN U.S." The "Colonel" shown in the picture below the headline was the 55-year-old Russian painter and guitarist who worked in the room directly below his, just one floor down. He was known by his fellow artists in the building as Emil Goldfus, but his real name, the story said, was Colonel Rudolf Abel, of the KGB. The first paragraph of the story explained that Abel was "the most important spy ever caught in the United States."[41] (Like in a spy novel, Abel had been caught after the FBI decoded a piece of microfilm a newsboy had found hidden in a hollow nickel.)

"I have always been overcome with that," Mailer told the interviewer. "It made me decide there's no clear boundary between experience and imagination. Who knows what glimpses of reality we pick up unconsciously, telepathically."[42] There's that T word again. But telepathy does not fit the facts of Mailer's case at all. He did not live or work in that building when he was writing *Barbary Shore*; at that point in his life he had never seen or interacted with "Emil Goldfus." When gripped by the Communist spy character "McLeod," who took over the novel-in-progress he was wrestling with at the end of the 1940s, Mailer is more likely to have been influenced by his own unsettled and shocked reaction to a *New York Times* cover story he would encounter seven or more years later—at least, as long as we do not chalk it up to chance.

Banging furiously at a typewriter and the other skilled activities I mentioned are all forms of rewarding physical engagement, for which Tyrone Slothrop's compulsive amorous activity (i.e., sex and seduction) is a perfect metaphor. The fact that Slothrop's "gift" is rooted in conditioning is thus highly realistic (even, as I suggested, prescient[43]). In fact, given precognition's connection to arousal, excitement, and athletic or creative flow states and the fact that it seems to operate almost entirely outside of conscious awareness or control, it may be fruitful to take a reductive, even behaviorist approach to defining it—or perhaps, "prehaviorist" might be a better term: Fundamentally, precognition seems to be not seeing or knowing or even feeling the future; rather, it seems to be a matter of *producing a behavior that is tied to a forthcoming reward*. The behavior could be a physiological response such as a movement or an emotion; it could be a dream, or an utterance, or a drawing, or a novel. The reward might be physical, as in sex or the gratification of other biological and social needs; or it could be the gratification of successfully accomplishing a task. In an ESP task, it could simply be the satisfaction of being right.[44] The reward could be intellectual, as in learning something new and exciting—such as reading a news story about a volcano eruption or the unmasking of a Russian spy. As we will see later in this book, the reward may often be existential: finding out we (will) have survived some chaotic or entropic threat to our survival.

Whatever the mechanism, this influence by future emotional rewards would be the basis of the intuitive guidance system that takes over whenever we follow our gut or whenever we act skillfully and instinctively in any domain. A premonition or hunch or creative inspiration that pays off in a confirmatory action is part of a reward loop, entraining the attentional faculty on those meaningful experiences coming down the pike. Engaged flow states may not only open the door to precognition by focusing the senses and busying the critical, conscious mind with other matters, they may also condition the precognitive apparatus, providing constant payoffs that propel us forward to the next reward in an ongoing chain—like feeding sardines to the dolphin of intuition.[45]

In this model, a presponsive behavior needs to be seen as one half of a two-part system, the other half being our everyday actions and experiences unfolding in linear time that serve to confirm it and thus give it meaning—for instance, Norman Mailer's encounter with the *New York Times* headline about the spy downstairs. The crucial role played by confirmation is part of what makes the whole topic suspect for skeptics and even for many parapsychologists open to other forms of ESP. Since hindsight is biased by a kind of selection, it is difficult or impossible in many cases to prove that ostensible precognition is not either memory error or "just coincidence." The difficulties go even deeper, in fact. As we will see later, a *retrospective* tunnel vision on events, especially after surviving some trauma—ranging from the most extreme, death and disaster, to minor chaotic upheavals like reading about a plane crash or a close brush with international espionage in the newspaper—seems to be precisely what people precognize or pre-sense in their future. *We precognize our highly biased hindsight*, taking us deep into a kind of recursive or fractal, M. C. Escher territory.

This fractal quality, coupled with our ignorance of precognitive or presentimental processes working in our lives, creates the causal circularity or time loops I have mentioned. Such loops may be a universal feature of a world that includes precognitive creatures who are unaware of their precognition. For instance, just imagine how weird it would have been for Mailer to read the headline about the spy in his building, as well as its vaguely unsettling subhead: "A NINE-YEAR PLOT—Suspect Said to Have Used Brooklyn Studio to Direct Network." Mailer noted that he probably shared the elevator with this KGB Colonel many times, without ever suspecting who he was. But the source of the headline's shock, and thus the whole reason Mailer would have been "inspired" by it years earlier, was not merely that the agent happened to be in his building, but the fact that he had already written about that exact situation: a KGB spy working in a Brooklyn Heights building full of artists and a novelist like himself. (We'll see another, oddly similar example of this kind of fractal literary time loop, also involving a bizarre encounter with a new neighbor a writer seemingly had "written about" years earlier, when we come to the story of Philip K. Dick later in this book.)

Remember my earlier warning about quagmires. There are way more wrinkles and nuances in this notion of hindsight and "selection after the fact" than has hitherto been supposed in simplistic "yes" versus "no" debates over the existence of precognition.

Orienting Toward Meaning

My likening of precognition or presentiment to a biological reflex might not have raised eyebrows in the Rhines' day, but it is a somewhat contrarian position now. Many parapsychologists today link psi abilities to the "extended mind"—that is, to some larger or higher consciousness that transcends the body, being metaphorically if not literally "entangled" with everything and everyone else.[46] Psychic ability is widely seen today as the ultimate disproof of the materialistic reductions of mainstream psychology and neuroscience. Consciousness, as something potentially irreducible to brain processes, assumes center stage in a what is seen by some as a new paradigm that will unseat and replace materialism.[47]

Disaffection with materialism, and the claim that it disenchanted the world with its insistence on physical mechanistic causes for all phenomena including mental phenomena, dates back to the Romantic period, and again, it was a driving motive for the earliest psychical researchers in the Victorian era. Frederic Myers saw telepathy as part of an enlarged, transcendent "subliminal self." The philosopher Henri Bergson argued for a kind of *panpsychism*, in which matter is itself a manifestation of mind and vice versa. Later, J. W. Dunne, as we saw, viewed precognition as reflecting our higher mind, "filling all space," equivalent to the higher consciousness of mystics. And in the middle of the 20th century, Carl Jung saw psychic phenomena as manifestations of the collective unconscious, which he suggested had a transpersonal (or even what today might be called "nonlocal") dimension. James Carpenter similarly sees first sight as a phenomenon resulting from our embeddedness in a universe of meanings that are found and not simply made by us, that extend beyond the body, and that are responsive to our intentions.[48] He sees first sight as much more than a mere reflex in the mechanistic sense most experimental psychologists might understand the term.[49]

As a cultural anthropologist by training, I agree that *meaning* is central. I do not agree, though, that perennial questions about consciousness in relation to materiality need to be resolved to explain ESP. (We will come back to the reasons why later, in Part Two.) Nor do I believe we need appeal to anything like a universe pre-saturated with meanings to explain these phenomena. Information encoded in material forms of language, art, artifacts, folklore, mythology, science, and the various "lived texts" that make up culture (as anthropologists understand the term) do precede and surround us—but information is different from meaning. Meaning is really what is made when intentional actors engage with that information, assign value to and internalize it, and use it to achieve their aims. Meaning is the *value* of information, in other words, and it is what we as humans constantly create and recreate as part of our social and cultural experience.[50] Rather than hovering over and above us, animating us, or exerting its own transpersonal causal (or, in Jung's paradoxical formulation, "acausal") force, meaning is constantly fashioned and refashioned by real embodied people in real physical interaction or physically mediated interaction. I suggest it is precisely such interactions that our first sight (as precognition) often orients us toward and that belatedly supply the meaning of our precognitive experiences.[51]

I am thus arguing for a hermeneutic (interpretive) approach to studying precognition, but I mean something specific and counterintuitive by this: Meaning may be precisely what is *lacking* in a dream or reflex action or other behavior that is inflected by our future, until the future inciting stimulus that will enable us to make sense of it. In other words, it seems to be that it is the future, physical *arrival at meaning* that *causes* the prior behavior, and the prior behavior may often *or even necessarily* be part of the causal backstory of that future arrival—time loops, in other words. This time-loop framework not only offers a new way of looking at precognition in creativity and dreams but even has interesting implications for rethinking psychoanalytic models of symptoms and neuroses. Instead of being rooted solely in past traumas and unresolved conflicts, it may partly be our baffling relationship to our future that makes us "sick" (at least in the psychoanalytic sense). And it offers, I think, a more compelling way of looking at "archetypal" phenomena like Jung's synchronicity too. If materially encoded cultural symbols exert some of their causative force or power *backwards*, through social actors' unconscious precognitive engagement with them, it would help explain why the universe often seems pre-saturated with meanings that, upon scrutiny, boil down to meanings actual concrete human beings have made themselves. These are possibilities we will explore in the second half of this book.

A hermeneutic orientation to precognition has specific implications for how we approach studying the phenomenon. If precognition orients us toward meaning, the purely scientific perspective—including even the rigorously acquired experimental data supporting its existence with astronomical p-values—cannot tell us the whole story, and thus cannot be taken in isolation from the anecdotal data: individual human beings' accounts of their anomalous experiences and what those experiences mean to them.[52] It has long been argued that ESP abilities of whatever sort would be unlikely to manifest strongly in sterile laboratory conditions where there is little personally at stake for the individual. What's more, the precognitive unconscious of the experimenter and of the test subjects may create effects that cannot be accounted for and that may be misinterpreted (a very interesting and potentially far-reaching argument made by Edwin May in the context of PK research[53]). Thus the "feeling the future" studies by Bem or the psychophysical studies by Radin and other researchers, with their impressive statistical significance but small effects discernible over milliseconds or seconds, may provide only an incomplete picture of precognition's scope. Individuals' personal accounts and recollections of anomalies lack the reliability and replicability that are essential to the scientific method, and they cannot be supported by significance tests, but they can reveal the *character* of precognition as it shapes our lives in a way laboratory experiments cannot.

The Future-Influencing-Present Effect

As mentioned earlier, in 1963 the playwright J. B. Priestley solicited viewers of a BBC program to send him examples of their precognitive experiences. He was inundated with roughly 1,500 letters. More interesting to Priestley than the hundreds of precognitive-dream reports in that pile were a smaller number of stories suggesting a more general and hard-to-define influence of future events on people's actions, thoughts, and emotions in waking life: "Somebody is in a queer state of mind, perhaps behaves oddly, and no reason for this can be discovered at the time. Later—a month, a year, 10 years—the cause of this effect reveals itself. Because of where or what or how I am now, I behaved in such a fashion then."[54] Priestley called this the "future-influencing-present effect"—not unlike what later researchers would call presentiment but unfolding in many cases across a much longer timeframe of an individual's life.

In his 1964 book *Man & Time*, Priestley described several examples. One letter-writer was a WWII veteran with what we would now call PTSD, who experienced a "breakdown" during the war and relapses of his condition thereafter. He credited his recovery to a somewhat older woman with children whom he met and married after the war and, by the time of his writing, had a teenage daughter with. But "for a year before he met his wife or knew anything about her, he used to pass the gate of her country cottage on the local bus. And he never did this without feeling that he and that cottage were somehow related."[55] Another, older letter writer recalled being a girl during the First World War and when out walking one night in London, "found herself looking up at a hospital, quite strange to her, with tears streaming down her cheeks." Years later, she moved in with a woman friend, and they remained partners for 25 years. "This friend was then taken ill and she died in that same hospital at which the girl so many years before had stared through her inexplicable tears."[56]

Priestley also gives an example from two acquaintances of his own:

> Dr A began to receive official reports from Mrs B, who was in charge of one branch of a large department. These were not personal letters signed by Mrs B, but the usual duplicated official documents. Dr A did not know Mrs B, had never seen her, knew nothing about her except that she had this particular job. Nevertheless, he felt a growing excitement as he received more and more of these communications from Mrs B. This was so obvious that his secretary made some comment on it.
>
> A year later he had met Mrs B and fallen in love with her. They are now most happily married. He believes … that he felt this strange excitement because

the future relationship communicated it to him; we might say that one part of his mind, not accessible to consciousness except as a queer feeling, already knew that Mrs B was to be tremendously important to him.[57]

Skeptics will immediately dismiss such stories as memory distorted by hindsight. Almost certainly, the woman who lost her partner did not write down that moment of tearfulness on her walk all those years earlier; it was recollected long afterward—so how can we be sure it really happened? Even if it did happen, how can we be sure she didn't break down crying before many buildings, all the time, and just remembered this one instance after her partner died at that particular hospital? Same with the shell-shocked man who said he felt an inexplicable connection to the cottage of his future wife. Similarly, Dr. A and Mrs. B (one wonders if she was a "Mrs." at the time of the official communications)—as well as Dr. A's secretary, abetting his memory—could have reframed their story in hindsight, shaping it into something much more fated-seeming. But while retroactive revision of memory must always be taken into account as a possible factor in such stories, it begins to appear simply stubborn and uncharitable to reject such accounts solely on the basis of that possibility, especially in light of the masses of similar and better-documented individual cases, not to mention the masses of experimental data also suggesting the possibility of something like Priestley's future-influencing-present effect.

And once again, hindsight arguably works *against* us noticing these phenomena more than it encourages us to notice (let alone report) them. We rarely become aware of the future-influencing-present effect, Priestley notes, for the same reason J. W. Dunne argued precognitive dreams so often escape notice—because we do not habitually record our "queer feelings" and thus can *only* reflect on them with the benefit of hindsight. It will seldom occur to people to make a connection between their thoughts or feelings at some time point A and an event occurring at a later, perhaps much later, time point B:

> [T]hough I describe this effect in terms of the future
> influencing the present, it can never be understood in
> the present that is being influenced by the future; it
> can be understood only when the effect is well into
> the past and the future that influenced it is now in the

present or the immediate past. It has now to be discovered in retrospect, and this makes it less dramatic and memorable, much harder to trace, than the precognitive dream.[58]

There is also an additional inhibiting force: the fact that such an effect seems so often to manifest in the highly meaningful but private context of love and romance. Sex and love, of course, are the most rewarding human experiences, toward which we might expect an adaptive presentimental ability to particularly orient us. But they are also the most intimate. Thus, among the many barriers to noticing presentiment's operation in our lives is the fact that it may so often be connected to the most private and unshareable dimensions of our experience.[59] This is one reason why the psychoanalyst's couch, a context where individuals are enjoined to discuss these intimate relationships along with their dreams and private thoughts, is the perfect place to study the future-influencing-present effect, as we will see later.

The anomalies produced when we engage precognitively with the world, including synchronicities, mystical or paranormal experiences, and so on may be the most profound and meaningful experiences in a person's life. Fortuities and coincidences are the basis of every love story, for example. It is when we fail to "wait for the sugar to melt," in Bergson's phrase—that is, when we try to force some sense out of our "queer feelings" without waiting for their meaning to arrive in the natural unfolding of events—that that "connection" (for that is what meaning really boils down to) will seem like something pre-existing, enveloping and surrounding us in the universe like some Platonic-Jungian amnion, or even like "the Force" in *Star Wars*. Instead, I suggest that our most meaningful connections to others and to ideas traverse the Not Yet, made possible by the 4-D nature of our meaning-making brain.

It is to the "how"—the possible nuts and bolts of precognition—that we now turn.

PART TWO

"How Can This Be?"

The future is more coherent than the present, more animate and purposeful, and in a real sense, wiser. It knows more, and some of this knowledge gets transmitted back to us by what seems to be a purely natural phenomenon. We are being talked to, by a very informed Entity: that of all creation as it lies ahead of us in time.

— Philip K. Dick, *Exegesis* (2011)

5

Catching Precognitive Butterflies — Chaos, Memory, and *Premory* in the Thermodynamic Universe

*One night, Zhuangzi dreamed of being a butterfly—
a happy butterfly, showing off and doing things as he
pleased, unaware of being Zhuangzi. Suddenly he
awoke, drowsily, Zhuangzi again. And he could not tell
whether it was Zhuangzi who had dreamt the butterfly
or the butterfly dreaming Zhuangzi. But there must be
some difference between them! This is called "the transformation of things."*

— Zhuangzi (4th century, BC)

Although it is mostly forgotten today, J. W. Dunne's *An Experiment with Time* was quite popular in the middle decades of the last century, going through nine editions and reprintings between 1927 and 1950. Readers were fascinated by Dunne's Serialism theory, and many took the engineer-dreamer up on his challenge to record their dreams in a daily journal and look for precognitive elements in them. His book exerted a particularly strong influence on writers. We have already met J. B. Priestley, who wrote several plays about the influence of the future on the present, such as *Time and the Conways* and *An Inspector Calls.* Dunne also influenced T. S. Eliot, C. S. Lewis, J. R. R. Tolkien, and H. G. Wells, among many others.[1] And over the course of three months in 1964, the insomniac Russian-American novelist Vladimir Nabokov undertook a systematic, Dunne-inspired dream experiment of his own, recording 64 dreams on index cards and comparing them to subsequent events. There were several "hits" in the series that would have merited Dunne's approval, as they fairly strikingly matched stories that would capture the writer's interest on television within the next few days.[2]

Nabokov's interest in dreams and dream precognition long preceded his reading of Dunne and his dream experiment, however. As a teenager, he had had a doozy of a "Dunne dream," which he would only recognize as such more than four decades later, when events in his life strikingly seemed to "confirm" what he had dreamed.

In 1916, the precocious, 17-year-old Vladimir Vladimirovich Nabokov lived comfortably on his family's estate in St. Petersburg, Russia, where he led an idyllic life collecting butterflies and writing. He was even about to have his first collection of poems published. Then came one of those life events that mix luck and misfortune, of the sort that always somehow appear at the heart of psychic occurrences: His rich Uncle Vasily Ivanovich Rukavishnikov died, leaving the young writer his fortune and his estate, Rozhdestveno. Although minus an uncle, the young Nabokov seemed set for a life of pursuing his hobbies with nary a care. But his new prosperity proved short-lived. The revolutionary fervor that engulfed Russia the following October overthrew the old class hierarchy. Nabokov lost his estate and his wealth, and his family had to flee the country.

It was during this time of tumult that Nabokov had his dream: His dead Uncle Vasily appeared to him and announced, enigmatically, "I shall come back to you as Harry and Kuvyrkin."[3] In the dream, Nabokov thought that these names represented a pair of circus performers. It was absurd—senseless—at the time, like most dreams are.

Fast forward to 1959: The 60-year-old émigré novelist and butterfly expert was now living in Ithaca, New York, where his friend Morris Bishop had landed him a teaching position at Cornell. *Life* magazine wanted to do a story on Nabokov, because of the popularity of his 1955 novel *Lolita*, and he was lunching with his wife and the reporters at his home when he received a call from Bishop, who eagerly asked him if he'd read that day's *New York Times*. He hadn't, so his friend read the news story to him over the phone: Harris-Kubrick Pictures, he said—Stanley Kubrick's production company—had just purchased the film rights to *Lolita* for a large sum: $150,000.

When the contract arrived in the mail, Nabokov was pleased to find himself, for the first time since his youth, a rich man. And he also remembered his uncle Vasily's crazy dream promise that his wealthy benefactor would return to him as circus performers "Harry and Kuvyrkin." The *v* in *kuvyrok*, which means "somersault" in Russian, would be a *b* in English, thus something like Kubrick. Harry and Kuvyrkin, from the "circus" world of Hollywood, had indeed come at last to restore Vladimir Nabokov's lost fortune.[4]

The Transformation of Things

Precognition, at least as it is usually understood, means a kind of time travel: Information from the future must travel backwards in time to affect a person in the present, for instance in a dream or an artwork or some "queer feeling." So, for example, if the 17-year-old Nabokov really had precognized the rewarding news of Stanley Kubrick's production company buying the film rights to a novel he would write decades later, it means that information about that occurrence, or the writer's reaction to it, was somehow received by the writer's unconscious 42 years beforehand, when he was 17, and was shaped into a dream. Another "precognitive butterfly," in other words.

While skeptics will scoff at such possibilities, many physicists have no trouble with the idea of time travel or backwards causation in principle. It is often pointed out that the equations governing fundamental interactions in the material world are *time-symmetric*.[5] If you could watch a video of interacting fundamental particles, and then played that video in reverse, there would be no easy way to tell which was the correct, forward-in-time version. There is no fundamental reason why effects cannot precede causes, and as we will see later, information is really just causation by another name. If causation can run backwards, so can information. The trouble is, a video of a person walking down the sidewalk, or an apple dropping off a tree, cannot be played in reverse without looking comical. On our scale, serious things seem to happen in a single direction only.

One big difference between the quantum realm of tiny particles and the classical, macro-scale world we are used to interacting with is that the latter is ruled by *entropy*, the constant tendency toward increasing disorder. Like a steep hill you can roll down with ease but cannot climb up, you cannot unscramble an egg, or unstir the cream from your coffee. That thermodynamic tendency for things to mix and mingle and equalize is, for most physicists, equivalent to the arrow of time. Entropy is a one-way-street. This is why most scientifically educated people, still living as they do in a classical, Newtonian world, will simply dismiss claims of precognition out of hand. The idea of information "flowing" in reverse is as absurd as the idea that things could get more orderly, rather than less.

Some of the absurdities are described in a 2016 history of time travel by James Gleick.[6] The idea that time is a dimension like space is a surprisingly young one, it turns out. The fourth dimension (not necessarily time) gripped the Victorian imagination right at the same time telepathy did, with fables like Edwin A. Abbott's *Flatland*. A sphere from "Spaceland" traversing Abbott's two-dimensional world appears to a bewildered local, the narrator, as a point enlarging to a circle, out of nowhere. The Stranger then "abducts" the narrator, bringing him on a higher-dimensional journey to show him the limitations of his perceptions. (The narrator is ultimately jailed for the dimensional heresies he tries to preach to his fellow, skeptical Flatlanders after his return.) Abbott's thought experiment was an invitation to imagine that our own 3-D reality may be similarly dimensionally challenged.[7] But it really took H. G. Wells in his 1895 novel *The Time Machine* to get people to realize that *time itself* was that fourth dimension, and that objects or information might traverse it in either direction, not just forward. Wells was prescient. Ten years later, Einstein's special theory of relativity made "past" and "future" fluid categories. Because the photons that carry information and causation have a fixed speed limit, an event in one observer's past may still be in another observer's future.

Einstein's teacher Hermann Minkowski extrapolated on this: The bodies we experience are really three-dimensional cross-sections of four-dimensional wormlike beings snaking some distance, several decades ideally, through a big four-dimensional block, *space-time*. This makes the idea of literally *moving* through time problematic, since everything is four-dimensional already. If you set the dial of your time machine for "T minus 10 minutes," would it collide with itself in its backward journey? Would it just "de-age" a bit, lose some iota of dust or tarnish? Don't cheat by having it fly through the air like Marty McFly's DeLorean in *Back to the Future*, which is just evading the issue.

What would those around you see? To your lab assistant watching your machine depart to some destination in the past, say a year ago, would you and your machine appear to vanish, like Doctor Who's Tardis? Theoretically, no—not unless you *moved* the time machine in the past ... but in that case, it would no longer be where it was ... er, is ... for you to get in it and travel backward. And what is "where it was" anyway? Is "here" relative to a point on the surface of the Earth, or to some arbitrary point in space that that point happened to pass through when you activated your machine?

If you set the dial for farther into the past—to some year before the machine was built, for instance—what about the individual histories of all its individual parts and particles? All the intertwining spaghettis of starstuff making up your time machine were somewhere else, living separate lives, before being woven together in their current form. How does time travel affect that?

And what about you, the passenger? If you "traveled" back to the date of your birth, would you yourself "age backward" like the wizard Merlin, getting younger and younger, smaller and smaller? Would you go back up inside your mother? Where did she come from? And ... how awkward! (We will see in the second half of this book, when we get to Freud, that the taboo of time travel is more entangled than you might think with the taboo of incest. Oedipus, who famously married his own mother, was essentially a premodern time traveler.)

"Moving" into the future, as Wells' time traveler initially does, is just as incoherent, albeit in a much more boring way. To move into the future, the time machine just needs to sit there ... and sit ... and sit ...

Einstein's theory does in fact permit physical time travel, but it requires traveling rapidly through space first. Traveling faster than light is tantamount to traveling back in time—and since you are flying through space in that case, it might get you around the awkward situation of finding yourself in an immobile time machine sitting there in your garage laboratory awaiting your arrival to get in and pull the lever. (So, okay, you can have your DeLorean.) But traveling faster than light would require infinite energy; it is possible on paper, not in practice. More recently, physicists have theorized other ways that physical travel into the past could be achieved, but they are still exotic and expensive. A technological civilization thousands or more years in advance of our own, one able to harness the energy of its whole galaxy, *could* create a wormhole linking different points in the fabric of spacetime and send a spaceship through it.[8] It is an idea explored widely in science fiction and depicted vividly in Christopher Nolan's 2014 film *Interstellar*.

But all this is academic for our purposes. For Gleick, what we are really talking about with time travel is a thought experiment about the experiencer—the passenger—in a novel, disjointed relationship to the external world. We can readily perform feats of "mental time travel," or at least simulate such feats, as well as experience a dissociation between our internal subjective sense of time and the flux of things around us and even our own bodies.[9] According to Gleick, part of what suddenly facilitated four-dimensional thinking in both popular writing and the sciences was the changing experience of time in an accelerating society. The Victorian age, with its steam engines and bewildering pace of urban living, increased these experiences of dissociation, and they have only intensified since then. Time travel, Gleick argues, is basically just a metaphor for modernity, and a nifty premise upon which to base literary and cinematic fantasies that repair modernity's traumas. It also shines a light on how confused we all are about time.

The most commonly voiced objection to time travel—and with it, precognition—is that any interaction between the future and past would change the past, and thus create a different future. The familiar term is the grandfather paradox: You can't go back in time and kill your grandfather because then you wouldn't have been born to go back in time and kill your grandfather (leaving aside for the moment the assumed inevitability of wanting to kill your grandfather, which is an odd assumption). The technical term for meddling in the past this way is "bilking," on the analogy of failing to pay a promised debt.[10] Whatever you call it, it is the kind of thing that, in *Star Trek*, would make the Enterprise's computer start to stutter and smoke and go haywire—the same reaction, in fact, that greets scientific claims of precognition. (As Dean Radin puts it, laboratory precognition results like those cited in the past two chapters "cause faces to turn red and sputtering noises to be issued from upset lips."[11]) Information somehow sent backward in time from an event cannot lead to a future that no longer includes that event—and we naturally intuit that it would be very hard not to have such an effect if we meddled in the timeline. Our very presence in the past would change things.

A 1952 short story by Ray Bradbury called "A Sound of Thunder" is a famous illustration of the problem. In Bradbury's future world, time-traveling safari hunters are allowed to hunt old, sick dinosaurs (ones soon to die anyway) in the Cretaceous period so long as hunters stay on an assigned walkway and do not disturb things too much. One hunter strays from the path during his hunt and returns to his own time (2055) to find that a Fascist who had lost the election prior to his departure is now President, along with other strange, minor differences from the world he left behind, such as differently pronounced words. He then notices a crushed butterfly on his boot and realizes that his killing of that butterfly had had somewhat significant effects on history. He pleads to be allowed to return to the past to make things right, but this is forbidden.[12] The "sound of thunder" of the title is the sound of his outraged hunting guide shooting him in the head for his carelessness.

Bradbury, like so many science-fiction writers, was weirdly prescient here. A little less than a decade after he wrote his story, an MIT meteorologist and mathematician named Edward Lorenz made a now-famous, serendipitous discovery: When he rounded off a parameter in a weather model running on his office computer—cutting off the last three of six digits to the right of the decimal point—his model unfolded differently than it had in other runs.[13] A one-part-in-1,000 difference in initial conditions quickly blew into a huge difference. This discovery, which came to be called the "butterfly effect," was the birth of *chaos theory*. As Gleick memorably put it in his 1987 bestseller *Chaos*, "a butterfly stirring the air today in Peking can transform storm systems next month in New York."[14]

Lorenz did not call his discovery the butterfly effect initially. When he wrote and presented about his discovery, he used the wingbeats of a seagull as his go-to example. But another scientist convening a session at a 1972 AAAS meeting where Lorenz was scheduled to speak wanted a snappy title for Lorenz's presentation and thought that a butterfly would make a more poetic and thus more memorable animal.[15]

Whoever really deserves credit for this metaphorical butterfly, it is thanks to Lorenz's discovery—and especially to Gleick's popularization of it—that we can no longer take seriously a simple time-travel scenario like "A Sound of Thunder," or for that matter the plots of any number of similar *Star Trek* episodes—such as "The City on the Edge of Forever," in which a time-traveling Kirk and Spock have to repair the damage done to the historical timeline by Doctor McCoy's accidental presence in depression-era Manhattan. What may have seemed to Bradbury and his mid-century readers like a major deviation of history since the Mesozoic—differently pronounced words and an altered election outcome—today looks like ridiculously small potatoes. The un-unscramble-ability of the egg goes way deeper than it is possible to imagine. Stepping on that butterfly all those millions of years ago would lead to a totally different 21st century—one without time machines, or at least with different time machines and different creatures to step in them.

One of the things that inspired people about chaos theory was that it suggested a kind of openness and possibility even in the mechanistic determinism that rules the physical world. The butterfly effect, along with the sublime recursive forms of fractal geometry, injected a slight bit of romanticism into that dull cold Enlightenment picture. No computer, no matter how many decimal places it can calculate out to, can predict the fate of the universe or even a human life. Implicit in the unpredictability entailed by chaos theory is the ability of the small to affect the large. The butterfly in Peking is a kind of David to weather's Goliath, and who doesn't thrill to stories about underdogs defeating much larger opponents? But even if it restores a little bit of the magic to the Newtonian billiard-ball world, the butterfly effect also, in the same wingbeat, trounces further our hopes for something truly enchanting like precognition ... or at least, it *seems* to.

The reason is the impossible complexity of causation. Even if a butterfly's flutter in Peking now can be a contributor to a storm in New York next month, the idea of somehow using that one butterfly to *predict* or *divine* New York's weather is unthinkable, because too many other butterflies, and seagulls, and individual photons warming individual molecules in the world's oceans also contributed to the storm. The causal antecedents of that storm are basically infinite in number. How could information about that incredibly complex event reflux back in time in any coherent way, for instance to one individual's head? Events like storms—and when you zoom in, even oft-prophesied calamities like plane crashes and terrorist attacks—are both hard to define and also very much like the martyr St. Sebastian, with whom Michael Richards identified in his seemingly precognitive sculpture of 9/11: *They are pincushions of causal arrows.* That sad-eyed, multiply pincushioned young man could be called the patron saint of complex causation, and he is for some critics the main thing standing in the way of accepting any form of foreknowledge not based on simple inference from sense data.

University of Maryland philosopher and parapsychologist Stephen E. Braude, a skeptic when it comes to retrocausal accounts of precognition, describes the problem:

> Any causal connection we identify will always be part
> of a larger causal nexus spreading indefinitely into the
> past and future. The particular causal connections we

find worthwhile to single out are individuated, on pragmatic grounds, out of an intrinsically seamless web of happening running from earlier to later and leading to and away from events we relate causally. And from out of that web we can distinguish many different causal lines, some converging toward the individual events and others spreading out from them.[16]

Braude argues that alleged precognitive experiences do not play fair if retrocausation is understood to be just a mirror image of "clockwise" classical causation, as is commonly assumed by its advocates. If causes can somehow project backward, then we ought to see the same kind of complex retro-causation determining precognitive experiences. Yet in a precognitive experience such as an alleged precognitive dream, Braude sees no sense that there are multiple causal arrows from multiple future events converging on the dream; the dream seems to be "of" a singular future occurrence. Nor does Braude see evidence that such dreams have radiating repercussions farther back in time, prior to the dream. In short, "retrocausal connections seem to stand out like a sore thumb on any causal map."[17] He adds: "No other sort of putative causal connection lacks an extensive surrounding causal history running temporally in the same direction."[18]

Arguments about prescience and its possible pitfalls often turn on ideal-typical thought experiments having the same structure as stories about time travel paradoxes. For instance, what if you received a premonition of a terrorist attack and alerted the authorities? If they averted the attack, from what future would your premonition have been sent? But in fact, precognition seldom if ever works so cleanly in the real world. "Prophetic" dreams and visions typically have a much more ambiguous, vague character. For instance, as uncannily precise as they seemed to be, David Mandell's or Elizabeth Krohn's precognitive dreams of news reports about disasters still lacked enough specificity about when or where the events were going to occur to use them to avert those outcomes. And premonitions are very often more oblique than that, or else they correspond to future events in unexpected and ironic ways. Failure to heed premonitions—either out of an overriding personal skepticism, fear of looking foolish, or simple failure to pay attention—is also a common pattern in the literature on this subject, as is "fulfilling" a premonition precisely in the effort to prevent it.[19]

Jeffrey Kripal relates a striking example of the latter type that was told to him by an academic colleague. The woman had sent her four-year-old boy to a petting zoo in the care of their nanny; at 10:06 AM she had a sudden vision of her son screaming in his car seat and the car filling with white smoke. She immediately phoned her nanny and told her to drive home immediately, and slowly. It was an uneventful trip home … but the boy was disappointed that he did not get to pet the animals as he'd been promised. So the next day the woman decided to take him back to the petting zoo herself. On the way, another car made a sharp turn on the highway ahead and crashed into them. No one was hurt—the airbags deployed—but the boy was screaming in the back seat, and just as in her vision, the car was full of "white smoke"—powder from the deployed airbags. It happened at 10:08 AM—24 hours and two minutes after the woman's premonitory vision. Kripal underscores that the premonition was actually self-fulfilling: "by preventing the child from a full visit at the zoo … the mother actually helped cause the future event to happen (since the child now wanted to return)."[20]

What, then, of the "foreseen calamities prevented" that are a perennial favorite kind of anecdote in books on precognition?[21] In her 1961 book *Hidden Channels of the Mind*, ESP pioneer Louisa Rhine describes cases in which an individual, suddenly aware of a déjà vu feeling or a remembered dream, narrowly averted some catastrophe. For example, a mother in Washington State reported a vivid dream in which her baby was crushed to death by a chandelier that had been hanging over the crib in their nursery. In the dream, she saw herself and her husband standing amid the wreckage, with the clock on the baby's dresser reading 4:35. Defying her husband's plea to just ignore the dream and go back to sleep, the worried mother rose and got their baby and brought her into their bed. Two hours later, the couple and their baby were awakened by a loud crash. She rose and rushed to the nursery, followed by her husband. "There, where the baby would have been lying, was the chandelier in the crib. They looked at each other and then at the clock. It stood at 4:35."[22] Since the woman evidently "used" her dream to protect her baby from harm, from what future did her premonition of the child being crushed come? Does such a dream challenge the Minkowski block universe?

Some who accept retrocausation get around the issues of paradox and associated questions of free will by suggesting that premonitions like this show us probabilities that are potentially alterable through our choices, not an etched-in-stone (or glass) future reality.[23] This is an idea that goes along with the popular "many worlds" interpretation of quantum physics attributed to physicist Hugh Everett in the late 1950s: the idea that at every decision point in nature, physical systems take multiple paths and thus endlessly proliferate new, alternative universes. According to such an interpretation, the woman's dream of her crushed child may have accurately showed her an event in a possible future, "a timeline not taken." J. B. Rhine thought that there may be a trade-off between the level of detail of a premonitory or precognitive vision and the amenability of the foreseen outcome to being altered.[24] Rhine was no doubt thinking of the analogous trade-off in quantum physics between an experimenter's level of certainty in a measurement and the extent to which the experimenter's probing interferes with the system being observed (more on which later).

A retrocausation skeptic might instead propose that the woman's premonition of her baby being crushed could have been an unconsciously drawn inference based on clairvoyantly gathered awareness of causal arrows converging on the imminent fall of the chandelier, or even that the chandelier's fall could have been psychically *caused* by the mother. Braude argues that what seems like information reaching a person from the future may really be a kind of psi-augmented inference, gathering information about the various causal antecedents of those events via clairvoyance or telepathy; he is also open to the possibility that the individual's own unconscious psychokinetic (PK) influence on events may contribute to outcomes that *seem* to have been simply foreseen.[25] In such an interpretation, linear causality is preserved, but by appeal to a wider (and ill-defined) array of psychic abilities, sometimes called "super psi." Those who refuse any form of psi on principle may suggest instead that an inference was made by the mother's unconscious mind, based on having subliminally registered a loose fitting in the chandelier the day before. As we will see later in this book, the super-abilities of the unconscious mind were an explanatory refuge for Sigmund Freud on many occasions when his own life and his clinical work seemed to supply evidence for some kind of anomalous knowing of imminent events.

None of these compromises or alternatives are very satisfying. Precognizing possible futures might be plausible when an event is imminent, but what about highly specific events more distant in time? Outcomes apparently foreseen years or decades beforehand—and there are plenty of such cases—seem to defy all sense in a butterfly-effect universe where every small decision should lead to a completely different future.

One imagines that even a single Swallowtail or Fritillary caught or not caught by Nabokov over the course of his life of butterfly collecting could have led to a different future that did not include writing *Lolita* or Harris and Kubrick Pictures buying the film rights.[26] Psi-augmented inference of future events based on their antecedents in the present is similarly implausible when a foreseen event involves something "random" like another driver making an unpredictable sudden turn a day in the future, let alone events of virtually any kind at longer temporal remove. Moreover, how could either psi-mediated inference or the unconscious mind's subliminal acuity account for the temporal coincidences in both Kripal's and Rhine's examples—the time of day being the same for the first mother's vision and the accident the next day, or the time on the clock being exactly right in the mother's chandelier dream?

The PK argument has problems of its own, even if we admit that thoughts or intentions (either conscious or unconscious) can be causal other than through the usual medium of willed human action. It is a vast question that goes well beyond the scope of this book, but ample experimental data do seem to support the existence of some kinds of PK.[27] An "active hypothesis" to explain ostensible precognition may also include the non-paranormal ability of individuals to unconsciously orchestrate or arrange events to fulfill their own "prophecies."[28] However, invoking an unconscious mental ability to orchestrate complex events like plane crashes or other disasters is hardly believable—and in any case is far less parsimonious than the precognitive alternative. In fact, as we will see later, there are several reasons it will be easier to mistake precognition for something like PK (or some supra-personal organizing principle like Jung's synchronicity) than vice versa.[29] Those "force fields" around precognition that I mentioned are quite strong, and they are powered by deep-rooted taboos. In any case, does it really help us to imagine—and is it really believable—that the mothers in the two examples might have psychically or otherwise *caused* the calamities that nearly claimed their children?[30]

The argument I am making in this book is that we precognize actual futures, and do so through a real, retrocausal mechanism—and moreover, that we do it all the time. The various objections to retrocausal accounts—including the seeming paradoxes—turn out to be butterflies that have been blown to hurricane proportions because of longstanding misunderstandings about just *where* (in space) informational time travel is occurring. The search for precognition in the physics of cause and effect as they apply to real occurrences like storms and plane crashes and fender benders "out in the world" is, I argue, to look in the wrong place.[31]

Premory

We really need to go back to Dunne and take seriously the distinction he drew on the basis of his own dream investigations—between objective physical events, embedded in their seamless web of complexly interacting mechanical causes and effects, and the very different phenomenological landscape of cause and effect that characterizes consciousness and especially *memory*. Braude is correct that in the world of classical, Newtonian physics there are no events that have only isolated, singular causes staggered in time with no subsequent downstream effects, but there are plenty of such *phenomena* in our experience. A *recollection* is an experience whose array of immediate neural causes and downstream behavioral sequelae may well be hidden from our awareness, or simply imperceptible, but it bears a distinct, direct, and coherent relationship to another experience distant—perhaps even many years distant—in time. And when it passes, it may be very hard to discern its effects on subsequent events or even on subsequent thoughts and behaviors until a similar recollection surfaces again.

For instance, as I write this, I am recalling a fender bender I got into about a decade ago in the parking lot of the Trader Joe's grocery store in Bethesda, Maryland. My recollection takes the form of a visual-sensory "reliving": a sense of the place, the sounds and feel of the collision, and so on. Between that event and my memory of it today, that experience had been "stored" as an unrealized possibility of connections across my brain. I didn't dwell on the accident after I exchanged insurance information with the other driver—no one was hurt, and we both went on with our lives. But lo and behold, today I can somewhat vividly summon the scene in my mind's eye (with some mix of accuracy and likely error), re-experiencing the brief shock, the feel of the impact, anger at myself for not looking more carefully in my blind spot, and other associated emotions. And in turn, once I'm done thinking about it, this recollection's effect on my future behavior will be subtle at most—maybe just a slight heightened alertness next time I'm in that parking lot. It might seem to some outside observer of my brain, God's fMRI, that that recollection, that memory, simply vanished again without further effect, like a storm that had dissipated.

We saw how, by bringing the same forensic sensibility to his pre-cognitive dreams that he brought to investigating a fatal crash of an ex-perimental monoplane, Dunne was able to show that it was the future occasion of his own learning of events that he was precognizing, not the events themselves. Many of Dunne's readers have been thrown by his somewhat non-sequitur conclusion, that part of our consciousness transcends the physical body; but as I argued, his Serialism theory never cohered with his core dataset, which consisted of dreams of events in his *embodied* future.[32] That in turn points to precognition's rootedness in the brain, as literally what Gerald Feinberg called a "memory of things future."[33] Various mechanisms have been proposed for how this might work, which we will come back to. But whatever the mechanism(s), precognitive (and other ESP) experiences as reported in life and lab do bear striking similarities to memory and memory-related phenom-ena.[34] Drawings made in telepathy experiments or in remote viewing exercises, for example, often look like sketches that could easily have been made *after* a brief, barely remembered or only subliminally regis-tered glimpse at the target stimulus.[35] The most parsimonious explana-tion—and as we will see, one that no longer flies in the face of scientific understandings of causation—is that the brain really, somehow, com-municates with itself across its history. I am arguing that precognition is just memory in reverse, or what we might for convenience call *premory*.

A basic principle of memory, one that is so obvious as to be almost not worth mentioning, is its rootedness in our own lived experience. I don't remember your childhood, or my wife's childhood—I remember my own. Insofar as I know about my wife's childhood, it is only from being told about it at some point. My knowledge about historical or world events like the Cretaceous period or Watergate is similarly traceable to books and movies and TV shows I have been exposed to in my lifetime, like *Jurassic Park* and *All the President's Men*. The experiences of Dunne and many others suggest that premory is exactly similar to memory in this respect: We precognize things that will happen in our own lives or things we are destined to learn about, rather than events as such that may remain outside our direct experience.[36] This fact becomes evident, ironically enough, when the future information source about some dis-tant event contains errors or omissions and the precognitive experience corresponds to those deviations from reality—the "tracers" mentioned earlier.[37]

An important, more specific principle about memory is one that was described already by German psychologist Hermann Ebbinghaus in the 19th century: that it operates on the principle of *association*—that is, connections among disparate ideas and experiences. For instance, when I hear the word "butterfly," my thoughts may go in several directions— to Vladimir Nabokov and his novels, for example, or to James Gleick's *Chaos* and the butterfly in Peking, or even to the Taoist sage Zhuangzi, who famously didn't know, when he dreamed about a butterfly, whether in fact his waking life was really the dream *of* that butterfly. (In fact, for years, I vaguely confused or conflated Gleick's Chinese butterfly with Zuangzi's—raising the question whether it was really Zhuangzi who caused the storm in New York!) Associations are like the wires or channels of memory. The strength of particular associations is determined in part by how strongly events in our lives reinforce them (through conditioning processes like those mentioned earlier); they change over time and seem to correlate with the strengths of synaptic connections between neurons.[38] The brain has a special appetite for making connections that are not logical, and this paradoxically makes memory strong and makes learned information (semantic memory) and autobiographical events (episodic memories) easily accessed by multiple pathways, multiple linkages in the brain.

Precognition and other ostensible ESP phenomena have also long been observed to operate on associative principles.[39] The ability to make broad and counterintuitive associations (*remote associates*) is one measure of creativity, which is a trait associated with ESP ability.[40] And precognitive dreams seem to build associations between past experiences and future ones, as well as using metaphor and other tropes like puns, which could also be thought of as kinds of association.[41] Association is the inner logic of Freud's "primary process" thinking, as we will see in Part Three, and this dovetails interestingly with recent research about memory consolidation during sleep and dreaming. Dreaming is coming to be understood as a process possibly intrinsic to the formation of new mnemonic associations, the brain's metabolism of the recent past by integrating new experiences into long-term memory in an associative manner.[42] I will argue that dreams may do the same thing with our future experiences.

Another principle about memory is that it is facilitated by strong emotion. Boring routine experiences don't get strongly encoded and may be—usually are—forgotten, but surprising and unsettling experiences are better remembered, and highly pleasurable behaviors are strongly reinforced. The same connection to strong emotion has been found with psychic phenomena, again as Dunne observed with his dreams and as Frederic Myers observed with the experiences he interpreted as telepathy.[43] There are good evolutionary reasons why strong emotion might play an important role in precognition (or James Carpenter's "first sight"): It needs to orient us to new information relevant to our survival so that we can update our knowledge about the world in a fruitful way. Survival and success demand we remember the things that reward and frighten us; it only makes sense that a precognitive orienting function would likewise focus on surprising rewards and threats.

Memory is also closely tied to our experience of place and geography, likely because the hippocampus, the brain's librarian/archivist, also contains our maps of space. Ancient orators used familiar architectural spaces as "memory palaces" to facilitate remembering arguments and speeches, a principle still utilized by modern memory champions.[44] Dreams—including precognitive dreams—use the same principles, activating absurd, punny associations to waking episodes and "placing" them as composite images in familiar spatial settings.[45] Elsewhere I have suggested that the link between premory and space is what facilitates hauntings and "time slips," phenomena that bridge a particular landscape to a *subsequent* reading or learning experience about that landscape.[46] Counterintuitively, this same principle may also explain *temporal* coincidences or resonances that are often observed in ESP phenomena—such as the mother's vision in Kripal's example occurring exactly a day before the event she seemingly precognized. Humans have a very hard time not thinking of time in spatial terms.[47] The visual/spatial calendars reported by people with synesthesia suggest what is possibly a more general principle: that our internal maps of space help structure our autobiographical map of time, our chronology.[48] If so, specific dates in the year or specific times of day may "premind" a person of experiences they will have in the future on that same day, or at that same time, the same way anniversaries remind us of events in the past.

Memory is also extremely malleable and subject to distortion over time. This reflects ongoing processes of brain plasticity involved in associating new experiences to older memories. Details of events gradually morph and change, and even memories that *feel* vividly accurate are often generic, schematic composites, less and less resembling actual events as they might be recorded by some God's-eye video camera. It is possible to make people believe events occurred in the past that didn't, such as the "lost in the mall" experiments made famous by University of California-Davis psychologist Elizabeth Loftus in the 1990s.[49] It is especially easy to modify or reshape people's memories of real events, modifying salient details. The same unreliability seems to characterize precognition. It is, at best, "good enough for government work"—an approximation of some future experience, but typically distorted.[50] As we will see later, distortion may arise not only as a function of elapsed time but for other, psychodynamic reasons as well. In fact, a certain degree of uncertainty, obliquity, or "noise" is precisely what may allow information from our future to influence us in the present without giving rise to paradox.

One feature of memory that distinctly does *not* apply to precognition is sort of the exception that proves the rule and may help account for why precognition often either goes unnoticed or is interpreted as something else like telepathy. This relates to what psychologists call *source monitoring*. Autobiographical or episodic memories are recognized as such (and accepted as accurate—too readily, in fact[51]) when they cohere with other events in our internal chronology. If a recollection seems plausible, given what else I know or think I know about myself, and especially if it is vivid, then why would I doubt it or puzzle over it? The same is true with our knowledge of facts. I don't at all remember where or how I first learned tyrannosaurs only have two digits on each forelimb while allosaurs have three, but my strangely extensive knowledge of dinosaur anatomy does not surprise me in the slightest: I wanted to be a paleontologist when I was a little kid, and my room was full of dinosaur books and toys. Even if our knowledge of our lives and the world is distorted and often inaccurate, our sense of self gives it coherence, and things we "know" may come along with some plausible sense of how we know those things.

In stark contrast, given the necessary absence of any autobiographical scaffold or structure in which to place information refluxing from our future, such information would have no "provenance" and thus would be subject to various other explanations—or just ignored. I would be puzzled by a vivid, spontaneous mental image of, say, riding a bicycle through the streets of Beijing, China. I have never been to China, so such a thing would seem anomalous. I'd assume it was a memory of a dream, or "just my imagination." If I believed in past lives or astral travel, I might shoehorn the experience into those conceptual boxes. If the image was really vivid and persistent, I might think I was going crazy. It would never occur to me that, in five years, I will be giving a lecture on time loops in Beijing, China, and will get around on a rented bike during my stay. Without knowing this, without having been to the future, there would be no way to situate this vision among the other items in my memory. And since most of our thoughts are as evanescent and hard to remember as dreams, I will be unlikely to remember this vision or notice how it corresponded to an actual event in my life some time afterward. It has often been suggested that déjà vu experiences may reflect this kind of "memory of a premonition," although neural signals of familiarity may misfire for more mundane reasons, so it would be hard to substantiate such a claim in many, or most, cases.

It is the same difficulty that J. B. Priestley identified in the context of his future-influencing-present effect: How often will it occur to people to (a) record their passing thoughts and moods in detail and (b) compare those recorded thoughts and moods to later events? Almost never. Yet as we will see later, when people's lives, thoughts, and feelings *are* recorded for some other purpose, such as in psychotherapy, it sometimes does—quite by accident—reveal suggestive evidence for something like the existence of a perturbing influence of future events on prior behavior.

"The brain is an illusion factory," as neurobiologist Dean Buonomano puts it.[52] Humans' ability to vividly and realistically imagine things that haven't happened (or haven't happened *yet*) poses a huge challenge to studying anomalous experiences and ESP phenomena. One of the million functions of the Swiss Army Knife in our skulls is to serve as a powerful all-purpose imaging device, a special effects studio that would put Industrial Light and Magic to shame. It is able to create from scratch, instantly, vivid images to dramatize any piece of information or idea, real or fictitious, as well as translate complex thoughts instantly into pictures. It does this not only in dreams but also in the hypnagogic and hypnopompic states on the edge of sleep, and even in waking reality when we "mentally time travel" or daydream or imagine possible scenarios.[53] Again, abundant research shows how readily this amazing capacity can be manipulated, and thus how memory can be distorted—especially in clinical situations. This body of research is often deployed to debunk psychic phenomena.

But the fact that memory may be unreliable and subject to manipulation cannot by itself explain away anomalous coincidences, such as between a dream and a later occurrence. It merely offers the skeptic a convenient alternative explanation. Life being messy and un-laboratory-like, one is forced to choose whom to believe, the experiencer or the debunker. I suggest that, rather than simplistically explain away precognition as memory distortion and wash our hands of the whole temporally obscene business—the skeptics' easy path—we need to include the putty-like malleability of memory, and the ability of the imagination to put vivid visual-sensory flesh on the bare bones of passing thoughts or things we read, within our account of precognition and how it might operate. In fact, it would help make sense of the characteristic obliquity of precognition.

Even just when daydreaming or mentally rehearsing scenarios, it is plain that our inner special effects studio "pre-presents" future events for which our memory lacks context by using stock images and "b-roll" we have already archived. Mentally preparing to give a presentation at a university I have never visited, I will picture it in my mind as some version of a room I am already familiar with. Precognitive visions and dreams seem to work this way too. The notion of bigshot American film producers purchasing the film rights to a not-yet-existing novel and restoring Vladimir Nabokov's affluence in his middle age would have had no context—would have made no sense—in the mind of the teenage Nabokov at the sunset of Czarist Russia. But "circus performers" embodying the return of Nabokov's recently deceased wealthy benefactor Uncle Vasily would be an apt approximation of that future milestone in his life, befitting of dreams' well-known representational cunning.

Another thing our deceptive and brilliant imagination can easily do is cloak any precognitive sensibility by disguising it as something else. The vividness and immediacy of many "psychic" experiences naturally lead people to think that they have seen actual events elsewhere or communicated long-distance with their loved ones in real time. Upon learning of the *Titanic*'s sinking, Clara Cook Potter may have interpreted her dream of terrified people hanging on a steeply angled railing as a clairvoyant vision of the real event, even though it could well have been (I suggest, probably was) precognitive of precisely the pictures she saw in the media. After learning of her brother's death in that disaster, Mrs. Henderson may have interpreted her waking vision of her grieving sister-in-law and niece as some telepathic contact, but it could just as easily have been a premory of a mental scene she would have formed about his family on receiving the bad news. In his dream of Lieutenant B.'s crash, Dunne felt like he was "in" the scene and being addressed by his friend, even though it later became clear that his dreaming brain was just putting imaginary flesh on the bones of his later interpretation of a news bulletin—and the same with his vivid dream about a volcano about to blow. In both cases, a discrepancy between the actual event and the way he learned of it enabled him to trace these images to his reading.

I argue—and we will see many examples of this in Part Three when we delve into Freud and the unconscious—that dreams and precognitive visions represent not just future experiences but also our thoughts and emotions associated with those experiences. This goes a long way toward explaining why they often do not depict events completely accurately or literally. For instance, on seeing a chandelier in her child's crib, the mother would certainly have been shaken by the terrible possibility that the baby could have been killed had she not brought her into bed with her. It is precisely this awful "what if" (i.e., what if she'd ignored her dream) that may have been pre-presented in her dream.

Precognition very often focuses on our future survival of some perilous (or at least chaotic and unsettling) outcome—in many notable cases, a tragic outcome that befalls someone else. Premonitions may not be "warnings" so much as previews of the equivocal reward of surviving some close call. In Kripal's colleague's case, as in Rhine's story, there was a big reward that will be missed if we focus simply on the car accident (and the fact that it occurred not only in spite of but because of her efforts to prevent it): the fact that *her son was okay*, and that what had seemed in her vision like the smoke of a burning car was just the dust of deployed airbags that had saved both their lives. The dominant emotion in her case and that of the mother who dreamed of the crashed chandelier would really have been relief, and intensified gratitude for the safety of a child. It is precisely in the context of surviving some close call that those existentially powerful feelings of being alive and safe (or of loved ones being safe) are intensified. The precognitive brain seems to have a voracious appetite for thoughts and emotions about survival and close calls of one sort or another.

Survival really is the key to precognition, and on multiple levels. In the 1980s, a Russian physicist named Igor Novikov postulated that any form of time travel, informational or otherwise, could only have a non-paradoxical outcome. Reality, he argued, will always be *self-consistent*, even in a universe that includes cosmological exotica like wormholes that can carry information and objects back in time.[54] Subsequently, wormhole expert Kip Thorne and two of his Caltech students, Fernando Echeverria and Gunnar Klinkhammer, confirmed that Novikov's self-consistency conjecture is guaranteed by the laws of probability. Any attempt to shoot a billiard ball through a wormhole at an earlier version of itself in order to deflect it away from the wormhole's mouth (and thus cause a paradox) could only have the opposite effect: nudging the ball into the wormhole instead.[55] Time-traveling billiard balls always survive their suicide attempts. We will see in the next chapter that there is a kind of causal Darwinism called *post-selection* that governs the flow of information backwards and forwards through the glass block of Minkowski spacetime. Information refluxing into the past only "survives" as meaningful insofar as it cannot be used to foreclose the future that "sent" that information.

It is because of this causal Darwinism that the grandfather paradox that scares so many people away from thinking about retrocausation really is an empty scarecrow, flapping harmlessly in the breeze. There is no rule dictating that time travelers are trying to kill (or even bilk) their grandfathers, and such a mission would never be successful in any case. In the block universe, the only time travelers who reach their destination in the past are ones who help bring Grandma and Grandpa together in the first place. This kind of matchmaking, although a little weird perhaps, is not paradoxical. It is also consistent with the essentially positive spirit of the messages the brain at time point B sends its younger self at time point A, even when they seem to involve dark outcomes.

"When retrocausation is allowed," writes Princeton physicist York H. Dobyns, "one may find that an event causes itself."[56] As long as a precognitive organism orients unconsciously toward a future that includes it, then the outcome will be a nice, safe, cozy causal loop. The term used in physics for such a formation is *closed timelike curve*. In myth and metaphor, we call it a self-fulfilling prophecy. "Time loop" is snappier though (and makes for a better book title). If we routinely orient to rewards in our future, and do so unconsciously, then causal tautologies and self-fulfilling prophecies ought to be constant features in our lives, dime-a-dozen formations in the Minkowski block universe. And like a volley of arrows converging on sad-eyed St. Sebastian, separate lines of research in a number of different scientific fields are rapidly converging on an explanation for how this might be possible.

6

Destination: *Pong* (or, How to Build a Quantum™ Future Detector)

The physical universe was a language with a perfectly ambiguous grammar. Every physical event was an utterance that could be parsed in two entirely different ways, one causal and the other teleological, both valid, neither one disqualifiable no matter how much context was available.

— Ted Chiang, "Story of Your Life" (2002)

In the evangelist Luke's account of Jesus's divine origins, the angel Gabriel visited the young virgin, Mary, to tell her the good news that she was going to give birth to God's son. The girl, no dummy, posed the obvious question to her visitor, "How can this be, as I know not a man?"

Gabriel cleared his throat and with a great flourish said, "*The* Holy Spirit will come upon you, and the power of the Highest will overshadow you; therefore, also, that Holy One who is to be born will be called the Son of God." In other words, not answering Mary's question—at all—but sounding very authoritative, and with a lot of what scientists nowadays call "vague hand waving."

Seeing the girl was still perplexed, Gabriel added that her relative Elizabeth had just gotten pregnant even though everyone thought she was barren, thus "With God nothing will be impossible." In other words, *just accept it.*

Countless Renaissance paintings depict Mary looking humbly quizzical before the flamboyant angel explaining all this. But it just wasn't a 13-year-old Galilee girl's place to question what a silken-robed messenger from heaven was telling her about God's plans for her body. So (we are told) Mary just bowed her head and said, "Behold the maidservant of the Lord! Let it be to me according to your word."

Mary's "how can this be?" is one way to look at the outrage of precognition. How can it be that we could see or feel or dream of events that haven't happened yet in the flow of time when we "know not the future"? We are all "virgins" when it comes to future time, aren't we? Anything that violates the time barrier would have to be a miracle—or at least, something supernatural—and that has no place in science.

For Luke's first-century audience, "The Lord" explained everything that couldn't be explained by common sense. In our accursed, godless age, that role is taken up by quantum physics, but the explanations are sometimes no less hand-wavy. People who write about the possibilities of ESP are particularly guilty of quantum hand-waving. There's even a specific version of Gabriel's evocative "overshadowing" in the ESP literature: the mysterious quantum concept of *entanglement*. When particles are created together or interact in some way, their characteristics become correlated such that they cannot be described independently; they become part of a single "entangled state." A measurement on one of the pair, "Alice," would have a corresponding effect on its entangled partner "Bob" instantaneously. Even if you send Bob to a lab orbiting Alpha Centauri, he and Alice will behave identically, almost as if they somehow communicated (you know, telepathically) to get their stories straight.

You'll be hard-pressed to find a book on ESP written since the late 1970s that doesn't mention entanglement, along with its corollary, *nonlocality*, as a possible explanation for the tendency of, say, twins to feel each other's pains or a remote viewer's ability to "see" a secret facility halfway around the world. Abuse of entanglement to explain ESP so angered some physicists that it nearly got the Parapsychological Association booted out of the American Association for the Advancement of Science. At the 1979 meeting of the AAAS, the eminent physicist John Wheeler thundered, "Let no one use the Einstein-Podolsky-Rosen experiment [the basis for the entanglement concept] to … postulate any so-called 'quantum-interconnectedness' between separate consciousnesses."[1] He added that such a notion was "moonshine."

Physicists famously have mini-strokes when quantum concepts are used by parapsychologists to explain "woo" like psychic phenomena, and even when those concepts are borrowed by researchers in more mainstream fields like psychology or economics to help illuminate problems in those domains. (Uttering the words "quantum consciousness" is especially guaranteed to make a physicist keel over, or punch you in the face.) But physicists do not hold an exclusive trademark on the word *quantum*. Knowledge evolves by the spreading of metaphors and the (mis)application of new concepts to different, seemingly unrelated questions—a healthy epistemic ecosystem depends on cross-fertilization, play, and error. The great anthropologist Claude Levi-Strauss called it *bricolage*, from the way handymen in France collect odds and ends from their past jobs and use them to solve new problems—a perfect metaphor for the ever-resourceful, ever-scavenging myth-making mind.[2] Often the result *is* moonshine … but nobody (not even John Wheeler) can predict what batch of today's moonshine might, after being aged a few decades, turn out to be the basis for some exciting and powerful new paradigm.

We may right now be in the midst of a monumental shift—if not even a paradigm shift—around how to interpret the famously "spooky" (and wavy) behavior of matter in the quantum world. It is a shift that could end up validating some of the woo-peddlers and hand-wavers. "Separate consciousnesses" might not be entangled across space; but everything made of matter, including brains, may bear the traces of their entanglements in both directions across time.

"I Was Told There'd Be Other Photons at This Party"

The Alice-in-Wonderland behavior of matter on a fundamental level can be seen in quantum physics' most famous object lesson, the *double slit* experiment. If you shoot a light beam through a barrier with a single slit, the photons will obediently pile on a screen behind it (such as a photographic plate) like a vertical smudge. You will see a dense area in the center fading out gradually on both sides, very much as if the slit was a stencil held in front of the screen and you sprayed the photons through it like spray paint. This doesn't tell us all that much about the nature of light, such as whether it consists of particles or waves. But if you shoot the beam through a barrier with two slits, you will not see two dark areas side by side, which you might expect if photons were like paint droplets or little solid bullets; instead you will see a rippling, zebra-stripe *interference pattern* on the screen, indicating that the photons passed through the slits like waves, cancelling each other where peaks and troughs coincided and amplifying each other where the wave peaks were in sync.

So far, so good. The discovery of this interference pattern in the early 19th century overthrew Isaac Newton's older dogma that light consisted of little particles. If light passing through parallel slits could interfere the way sound waves or ripples on a pond do, its true nature had to be wavy.

But wait. Where it gets weird—or indeed, "impossible," from a classical physics point of view—is if you dial down the intensity of your expensive laboratory flashlight to such a low setting that it shoots just single photons, individual *quanta* of light, through the slits, one at a time—one every second, one every minute, or one every day. If you do that, at the end of your experiment you will *still* find an interference pattern on the screen, not a twin pair of smudges, as you might expect.[3] The same is true with electrons and other larger particles, even atoms and certain molecules—they interfere with *something* even when they are by themselves.

How can this be? What are the individual photons interfering with so that they still land on the screen in the distinctive zebra-stripe interference pattern? How does each photon "know" there were other photons before them, and other ones coming later? Or are they really interfering *with themselves* in some weird way? It was enough to turn grown male scientists into teenage girls from Galilee.

In 1935, the Danish physicist Niels Bohr described a variant of this experiment. What would happen, he wondered, if you attached some kind of detector to one of the slits so it was possible to determine which path each individual particle took on its way to the screen? According to his predictions, if you attempt to spy on the individual particles, they will suddenly change their behavior and pile on the screen the way they would if they were just boring old bullets (or droplets of spray paint)—in two dark lines, with no interference pattern, regardless of whether they are shot through the slits individually or en masse. In the last few decades it has become possible to actually test Bohr's idea, obtaining "which path" information in double-slit experiments that use beams of atoms and a non-interfering detector at one of the slits. Bohr's prediction has been proven right. They somehow know what's up and behave like little solid paint droplets in that case—even the ones flying through the slit that doesn't have the detector attached to it.[4]

Even more mind-bogglingly, none other than John Wheeler showed in 1978 that if you change the parameters of the double-slit experiment while particles are already in mid-flight, they appear to change their nature *retroactively*—again, almost as if they "know" in advance what they are being asked to do.[5]

The central dogma of quantum physics is that there is no way to predict how any individual photon or electron or any other particle will behave in any situation—for instance, which path it will take through the slits of the double-slit experiment. The equations that make quantum physics the most powerful and precise scientific theory ever devised only apply to large numbers of particles. The unpredictability of a single particle's behavior goes way deeper than the butterfly effect: Even knowing all the initial conditions out to the last decimal place would not be enough to enable an experimenter to predict how the particle will behave. Until you actually make a measurement of its position, or its momentum, or its *spin*, or any of the other variable states it might possess, you must assume those things only exist as a vague cloud of mathematical probabilities, what's known as a *wavefunction*. It is not simply that the behavior of particles before measurement is unknown. It is that there is no "already existing" reality to these particles at all until they are observed.

This at least is the most famous interpretation of the evidence, called the Copenhagen Interpretation, which was arrived at by Bohr and his friend Werner Heisenberg in the mid 1920s. It radically redefined the whole business of physics: from describing a preexisting, stable reality "out there" to describing what happens in experiments only—because in some very real sense, there seemed to be *nothing* out there, outside of or prior to the act of observation … at least nothing you could ever put your hands on. According to one of quantum theory's axioms, the "projection postulate," it takes an observer (or at the very least a measuring device) to cause the mathematical cloud of probabilities, in their state of self-interfering *superposition*, to "collapse" into a single definite particle-like value.

This need for an observer to be the midwife for reality has a further strange implication, which Bohr also discovered. Each of a particle's knowable features (like its position) is only knowable when you sacrifice your ability to know about another, complementary feature (like momentum). It is not simply that measurement interferes with what is being measured—Heisenberg's famous *uncertainty principle*—but that the tools needed to measure one kind of information are physically antithetical to the kinds of tools needed to measure the other kind. This is known as *indeterminacy*.[6] Thus, when the observer delivers the object into the world, her choice of how to perform her measurement really determines the form it takes: particle or wave. Her choice influences that particle's destiny. John Wheeler, who studied under Bohr, underscored that observation not only brings the world into being but actually shapes it—an idea known as the "participatory universe."[7]

Exactly what it is about observation or measurement that might cause the "collapse of the wavefunction," and what really happens in that magic instant, has been widely debated.[8] One idea floated by John von Neumann in a 1932 textbook and now popular with the wider public (and especially writers on psi phenomena) is that *consciousness itself* is what collapses wavefunctions during observation.[9] A more modest, non-anthropocentric theory that has come to prevail in the last few decades within physics is known as *decoherence*: Fluctuations in the environment act as an "observer," constantly converting matter's waviness into something solid and definitive.[10] Whatever the case, for most physicists, the collapse of the wavefunction is held to be a real transformation in reality, and it is generally held to be irreversible—a one-way change.

Einstein, who famously quipped that God doesn't play dice, wasn't happy with any of the arguments about uncertainty and wavefunctions collapsing and the complementarity of position and momentum and all the rest. He had trouble accepting that randomness could be somehow built in to the structure of reality at a fundamental level, and especially that it would take an observer to "realize" matter's definiteness. In many histories of quantum physics, Einstein comes across as the grumpy old man, shaking his cane at the young'uns, telling them to get off of his beautiful relativistic lawn. In fact, Einstein's criticisms—even if they reflected an old-fashioned realism—were incisive, and his contributions not only helped hone the reasoning of his younger, more surrealistically minded peers like Bohr but also gave the field what has remained its most "magical" showpiece: the phenomenon of entanglement (more on which momentarily).

Einstein was also far from alone in his distrust of the Copenhagen

Interpretation. A minority of physicists over the years have also suspect-ed that quantum formalisms obscure what is actually happening during measurement. Some have even argued that there has to be a *hidden variable* accounting for the apparent randomness and uncertainty of unmeasured physical systems. Recent developments are making it look like the truth may indeed lie somewhere between Einstein's retrograde realism and the resignation to indeterminacy and uncertainty preached by Bohr and Heisenberg. *Time* seems to hold the answer.

Bass-Ackwards

A big problem with the idea of wavefunctions collapsing is the irrevers-ibility of it. This time-*a*symmetry comports well with our understand-ing of thermodynamics and the one-way-ness of entropic physical pro-cesses we observe in daily life, and thus with our intuitive billiard-ball understanding of cause preceding effect. But it goes against most of the rules of physics and the equations describing electromagnetism, which leave open the possibility that systems could evolve in both directions in time.[11] Most physicists have just shrugged and thrown out the "back-ward" solutions to these equations. But it feels wrong somehow.

In the early 1940s, Wheeler and his student Richard Feynman made a stab at reconciling the temporal symmetries suggested by most of physics' laws with the seemingly asymmetric behavior of light—the way it ordinarily radiates outward from a source, dissipating through a medium according to thermodynamic principles of entropy, and thus seems to carry causation in a single direction (outward). According to their *absorber theory*, objects that receive (or absorb) radiant energy emit waves of their own, called "advanced waves," which interact with the "retarded waves" from the radiation source and produce the apparently asymmetric behavior of radiation. The single direction of light-carried causality is not some a priori, in their theory, but is a product of the interaction of these advanced and retarded waves.[12] Wheeler and Feyn-man's absorber theory does not presume that the destination of a pho-ton has advanced knowledge that it is going to receive the photon; thus, even though it is a time-symmetric solution, it is not exactly retrocausal. But others have gotten more radical in their thinking.

In the 1960s, an Israeli physicist named Yakir Aharonov basically agreed with Einstein about God not playing dice, and he proposed that *the future* is the hidden variable underlying quantum strangeness.

Individual particles, such as those photons passing through the slits of the double-slit experiment, are actually influenced by what will happen to them *next* (i.e., when they hit the screen), not just by what happened to them a moment ago (when they were shot out of the expensive flashlight and passed through the slits). The randomness that seems to rule the quantum casino, Aharonov suggested, may really be the inherently unknowable influence of those particles' future histories on their present behavior. Measurement thus becomes part of the particle's "backstory"—precisely the part that always looked like randomness, or quantum uncertainty.

Physicists like to give innocuously obscure names to their ideas, partly to keep the rest of the world from abusing those ideas in ESP books, like I'm doing here. The time-symmetric, retrocausal framework advanced by Aharonov and his colleagues is sometimes called the *two-state vector formalism*. It is not the only, or even the most well-known, retrocausal solution, however.

In the 1980s, University of Washington physicist John G. Cramer argued for a *transactional interpretation* of quantum mechanics that resembles in many ways Wheeler and Feynman's absorber theory but is actually retrocausal. Like Wheeler and Feynman, Cramer proposed that the wavefunction of a particle moving forward in time is just one of two relevant waves determining its behavior. The retarded wave in Cramer's theory is complemented by a *response wave* that travels specifically from the particle's destination, in temporal retrograde. In his theory, a measurement, or an interaction, amounts to a kind of "handshake agreement" between the forward-in-time and backward-in-time influences.[13] This handshake can extend across enormous lengths of time, if we consider what happens when we view the sky at night. As Cramer writes:

> When we stand in the dark and look at a star a hundred light years away, not only have the retarded waves from the star been traveling for a hundred years to reach our eyes, but the advanced waves generated by absorption processes within our eyes have reached a hundred years into the past, completing the transaction that permitted the star to shine in our direction.[14]

Cramer may not have been aware of it, but his poetic invocation of the spacetime greeting of the eye and a distant star, and the transactional process that would be involved in seeing, was actually a staple of medieval and early Renaissance optics. Before the ray theory of light emerged in the 1600s, it was believed that a visual image was formed when rays projecting out from the eye interacted with those coming into it. It goes to show that *everything*, even old physics, comes back in style if you wait long enough—and it is another reason not to laugh too hard, or with too much self-assurance, at hand-waving that seems absurd from one's own limited historical or scientific standpoint.

In short: Cramer's and Aharonov's theories both imply a backward causal influence from the photon's destination. The destination of the photon "already knows" it is going to receive the photon, and this is what enables it to behave with the appropriate politeness. Note that neither of these theories have anything to do with billiard balls moving in reverse, a mirror of causation in which particles somehow fly through spacetime and interact in temporal retrograde. That had been the idea at the basis of Gerald Feinberg's hypothesized tachyons, particles that travel faster than light and thus backward in time. It inspired a lot of creative thinking about the possibilities of precognition and other forms of ESP in the early 1970s (and especially inspired the science-fiction writer Philip K. Dick), but we can now safely set aside that clunky and unworkable line of thinking as "vulgar retrocausation." No trace of tachyons has turned up in any particle accelerator, and they don't make sense anyway. What we are talking about here instead is an *inflection* of ordinary particles' observable behavior by something ordinarily unobservable: measurements—that is, interactions—that lie ahead in those particles' future histories. Nothing is "moving" backwards in time—and really, nothing is "moving" forwards in time either. A particle's twists and turns as it stretches across time simply contain information about both its past and its future.

A prominent advocate of time-symmetric, retrocausal solutions is Cambridge University analytic philosopher Huw Price. It is not the ostensible randomness and observer-dependence of the microworld that nags Price so much as entanglement, everybody's favorite quantum quirk. Einstein and two of his younger colleagues, Boris Podolsky and Nathan Rosen (collectively known as "EPR"), originally predicted the existence of entangled states in a 1935 paper that was intended to show the incompleteness of quantum theory. Despite being predicted in the equations, entanglement seemed intrinsically impossible because it would require information to travel between entangled particles at a speed faster than light (i.e., instantaneously), violating light's strict speed limit and thus violating unilinear causality. Yet in 1964, a CERN physicist named John Bell published a theorem proving the EPR prediction, and subsequent experiments supported the existence of entangled states. Since then, entanglement has gone from a curious special case to the state of almost everything in the universe—all particles that interact become entangled, at least to a degree. However, no one has ever been able to explain just how entanglement works—it is just one of many quantum bizarreries that physics students are instructed to take on faith. But Price thinks retrocausation (or what he also calls "advanced action") holds the answer: The measurement that affects one of the two entangled particles sends information back in time to the point when they interacted and became entangled in the first place. Thus, that future event in the life of Alice became part of the destiny of Bob too—a kind of zig-zagging causal path cutting across Minkowski's four-dimensional spacetime block.[15]

Price didn't come up with the idea originally. It was first suggested in the 1950s by the French physicist Olivier Costa de Beauregard as a way of rescuing Einstein's relativity from his own proposal of entanglement (and at the same time, rescuing entanglement from relativity). But that was before Bell established the reality of entangled states with his theorem and before the many experimental demonstrations that followed. More recently, Price and his collaborator, San José State University physicist Ken Wharton, have reinterpreted some of those experiments, showing that entanglement is really better explained through Costa de Beauregard's "Parisian zigzag" than through the "spooky action at a distance" that is implicit in standard descriptions of the phenomenon.[16]

Price's assumption when he first advocated a less temporally biased view of causation in his 1996 book *Time's Arrow and Archimedes' Point* was that, even though time-symmetric solutions to quantum mechanics seemed persuasive on many levels, it would be hard or impossible to test them directly because of the famous uncertainty that rules the quantum realm. Since every measurement changes what it measures, how could you ever get direct evidence of a future influence? Your measurement is changing that future, making it impossible to distinguish any backwards influence from the perturbing effects of your measurement. For the same reason, advocates of retrocausal solutions often emphasize, as though anticipating the abuse of these ideas by the uninitiated, that it would be impossible to actually send a signal into the past.[17] But developments over the past two decades in laboratory methods—some of which were developed by Aharonov and his colleagues specifically to study aspects of his two-state vector formalism—have opened new doors for testing retrocausal hypotheses experimentally. They may even open doors to a real kind of informational time travel.

For instance, in 2009, a team at the University of Rochester led by physicist John Howell shot a laser beam through a beam splitter and then at a mirror attached to a very sensitive motor; the motor could measure the extremely tiny amount that the mirror was nudged or deflected by the photons in the beam. This experiment used a new technique proposed by Aharonov called "weak measurement" that manages to partly get around the old limitations imposed by Heisenberg's uncertainty principle. Each individual weak measurement interacts trivially with the particle in order not to perturb it too much; that measurement, in isolation, is too imprecise to tell you anything useful, but when aggregated over many particles, such measurements can produce valuable information without disturbing the light beam. The weakly measured laser light in this experiment then passed through either of two gates, beyond which one portion of the split beam was measured a second time in the usual, "strong" way. This after-the-fact selection of some of the light to measure again is known in these experiments as *post-selection*—a key concept that we will be returning to throughout the remainder of this book. The astonishing finding was that the post-selected light, the portion of the laser beam measured at the later time, turned out to have been *amplified*, deflecting the mirror *previously* about a hundred times more than the light that wasn't destined for the second measurement.[18] In other words, that second measurement seems to have influenced the light's behavior *in its past*.[19]

As hard as it is to wrap our heads around, retrocausation could radically simplify—even "collapse"—much of the famously mystical weirdness of quantum mechanics and explain why particles so often seem to know so much about their destinies. Take for instance a phenomenon called *frustrated spontaneous emission*. It sounds like an embarrassing sexual complaint that psychotherapy might help with. In fact, it involves the decay of radioactive particles, which ordinarily takes place at a predictably random rate. The exception, however, is when radioactive material is placed in an environment that cannot absorb the photons that are emitted by decay. In that case, decay ceases—the atoms become "frustrated." How do these atoms "know" to stop decaying until conditions are suitable? According to Wharton, the unpredictable decay of radioactive particles may be determined in part by whatever receives their emitted photons in the future.[20] Decay may not really be random at all, in other words.

Another quantum mystery that arguably becomes less mysterious in a retrocausal world is the *quantum Zeno effect*. Usually, the results of measurements are unpredictable—again according to the famous uncertainty believed to govern the quantum kingdom—but there is a loophole. Persistent, rapid probing of reality by repeating the same measurement over and over produces repetition of the same "answer" from the physical world, almost as if it is "stopping time" in some sense (hence the name of the effect, which refers to Zeno's paradoxes like an arrow that must first get halfway to its target, and then halfway from there, and so on, and thus is never able to reach the target at all).[21] If the measurement itself is somehow influencing a particle retrocausally, then repeating the same measurement in the same conditions may effectively be influencing the measured particles the same way *in their past*, thereby producing the consistent behavior.

Retrocausation may also be at the basis of a long-known but, again, hitherto unsatisfyingly explained quirk of light's behavior: *Fermat's principle of least time*. Light always takes the fastest possible path to its destination, which means taking the shortest available path through different media like water or glass. It is the rule that accounts for the refraction of light through lenses, and the reason why an object underwater appears displaced from its true location.[22] It is yet another example of a creature in the quantum bestiary that makes little sense unless photons somehow "know" where they are going in order to take the most efficient possible route to get there. If the photon's angle of deflection when entering a refractive medium is somehow determined by its destination, Fermat's principle would make much more sense. (We will return to Fermat's principle later in this book; it plays an important role in Ted Chiang's short story, "Story of Your Life," the basis for the wonderful precognition movie *Arrival*.)

And retrocausation could also offer new ways of looking at the double-slit experiment and its myriad variants.[23] Again, we would have to assume that the photon's path through the slits is already determined in part by its future interaction with the screen, not just by the slits themselves (or the light source). The interference pattern may not simply reflect possible paths interfering with each other in some quantum nowhere prior to measurement but may reflect the entanglements between photons and the whole experimental apparatus (including the screen) *across time.*

In other words, particles may know so much about the future because they have already been to the future … although again, a more correct way of looking at it is that they are halfway "in" the future already.

Think back to that glass block of Minkowski: Every particle is really a spaghetti strand snaking across time. Or better yet, imagine particles as colored threads on a vast and chaotic loom; everywhere a thread entwines with another thread is an interaction (or "measurement"), and the patterns woven by the zig-zagging, criss-crossing threads as they are stretched between both sides of that loom would not appear random at all if we could take a higher, Archimedean vantage point outside of time, as Price recommends.[24] From a viewpoint that could grasp the whole cloth, it would be strange—indeed, ridiculously biased—to privilege one side, or one direction of causation, over the other. It would be like saying the pattern created by the interwoven colored threads in a blanket is "caused" by its lefthand side, with a component of capriciousness in the threads' turnings as we scan the blanket from left to right, and the righthand side of the blanket exerting no "leftward" influence on the pattern at all. With retrocausation, we can no longer privilege the past, as though causation is only a matter of "pushing" (sometimes called *efficient causation*). The real mystery becomes why those efficient causes are so much more apparent and intuitively understood, and why influences propagating in reverse give us headaches to even think about. This is a mystery that physics alone might not be able to solve, but the first step toward finding a solution may be to train ourselves to "think backwards" about events. (Consider this book a primer in doing exactly that.)

What at least some retrocausal frameworks suggest is that the so-called collapse of the wavefunction may really be just a handy fiction, a statement about our current lack of knowledge not only about the outcome of a measurement but also about how our measurement will turn out to have affected the particle's *prior* behavior once we have interpreted the relevant data. In other words, the many supposedly "superposed" possibilities, and the statistical contours of that landscape of possibility, reflect not simply our lack of knowledge about something that already possessed definite properties independently of us (the old-fashioned, realist view never quite given up on by Einstein) *or* that measurement creates actuality out of a cloud of mathematical nothing (the Copenhagen Interpretation). Instead, the measurement itself is what will determine those prior, uncertain properties. Measurement creates—but really, cre-at*ed*—the past. Aharonov and his colleague Jeff Tollaksen write that time-symmetric reformulations of quantum mechanics

> change the meaning of uncertainty from 'capricious-ness' to exactly what is needed in order that the fu-ture can be relevant to the present, without violating causality, thereby providing a new perspective on the question 'Why does God play dice?' … [It] suggests that two 'identical' particles are not really identical, but there is no way to find out their differences based only on information coming from the past, one must also know the future.[25]

It is important to pause at this point and "absorb" the implica-tions of all this. What it does *not* mean is that, tucked away safely in a few laboratories on a few university campuses there might be funny, exceptional situations where trivial teensy-weensy effects precede trivial teensy-weensy causes. The implication of experiments like John How-ell's beam-amplification experiment at Rochester or numerous variants of the double-slit experiment like Wheeler's delayed-choice experiment is that the behavior of all matter at a fundamental level is determined not just by its past but also by its future. *Everything* that happens to ev-ery photon or electron, every interaction it has with other photons and electrons, other objects, other forces, sends ripples into its past history as well as its future history. What looked for all the world like random-ness, quantum uncertainty, really has been hiding a variable we didn't understand or have any way of measuring until recently: *the influence of the Not Yet on the Now.*[26]

Even if it represents a new way of looking at the measurement problem, the idea that measurement "creates the past" flows in some ways from insights articulated by Bohr already in the 1930s. Bohr argued that quantum reality undermined *totally* the classical assumption Einstein adhered to, that subject and object, observer and observed, could be distinguished. There is *no pre-existing reality* apart from and indepen-dent of the observer and the apparatus used to measure that reality, and thus no a priori distinction between observer and observed. They are all of a piece: Not only is the wavelike (versus particle-like) nature of an electron "created" under the influence of a certain specific kind of measuring apparatus, but the creation of and choice to deploy that apparatus is itself a product of the social conditions making the experiment possible, the history of science that led to it, and even the biological and cultural forces that converged to produce the experimenter herself. The measurement sits at the center of infinitely widening gyre of what theoretical physicist and feminist scholar Karen Barad, using a more modern idiom, calls "entanglements."[27] Other apparatuses, other conditions, and another experimenter making other choices would produce a different reality.

In her stunning 2007 meshing of critical theory, physics, and gender studies, *Meeting the Universe Halfway*, Barad revisited Bohr and his then-untestable *Gedanken*-experiments from the standpoint of recent developments in what she calls "experimental metaphysics"—the use of new, highly precise laboratory techniques to probe the once-insoluble questions that Bohr and Einstein (and Heisenberg and Schrödinger) debated, never thinking empirical answers would ever be forthcoming. The Rochester experiment and others using weak measurement might be examples of such experiments. Variants of the double-slit experiment that spy on individual photons to see "which path" they took through the slits are among those that Barad cites. In the early 1990s, Marlan O. Scully and colleagues at the Max Planck Institute described an experiment collecting which-path information on atoms passing through two slits using newly developed *micromaser* technology. Again, Bohr had predicted that the screen would show no interference pattern in such a case—the atoms, "knowing" they had been spied on, would behave like particles, not waves. This turns out to be the case. But astonishingly, Scully and colleagues described that if the experimenters erase the which-path information they have collected (but not yet analyzed) after they run the experiment, an interference pattern is restored.[28] It is a delayed-choice version of the double-slit experiment in which the experimenters seem able to *dictate what happens it the past* by erasing (versus not erasing) quantum information in the present.

From this and other similar experiments, Barad argues that we can no longer think of time as some objective framework, some empty container holding and preceding its contents. It too is shaped and in a very real sense *created* by our experimental choices and by the scientific and discursive practices that we bring to bear on reality when we investigate it—a radical form of what is sometimes called the "social construction of reality" but penetrating to the very heart of matter, space, and time. She writes:

It's not that the experimenter changes a past that had already been present or that atoms fall in line with a new future simply by erasing information. The point is that the past was never simply there to begin with and the future is not simply what will unfold; the "past" and the "future" are iteratively reworked and enfolded through the iterative practices of spacetimemattering … neither space nor time exist as determinate givens outside of phenomena.[29]

(Yes, she said "spacetimemattering.")

To be clear, Barad is *not* adopting an interpretation like that of John von Neumann or any number of more recent writers excited by the possibility that consciousness is somehow constitutive of reality, or that consciousness is even an intrinsic part of observation and measurement.[30] And she is not simply repeating the quantum truism that our choice of how to measure a particle effectively determines the face it reveals going forward. She is instead asking the reader to grapple with the fact that time itself does not escape the skein of entanglements in which the experiment and the experimenter are not only embedded but actually constituted. *Everything* is entangled. It is a radical kind of contextualism that extends entanglements not only across space but across history (in both directions). There are no individual agents acting upon separate objects, for Barad, and thus no way to separate the knower from the known. It is all "intra-action" in which agents and objects come into being, along with their histories, through the enactment of cuts (meaningful distinctions) in an otherwise undifferentiated phenomenal reality.

Barad does not use the idiom of retrocausation, which has gained in popularity in the decade since she wrote her book—and she might not necessarily endorse the two-state vector or transactional interpretations described here. But what she is articulating is the literal participation of measurement (and by extension, all physical interactions and entanglements) in producing the historical conditions that led to them. The particle's past is determined by how the experimenter makes contact with it in the present, as well as further decisions that will be made about that contact going forward. The past never ceases being made by the future, and we ourselves never cease being made in the intra-actions that create this new knowledge. We and time are all of a piece—an idea we will loop back to at the end of this book.

* * *

"The herd of mainstream opinion has resigned itself to the spooks," Huw Price and Ken Wharton lament, "but there is an open gate leading in a different direction."[31] They argue that there really are no good arguments against retrocausation from a physics standpoint. The objections are purely philosophical: The problem of free will is what has tended to deflect physicists from confronting time-symmetric interpretations of quantum mechanics with the seriousness that these quite elegant solutions deserve.[32] When suddenly confronted with the radical and troubling idea of the block universe implied by retrocausation, physicists frequently turn into philosophers, anxious to preserve and protect one of the philosophical pillars of our individualistic, freedom-loving society. Even when retrocausation advocates broach the subject in polite company, either in journal articles or the popular science press, they generally do some obligatory rhetorical dance promising that free will is safe and sound (even if it really may not be).[33] This kind of anxiety tells us we are in the world of powerful taboo. We'll come back to that too.

But even if it remains a minority interpretation in physics and touches on deep-seated hangups, the resistances to retrocausal thinking are softening. If you follow the science news, it seems like every month some new theory or experiment is throwing the universality of cause-*preceding*-effect into question.[34] For example, research in quantum information theory by Časlav Brukner and Philip Walther at the University of Vienna and by Giulio Chiribella at the University of Hong Kong is showing that causal order can be "indefinite" at the quantum level.[35] Recent experiments are even showing that quantum-entangled systems can defy the second law of thermodynamics: Heat can be made to flow from a colder object to a hotter one—another kind of "time reversal."[36] "Time crystals" are also now being created in laboratories: little perpetual motion machines that continually oscillate without any energy being added to them, as though they are stuck in an endless, timeless loop, little chunks of eternity.[37] What do these new developments and possibilities tell us—or not tell us—about the possibility of gaining useful information about the future before it arrives—effectively the obverse (and thus, equivalent) of "sending a signal into the past"? Even on this question, the skeptics and deniers may have less of a leg to stand on than was once believed. That "gate" Price and Wharton mentioned really is wide open to a lot of amazing possibilities.

Information vs. Meaning

Retrocausation is increasingly thinkable nowadays thanks to another, much bigger, slower, and less controversial paradigm shift that has been occurring across many physical sciences over the past few decades: a trend away from describing natural phenomena in terms of causes and effects to instead describing them in terms of *information* and its transformations.[38] Such a reframing not only frees us conceptually to understand the kinds of backward influences being detected in physics laboratories, but it also enables us to better consider what these influences may have to do with, or not do with, questions of *meaning*. It may be that we cannot understand matter on a fundamental level (let alone such notions as "sending signals back in time") until we understand meaning and how it gets made, and more often *not made*, from the raw material of information.[39]

First, what does it mean to redescribe causation in terms of information? Every process in nature, every collision, every interaction of matter and energy, boils down to a transformation in some theoretically measurable state of the atoms and photons and electrons involved. It changes the states of those particles the same way energy flowing through a computer changes binary switches—it "flips bits." Thus causation is, when it comes right down to it, synonymous with *computation*.[40] John Wheeler famously described the physical universe as the product of computation, "it from bit"[41]; and quantum computing pioneer Seth Lloyd argues we should really think of the whole universe as a giant computer, because you could theoretically use any lump of matter in the universe, or even the universe as a whole, to compute things.[42] You just need to measure the particles first, "program" them by interacting with them in some way, and measure them again to find out how they have changed; the latter is your "output."

"The universe is a computer" is a bit of a misleading metaphor, however, for a couple of reasons. For one thing, it calls to mind a "user" who can derive meaning from all this computation and apply it to some problem. Mere computation, the transformation of information, is not enough for the making of meaning. You can theoretically quantify the information in a system, even the amount of information in the universe as a whole (the universe can store roughly 10^{92} bits of information, in case you were wondering[43]) or the amount of information processing in any subsystem of the universe—like a computer, a rock, a star, or a starfish—without necessarily paying attention to whether a given bit flip has any value or utility to someone in guiding behavior or communicating a message. Meaning, while often confused with information, really refers to the value of a piece of information to some agent (conscious or not) who can use it to convey a message or otherwise effect some change.

Because meaning is relative to the needs of the agent holding or using the information, it cannot be measured in any absolute way. This is what mathematician Claude Shannon realized in the middle of the 20th century when he tried to turn information theory into something rigorously scientific.[44] Shannon, who worked at Bell Labs during WWII and later taught at MIT, was interested in technical problems in cryptography, telecommunications, and computing, and it was safe to assume for all these human purposes that the information we are concerned with *can* be meaningful (otherwise why would we care about it?). But it is hard to quantify the truth versus falsehood of a signal, and impossible to quantify its value to a recipient (or sender)—indeed its value to different agents could differ. Formalizing his theory thus meant setting aside these "psychological factors." It was an important move that later paved the way for thinking of causality on a fundamental (quantum) level in information terms. Yet lingering confusions about information and whether it must be meaningful have persisted and have even led to some of the most interesting byways in late-20th-century science.[45]

The most colorful of these byways is described by David Kaiser in his 2011 book *How the Hippies Saved Physics*.[46] Because their funding came directly or indirectly from the military-industrial complex, whose overriding imperative was to technologically out-compete our global rivals, postwar American physicists fully internalized the Copenhagen ideology of not questioning quantum mysteries—"shut up and calculate" was the motto. But in the 1970s, especially in California, a younger generation undaunted by their elders' warnings dreamed of using John Bell's theorem proving the existence of entangled states to do really nifty tricks like sending messages faster than light. Since a measurement of one of a pair of entangled particles seems to determine what its partner does instantaneously, no matter how far apart they are, it naturally invites thoughts of instantaneous communication across space without some intervening transfer of energy. The out-of-the-box California physicists beat their heads against this problem for years, but by the early 1980s, it became apparent that there is no way to send a signal via entanglement alone. For one thing, if you force one of a pair of entangled particles into a certain state, the entanglement with the other particle will be broken, so it will not "send" information about its state to its twin. You are limited to performing measurements of a particle's uncertain value, which compels it to make up its mind about the (previously uncertain) state it is in. In that case, you can be sure its entangled twin will make the same choice, but then some additional information channel needs to be available to let your distant partner know what measurement you performed and what result you got.

The latter part of the problem has an analogy in basic semantics. For a piece of information to be meaningful, it needs to be reliably paired with another piece of information that gives it context or serves as its cipher. If I say "yes" to my wife, it can only be meaningless noise, a random word, unless my utterance was produced in the context of a question, like "Are you going to the store later?" Without knowing exactly *how* the physicist on Earth measured her particle, Alice, and what result she got, the change in Alice's entangled partner Bob four light years away in that lab orbiting Alpha Centauri cannot be meaningful, even if it is information. The Earth physicist needs to send some slower-than-light signal to inform her distant colleague about her measurement and its outcome ... which defeats the whole purpose of using entanglement to carry a message.[47]

This is also the problem with the metaphor of the universe as a computer. No matter how much computation the universe can perform, its outputs can be little more than out-of-context yesses and nos, addressed to no one in particular. If there is no "outside" to the system, there is nothing to compare it to and no one to give all those bit flips meaning. In fact, it is a lot like the planetary supercomputer "Deep Thought" in Douglas Adam's *Hitchhiker's Guide to the Galaxy*: When, after millions of years of computation, it finally utters its output, "42," no one knows what it means, because the question the computer had been programmed to answer has long been forgotten.

We are now perhaps in a better position to understand how the behavior of atoms, photons, and subatomic particles could carry information about their future—*tons* of information—without any of it being meaningful to us, and why we would naturally (mis)construe it as randomness: It is noise to our ears, stuck as we are in the Now with no way of interpreting it. It is like the future constantly sending back strings of yesses and nos without us knowing the questions. We are only now realizing that there may indeed be words in all that noise—it's not just gibberish. But how to decode them?

Post-selection, used in the Rochester team's beam-amplification experiment, is one principle that may allow backward-flowing influence from the future to assume a semblance of meaning in the present. If an experimenter could be confident that a certain behavior of a group of particles (such as amplification of a laser beam) at time point A was correlated with some known measurement (e.g., versus no measurement) at a pre-ordained time point B, information from the first measurement might be readable as a meaningful retrograde "signal" (although it would really not be a signal so much as a correlation between a present state and a future state). Something else that may be of use here is the discovery that the interference that goes along with measurement is not, as was once thought, a zero-sum, all-or-nothing proposition. It is possible to extract a net gain of meaningful information even when interfering. The new technique of weak measurement, for example, seems to let researchers obtain a margin of meaningful information without badly perturbing a quantum system, so long as they are willing to accept some degree of uncertainty or imprecision as a trade-off. In other words, the relationship between the amount of meaningful information it is possible to gain through measurement and the amount of interference the measurement produces is *non-linear*.[48] These principles may just make the impossible—detecting the future—possible.

So, at the risk of giving mini-strokes to the few quantum physicists who may be slumming it reading a trashy book on ESP, here are a couple admittedly hand-wavy possibilities for how a *future detector* might be created. The simplest method uses the same principle as John Howell's beam-amplification experiment: measuring particles at time point A in a "gentle," relatively non-interfering way so that a predictable subsequent stronger measurement of some of them at time point B— the post-selection phase—reliably shows a difference between the two groups. Tying some real-world outcome to the measurement of a previously weakly-measured group of particles could create something like Asimov's "endochronometer" that used thiotimoline's pre-dissolution in water to detect future events. Measuring the amplification of a laser, specifically, might not be your best choice of system to use because you'd need some way of slowing down the speedy photons (or shooting them a long distance across space) for the setup to provide any useful temporal window between weak measurement and post-selected measurement. However, whatever system you use, you could in principle amplify such a device by daisy-chaining multiple future detectors together, just as Asimov did with his endochronometers to create a "telechronic battery."

Another possibility for a future detector is more complicated and uses one of several serendipitous fruits of the hippie physicists' failed attempts to crack the nut of faster-than-light signaling: *quantum teleportation*.[49] Even if you can't use entanglement by itself to send a signal faster than light, you can combine conventional signals with entanglement to "beam" information or even matter short distances across space. For teleportation to work, the entangled couple Alice and Bob need to both be back on Earth, near enough to each other that a conventional signal can be sent between the separate laboratories that house them. It is usually described more or less like this: The physicist who holds Bob in his possession can compare Bob to another, third particle Chris—the object he wants to teleport—to determine the relative properties of the two particles (destroying the properties of Chris in the process, because measurement interferes). Once this is done, the physicist can phone up his colleague who has Alice and tell her how Bob and Chris compared. His colleague can then measure Alice (destroying Alice's unique properties) and from the knowledge she got from her colleague, reconstruct information about Chris at her location, since she knows Alice was just like Bob.[50] It sounds like a crazy-complicated Rube Goldberg contraption, but it is cool because it is basically a transporter, like in *Star Trek*—destroying matter or information in one location and reconstituting it some distance away. Or, if you remember the 1982 Disney movie *Tron*, you can picture the memorable scene of video-gamer Kevin Flynn (Jeff Bridges) being digitized and disassembled by his office laser and reconstituted inside the virtual world of his favorite arcade game. First proposed by IBM physicist Charles Bennett in 1993, quantum teleportation has since been demonstrated experimentally many times, over distances of as much as 870 miles (the current record, as of this writing), using lasers to send one of a pair of entangled photons to a satellite in orbit.[51]

Seth Lloyd and his colleagues developed and even tested a variant of this method that combines teleportation with—you guessed it—postselection, to send information *back in time* instead of across space.[52] It involves breaking the entanglement of Alice and Bob and then re-entangling one of them (Bob, say) with Chris. Information associated with Chris will in certain, post-selected circumstances be found to have been correlated with information associated with the divorced particle, Alice, prior to this procedure.[53] "It's complicated," as they say of relationships on Facebook, so don't bother trying to wrap your head around it—but for a mental image, you could picture Jeff Bridges being digitized by the laser, same as before, and instead of materializing inside his slick 1982 Tron game, he would materialize *several years earlier* inside a mid-1970s Pong console. (In the prequel, *Pong: Legacy*, we'd find that Flynn had become ruler of a dull virtual table tennis scenario and gone mad from the boredom.) In their experimental test of this idea, Lloyd and colleagues successfully made a particle interact with itself in the past and, as predicted by Igor Novikov's self-consistency principle, only in a non-paradoxical way—"no matter how hard the time-traveler tries, she finds her grandfather is a tough guy to kill."[54] Before you get too excited, it was only a few billionths of a second into the past. Still, it was an important proof of principle. Lloyd considers this a way that information and potentially even matter could be teleported into the past, creating what physicists call a closed timelike curve—that is, a time loop.[55]

If there is one technology that may really open the door to the future detectors of tomorrow, it could be quantum computing—the biggest, juiciest, most expensive fruit of those hippie physicists' tireless attempts to figure out what science-fictional things could be done with entangled particles. A quantum computer is a supercooled matrix of entangled (or quantum-coherent[56]) atoms or other particles, whose parameters such as "spin" are assigned values and used to encode and process information. These quantum bits or *qubits* play a role similar to the binary switches in a conventional microprocessor, except that each qubit can assume multiple values simultaneously (0 *and* 1, off *and* on) thanks to the magic of superposition. The system needs to be kept extremely cold to maintain the precious entanglement between qubits, which washes out very easily when there is any interference by the environment.

The typical explanation for why a quantum computer ought to be vastly more powerful than a classical one is that it can simultaneously take multiple computational paths to the right answer to a problem. A somewhat more precise characterization, according to Scott Aaronson, is that quantum computers "choreograph a pattern of interference" in which wrong answers cancel each other out and only correct solutions remain.[57] Either way, it boils down to the assumption that probabilities (or "amplitudes" as they are known in the field) interact constructively or destructively like waves to produce a single outcome. Like light rays finding the fastest path to their destination, a quantum computer finds the fastest path to the solution of the problem it was programmed to solve. But there is still a surprising amount of disagreement about how quantum computers actually work (and even *if* they will work as expected[58]), partly because there is still so much disagreement about how quantum mechanics works more generally.

Remember that the standard (Copenhagen) view that particles are totally wavy until collapsing on measurement is not the only possible interpretation. Retrocausal frameworks suggest instead that particles' behavior is determined by their subsequent interactions as well as their previous ones, and that it is our inability to know about the former that makes their pre-measurement behavior seem more wave-like than it really is. Also, remember what Olivier Costa de Beauregard, Huw Price, and Ken Wharton proposed about entangled particles: that their fates are really interwoven across time. Thus, the term "nonlocality" commonly used to characterize entanglement may be a bit misleading: Entangled states really seem to partake of a kind of *eternity*, the quintessence of the Minkowski glass block. *If* this is true (or at least, insofar as it might characterize what is happening in the expensive guts of a quantum computer), what may give a matrix of entangled qubits its extra computational oomph is not a kind of massive *parallel* processing but, rather, an ability to draw on its processing power over its history. Could it be that quantum computers really *compute across time*?

Call an ambulance! That thud you just heard is an "actual real-life physicist" somewhere keeling over from a stroke as a result of a non-physicist being wrong (or too simplistic) about quantum computing in an ESP book. But there is mounting evidence that there is indeed something special, even "timeless," about entangled states like those that a quantum computer relies on. Again, new research in quantum information theory is showing that the causal order in quantum computational operations can be indefinite—it is possible to scramble cause and effect in operations using entangled particles.[59] This is being proposed as a principle that could be used to radically accelerate quantum computation.[60] Whether a quantum computer could ever be used to "precognize" its own future states remains to be seen.

In any case, it is fun to speculate that one or more of the possibilities proposed might, decades down the road, lead to the development of a real precognitive circuit. Given human nature, whoever builds the first one will probably use it to make a killing by predicting microfluctuations in the stock market. If miniaturized enough, though, such technology could serve as the basis for security systems, safety features in vehicles, and medical devices, among other applications. It would not provide a reliable fore-warning of preventable outcomes, for the same reason it may never be possible to create a "psychic early warning system" to prevent things like terrorist attacks (if, as I argue, precognition is of actual, not just possible, futures). Or, the error or noise quotient would escalate as the possibility of "bilking" a pre-detected outcome increased. But such a circuit could detect an inevitable imminent event and trigger a preparatory response in advance. In certain circumstances, even a forewarning of a second, or a fraction of a second, could provide a decisive margin to initiate a preparatory response—such as triggering the deployment of an airbag in advance of an imminent collision.

And, of course, there is the scary/awesome thought of "precognitive AI." But before we get too frightened about precognitive Terminators hunting down the remnants of humanity in some post-apocalyptic waste, peering into the future to anticipate their quarry's every move, we should realize that precognition may actually be intrinsic to what we think of as intelligence. If that's the case, nature has a few-billion-year head start on building a future detector. Spoiler alert: You may already be equipped with one of these devices.

7

A New Era of Hyperthought — From Precognitive Bacteria to Our Tesseract Brain

*Time is the substance I am made of. Time is a river
which sweeps me along, but I am the river; it is a tiger
which destroys me, but I am the tiger; it is a fire which
consumes me, but I am the fire.*

— Jorge Luis Borges, "A New Refutation of Time" (1946)

In Madeleine L'Engle's 1962 novel *A Wrinkle in Time*, 13-year-old Meg Murry, along with her telepathic little brother and a classmate, travel to a series of distant planets via a fold in the fabric of the universe called a *tesseract*. They are trying to find and rescue their missing scientist father, who happened to be researching precisely such higher-dimensional possibilities when he vanished months earlier. In a memorable scene, "Mrs. Who," one of three librarian-like spinsters who understand higher-dimensional cosmology and use tesseracts to get around, demonstrates the principle to the schoolkids by holding her robe out flat and drawing it together, showing how such a "wrinkle" can bring distant points together and make a hypothetical insect's traverse of her robe much shorter.[1] The concept paved the way for newer concepts like wormholes as shortcuts through space and time. But such higher-dimensional doorways (or at least the idea of them) have a surprisingly long history.

The fourth dimension, as we saw earlier, was catnip to thinking Victorians.[2] Tesseracts were originally the brainchild of a British mathematician named Charles Howard Hinton. In his 1888 book *A New Era of Thought*, Hinton coined that term to refer to a four-dimensional version of a cube (also called a "hypercube"). Hinton's fourth dimension (like that of Edward A. Abbott in *Flatland*) remained an added *spatial* dimension, not the dimension of time—again, it was H. G. Wells who made that further leap—but Hinton saw that our human ability to conceive of higher dimensions and manipulate them in our imagination reflected the likelihood that our brains somehow partook of this higher dimensionality. "We must be really four-dimensional creatures," he wrote, "or we could not think about four dimensions."[3]

As is irresistible and probably unavoidable when you're trying to blow your readers' minds with a speculative new idea and also justify it scientifically, Hinton engaged in a little bit of hand-waving to show how this might be possible. He proposed that it was the brain's computational units, what he called "brain molecules," that behaved in this four-D way and enabled our contemplation of higher dimensions:

> It may be that these brain molecules have the power of four-dimensional movement, and that they can go through four-dimensional movements and form four-dimensional structures. …
>
> And these movements and structures would be apprehended by the consciousness along with the other movements and structures, and would seem as real as the others—but would have no correspondence in the external world.
>
> They would be thoughts and imaginations, not observations of external facts.[4]

Sometimes, hand-waving that looks like drowning is really saying hello to a future the rest of us cannot yet see. Hinton's "brain molecules" able to perform four-dimensional gymnastics sound whimsical, but a growing number of researchers think the brain could have real quantum computational properties. And if the retrocausal hypothesis gaining ground in physics is right, those properties could even be time-defying. Although it remains speculative at this point—and thus, yes, hand-wavy—it is not unthinkable that the brain may turn out to be something like a squishy, pinkish-gray tesseract—a roughly six-inch-in-diameter information tunnel through time, corresponding more or less to what J. W. Dunne called a person's "brain line."[5] Moreover, its super-dimensional abilities, if real, will likely turn out to be based, as Hinton presciently intuited back in 1888, on *molecular* structures that the brain's cells share with distant bacterial ancestors of all complex organisms on our planet.

Scientists and philosophers have long sought to understand how order, and specifically life, could ever have emerged within a universe governed by the physical laws formulated during the Enlightenment. Classical physics, with its totally determinative, forward-in-time, billiard-ball causation, not only required sweeping anomalies like prophecy under the rug, it also replaced the order and beauty of God's creation with a bleak mechanistic universe forever slouching toward cold chaos. The second law of thermodynamics insists that everything is, on the whole, cooling off and descending into disorder. This produced a seeming paradox: How could a natural world governed by entropy produce systems that bind energy, replicate themselves, and create ever more complex forms? What principle in the ever-more-disordered universe allows things like seashells, eyes, brains, or Beethoven's Fifth Symphony?

Beginning in the middle of the last century, scientists like Austrian biologist Ludwig von Bertalanffy, Russian chemist Ilya Prigogine, and American mathematician-meteorologist Edward Lorenz applied new scientific and mathematical tools to model the emergence of complex systems within the traditional regime of thermodynamics. According to Prigogine's idea of "dissipative structures" (for which he won the Nobel Prize in 1977), systems become orderly by exporting (dissipating) entropy itself. In this way, they generate complex emergent forms, including the complex forms of animal and plant life.[6] In the 1970s, Austrian astrophysicist Erich Jantsch argued that these same basic principles underlie the regularities of social existence too, up to and including the cultural symbol systems used by humans to encode meaningful information and guide our behavior.[7] Today, quantum information theory, discussed in the last chapter, is also being applied to study the emergence of complex systems.[8]

Yet, voices on the margins of mainstream science have again and again felt that, to really explain the "balance within imbalance" of the cosmos, the miraculous rise of life and mind, there must be some as-yet-undiscovered anti-entropic force or principle to supplement the mechanistic laws formulated in the Enlightenment. Vitalism was a popular idea in the Victorian era, for instance. Around the turn of the century, Henri Bergson proposed the existence of an *elan vital*, a life force, as the missing X-factor.[9] A couple decades later, the Lamarckian biologist Paul Kammerer argued for "seriality" as a kind of convergence on meaningful order.[10] In the 1980s, the maverick biologist Rupert Sheldrake proposed that complexity and extraordinary convergences in nature (including psi phenomena) could be explained by a "resonance" among forms. *Morphic resonance*, he argued, is a kind of active non-material memory and causative principle all of its own.[11] Today, some researchers are proposing that *consciousness* is a fundamental organizing principle in nature, perhaps even driving life and complexity.[12]

The problem with these anti-materialist alternatives, of course, is that (almost by definition) they cannot supply any underlying physical mechanism, and thus most mainstream scientists will call them hand-wavy (if not worse epithets). Sheldrake's formative causation, for example, cannot explain how or why forms impose themselves on matter at a distance. While he has accused neuroscience of "promissory materialism" in its assurances that consciousness will eventually have a materialist, brain-based explanation, his theory of morphic resonance is also promissory in that it lacks any existing basis in physics as we know it—it too rests on future discoveries.[13] A more basic problem may be the question of how forms could be defined objectively, independent of some "comparing" God-like observer that decides what counts as a form in the first place. In other words, what is it that causes two spatial (or temporal) arrangements of things, be it seashells, strands of DNA, or patterns of brain activity dictating the behavior of a mouse, to count as formally similar?

Rather than imagine hard-to-define consciousness or invisible morphic fields driving the emergence of life, a simpler answer is liable to come from retrocausation, the ability of future states of systems to influence prior states. This possibility was already floated in the middle of the 20th century, in fact, by a mathematician named Luigi Fantappiè. Fantappiè proposed a retrocausal principle drawing systems toward complexity, coherence, and order, which he named *syntropy*. Two Italian psychologists, Ulisse Di Corpo and Antonella Vannini, have lately resurrected this idea, drawing on research in physics and parapsychology to support Fantappiè's theory.[14] They propose that future nodes of convergence and harmony, or "attractors"—a concept borrowed from Edward Lorenz's work in chaos theory—exert a pull on the past, and they describe some physical mechanisms that may facilitate this. Water itself, they suggest, may provide a physical basis for the pull toward order. On the molecular level, the unique properties of hydrogen bonds (the "hydrogen bridge" discovered by physicist Wolfgang Pauli) make water especially suitable to serve as the basis for the emergence of complex, self-organizing biological systems out of the entropic, prebiological matrix. In animals and humans, di Corpo and Vannini argue, syntropy expresses itself as precognition and presentiment; the emotion of love, they argue, is basically a syntropic signal drawing individuals toward meaningful convergences in their future.

The idea that some kind of retrocausation may explain life, order, and complexity is no longer only being discussed on the scientific fringes. Huw Price has tentatively speculated that some form of primitive precognition may have been a force in evolution.[15] And Arizona State University physicist Paul Davies has suggested that it might turn out to be *post-selection*, applied to the vast quantum computer that is the universe, that will explain the rise of life from lifeless matter:

> Perhaps living systems have the property of being post-selective, and thus greatly enhance the probability of the system 'discovering' the living state? Indeed, this might even form the basis of a definition of the living state, and would inject an element of 'teleology without teleology' into the description of living systems.[16]

A Time Eye

Erwin Schrödinger speculated about quantum mechanics' possible role in biology in a 1944 book, *What Is Life?*, which inspired James D. Watson and Francis Crick in their hunt for a molecular basis of the genetic code. But while Schrödinger's book gave a fore-taste, the quantum biology revolution really didn't begin until the first decade of this century, when a process called *quantum tunneling* was found to be essential to photosynthesis.[17] When photons strike magnesium atoms in chlorophyll molecules, they release energy in the form of free electrons. These liberated electrons find the shortest route to the reaction center of a plant cell by tunneling—also known as taking a "quantum walk"—through the cytoplasm. A quantum walk is usually explained using the language of superposition: By remaining in a wavelike unmeasured state, particles can pass through solid physical barriers or expeditiously find their way to distant points in space by taking multiple paths simultaneously. An alternative, retrocausal way of looking at it is that the particle's path may be partly determined by the interaction at its destination—that same business of a particle "knowing" where it is going in advance. Biologist Graham Fleming, in announcing the dependence of photosynthesis on quantum mechanics in a 2007 *Nature* article, suggested that plants are quantum computers because of this phenomenon. (Remember that, at the quantum level, any manipulation to produce an effect—that is, cause something—can also be described as performing a computation.)

Since then, quantum processes have been confirmed in other biological systems. Tunneling has been discovered to be essential to the catalytic action of enzymes, for example; and entanglement turns out to be the answer to the longstanding mystery of bird navigation. A pair of entangled electrons in the retinas of migratory birds enables them to "see" the angle of a magnetic field in relation to the Earth's surface, making them sensitive to latitude.[18] Some researchers have proposed that quantum processes may be involved in the sense of smell, which depends on an acute ability to detect the difference between structurally identical molecules whose only difference is their quantum vibration.[19] These functions undoubtedly represent just the tip of the iceberg of quantum behavior in living systems, and as we will see, there is currently a kind of gold rush to discover quantum processes in the brain that may help explain consciousness.

According to some retrocausal interpretations of quantum mechanics, we are awash in information from the future—every physical interaction, including in our bodies, is conditioned or inflected by what will happen to every interacting particle *next*. The reason we are mostly unaware of this fact is that we lack the context for interpreting that inflection—a cipher turning that information into something meaningful. Information at the quantum level remains noise—seemingly probabilistic or random—unless there is a suitable apparatus for measuring and comparing different groups of particles whose next interactions can be predicted with some degree of reliability. Since it is now possible to design an experimental apparatus to measure retrocausal effects via post-selection, there seemingly are exceptions to the rule that information from the future is always or only noise. In the previous chapter, I described some possible avenues for building a "future detector"—one that uses a technique called weak measurement, others that use serial entanglement of particles or perhaps a matrix of entangled qubits (as would be found in an artificial quantum computer) to decipher information in the past correlated with a future state of the system. These methods would use post-selection to impose a constraint on the outcome, such that a prior "readout" of information correlated to a future "input" can give meaningful insight about that future state (and at the same time, prevent paradox).

As the "chaotician" Ian Malcolm (Jeff Goldblum) famously says in *Jurassic Park*, "life will find a way." It stands to reason that if it is possible to detect the future in laboratories, then life too would have found a way to use post-selection to tell the difference between particles that will receive a predicted later measurement from those that won't be—in other words, to evolve a quantum-biological future detector.[20]

To see how such a thing might work, we can use the analogy of a simple eye. Some single-celled organisms like the euglena possess photoreceptors that can distinguish light from dark, but the simplest eyes in more complex animals like planarian worms consist of a patch of photoreceptive cells at the base of a shallow pit. For reasons that will be clear later, let's picture a simple eye as a pit on the *upper* surface of the animal, with light flowing *down* from above. There is very little that a simple photoreceptor array can determine about the environment overhead. It can tell the organism about the presence of light and its intensity or frequency and perhaps roughly its direction, and it can tell when it is in shadow, but it cannot *image* the environment or tell the animal exactly what is casting that shadow or how far away it is. (This is analogous in spatial terms to how the back-flowing influence of future interactions is interpreted by us in the present as randomness or chance—it appears as a kind of noise that, at most, can be quantified in the form of probability.)

But what happens when you set those photoreceptors inside a deeper recess that is mostly enclosed except for a small pupil-like opening? Evolution did this multiple times—it's the intermediate stage on the way to a proper eye. Even in the absence of a lens to enhance the photon-gathering capacity, a narrow aperture acts as a *pinhole camera* to project an image onto the photoreceptive cells. All the sudden, you have the ability to capture a picture, a re-presentation, of what is outside in the environment, such as a predator circling a few inches above. In other words, when you constrain the in-falling light, you actually gain much more usable or meaningful information about the outside world even though you have eliminated most of that light in the process. Photographers understand this as the inverse relationship between aperture (f-stop) and depth of field: The sharpness of the image, and the amount of the scene that can be in focus, increases as the aperture narrows. This is exactly like a spatial analogue of post-selection. The pupil, the aperture in an optical eye, acts as a *selector* of light rays in space; by admitting only a small bundle of rays, it generates much more coherent information about energetic events unfolding beyond it (you might call the pupil a "far-selector").

In contrast, the basic pre-sense enabled by intracellular quantum computing would be a temporal sense, a *time eye*, which amounts to an ability to gather information about outcomes ahead of the organism in its future rather than objects at some distance away in space. To create a time eye, evolution would have needed to create a system that is able to tell the difference between two or more groups of otherwise identical particles that will receive different measurements later. This requires the system to have a potential "measuring presence" at two points in time, not just one, the same way a primitive eye requires bodily tissue at two different distances from the external "seen" object (i.e., the retina and the aperture or pupil). That is no problem: In the block universe of Minkowski spacetime, organisms are continuous in time, worm-like beings that have beginnings, middles, and ends, like stories, just as they have extension in space. Thus, we are now talking about a kind of "sensory apparatus" that "points" along the direction of the organism's world line through the glass block—that is, along the time axis instead of along a spatial axis like an eye.

By convention, most graphs put time along the horizontal x-axis, and intuitively in our culture we often think of time as "running" from left to right. So to visualize such a system, mentally rotate your simple optical eye away from the vertical y-axis of space so it is directed instead horizontally, facing to the right, along the x-axis. Instead of an in-falling rain of light being constrained by a narrow aperture to form a coherent image on a recessed surface, the noisy back-flow of influence from the future needs to be constrained, or post-selected, later in time, on the right, to form a coherent "image" at an earlier time point, on the left, when it is (er, *was*—we have to fudge our tenses here) measured initially, perhaps via some form of weak measurement. What would be the post-selection parameter acting as the temporal "aperture" in this time eye? Most simply, it could be existence at that later time point: *survival,* in other words … if not the survival of the organism as a whole, at least the persistence of the molecular apparatus doing the measurement.

Weak measurement is a sophisticated tool used in experimental situations to (among other things) detect possible retrocausal influences. But with billions of years of trial and error in the primordial soup, it may not have been necessary to engage in something as subtle as that. All a quantum presponsive circuit, a molecular future detector, needs to have done is learn to somewhat reliably detect a difference between groups of identical quantum-entangled objects (particles, atoms, even molecules) whose only difference is what happens to them *next* (e.g., in a few milliseconds). An array of entangled qubits in a molecular quantum computer, representing multiple options in a decision space (such as moving to the left versus moving to the right), could serve as a precognitive guidance system, orienting the organism generally toward positive outcomes ahead in its timeline.[21]

My hand-waving makes it sounds nice and easy—but do we actually know of any molecular structures or systems in nature that could be capable of detecting optimal outcomes (most basically, survival) in their future? *Maybe*. It just so happens that the ongoing search for the roots of consciousness in quantum biology has turned up an excellent candidate—if not for consciousness, then at least for cellular quantum computation, and with it perhaps the temporal shenanigans that would make a time eye possible.

The cytoskeleton or internal structure of all complex cells is formed from tiny tubular polymers called *microtubules*. Originally thought to be merely the bones of cells, giving them their shape, these highly dynamic structures are now known to drive cellular movement and shape-changing and to control cell division. They seem to act as the "brains" of cells. Thus, their information storage and computation abilities have attracted a great deal of attention in recent years.[22] Interest in these structures as computing devices is often associated with the work of Stuart Hameroff. As an anesthesiologist at the University of Arizona in the 1980s, Hameroff noticed that anesthetics seem to cause unconsciousness via their actions in microtubules, which are particularly numerous and complexly arrayed in neurons. Thus, he hypothesized that these structures may be the quantum computational basis for consciousness.[23]

A quantum computer, remember, is a matrix or lattice of entangled atoms or other particles that are kept isolated from their surroundings to preserve their entanglement and can act as quantum bits or qubits. Whatever you do to one of the particles affects all the others simultaneously—although again, entanglement may really reflect a zig-zagging connection across time. Conveniently, microtubules are perfect tubular lattices built from individual cup-shaped proteins called tubulin. Proteins like tubulin have multiple ways they can fold, called *conformational states*. After several researchers had suggested that quantum mechanics may play a role in determining how proteins select one versus another state, Hameroff suggested that tubulin molecules could play the role of qubits through their variable conformational states.[24] The lattice structure of microtubules places the individual tubulin molecules, and electrons in bonds within them, at distances that would enable entanglement to occur. Hameroff and his colleagues subsequently confirmed that microtubules transmit electricity according to quantum principles: Like semiconductors, they offer no resistance. This makes it increasingly promising that his hypothesis—at least about their quantum computational abilities, if not their role in consciousness—could be right.[25]

The possible role of microtubules as the central information processors of complex cells also interested the pathbreaking evolutionary biologist Lynn Margulis.[26] According to Margulis, complex nucleated cells (*eukaryotes*) formed originally over two billion years ago from the *endosymbiosis* or merger of bacteria having different lifestyles and able to make different contributions to the collective. For instance, the engulfment of specialized bacteria gave eukaryotes their oxygen-burning mitochondria and the chloroplasts that enable plant cells to photosynthesize. Both of these structures still retain their own DNA separate from that found in the cell's nucleus, proving they were once independent-living organisms.[27] Establishing the origins of microtubules has been more difficult, but Margulis argued that those structures, as well as the cilia and flagella that facilitate motion in many eukaryotic cells, are the inheritance of an early engulfment of the distant ancestors of today's *spirochetes* (a group that includes the pathogens that cause modern syphilis and Lyme disease). These bacteria were little corkscrews that distinguished themselves from other early bacteria by speedily moving from place to place. The undulatory movement of spirochetes, as well as the motors that drive the movement of cilia and flagella in more complex cells, are made possible by the dynamism of microtubules.

The link between microtubules and movement could be consistent with the hypothesis that microtubules were the first cellular guidance systems, even the first future detectors. You do not need to "decide" much if you are a relatively stationary bacterium floating in muck or clinging to some surface. And most types of bacteria do not have microtubules. (Today, bacteria are thought to navigate mainly by orienting toward or away from chemicals in their environment, called *chemotaxis*.) But if you are a speedy mover, a way of making informed choices about whether to move to the right or move to the left (or up or down) could come in very handy. If microtubules are quantum computers prepsonsive to post-selected outcomes (i.e., survival) in addition to perhaps encoding a record of past successes, then there you have it: Engulfed spirochetes may have endowed eukaryotes not only with motility but also with quantum pre-sense, and perhaps simple learning ability, via their microtubules. If such a molecular quantum computer could detect the relative favorability of multiple decisional options, even a few milliseconds into the future, it would obviously have conferred a valuable selective advantage on any cell equipped with it. It would have given that cell the ability to *bind time.*

Time binding was a term originally coined by the philosopher Alfred Korzybski to denote our species' unique ability to transmit information to later generations and thereby pursue goals that transcend the span of an individual's lifetime. For Korzybski, who influenced many 20th-century science fiction writers like Philip K. Dick, Robert A. Heinlein, and Frank Herbert, time binding was implicitly higher than both *space binding*, the activity of animals who live in an eternal present and are dominated by the imperative to forage and hunt for food in their environment, and *energy binding*, the activity of plants that, via their chloroplasts, convert energy from the sun.[28] Korzybski wrote before the era of quantum biology, and he was not thinking in terms of any ability to use information from an organism's future as well as its past. But something like time binding, mediated perhaps by a molecular future detector along the lines I have proposed, may be as old as those energy- and space-binding functions of life, truly a "first sight." Earth's primordial soup may have been a precognitive soup.

The Big (6-Inch-in-Diameter) Picture

Starting right around the time Charles Howard Hinton wrote his *A New Era of Thought*, the Spanish pathologist Santiago Ramón y Cajal was using paint and ink to depict the animal neurons he saw under his microscope with great detail, revealing that these cells were like trees with often hundreds of branches and countless bud-like projections, each making a connection to another neuron. At that time, it was not yet widely believed that neurons were the building blocks of thought, but their importance rapidly became apparent to Ramón y Cajal. Around the turn of the century, he drew and painted even more mindbogglingly complex human neurons, vast and sublimely intricate despite being so tiny. He called neurons "mysterious butterflies of the soul whose beating of wings may one day reveal to us the secrets of the mind."[29] Ramón y Cajal's work paved the way for 20th and 21st century neuroscience.

With recent visualization technologies, even a one cubic millimeter spec of mouse cortex looks like a dense Amazonian rainforest—a vast jungle of trees with roots and tendrils making millions of connections. The human brain, an object a little bigger than a grapefruit, contains about 86 billion of these cells, each one making about 1,000 synaptic connections with neighboring cells, amounting to about 80 trillion connections across the brain. It is sometimes said that there are more possible paths that a signal can take through this structure than there are atoms in the entire universe. Neuroscientist Christof Koch famously declared that the brain is "the most complex object in the known universe."[30] This is true even just at the "macro" scale neuroscientists can easily study with present-day imaging technology, and trends in several research fields promise to exponentially increase our knowledge of the brain's complexity in coming decades.

The most publicized controversy in neuroscience and philosophy today concerns the brain's role in relation to consciousness—whether experience and awareness arise solely from brain processes, whether consciousness is an "emergent property" that rests on those processes yet cannot be predicted by them, or, again, whether it may be somehow more basic and universal in nature. Some, like Koch, suggest that consciousness is intrinsic to complexity itself, and that while the brain may be super-conscious, even a rock may possess a tiny bit of that ineffable quality. Critics of Enlightenment materialism (including many parapsychologists) are particularly keen to reject neuroscience assumptions that consciousness is a product only of brain processes or even that it is some kind of higher-order emergent property.[31] (Again, Rupert Sheldrake has called this assumption "promissory materialism."[32]) Alternative theories have long been proposed, such as that the brain merely acts as a kind of prism or radio receiver for consciousness—a view argued by Frederic Myers, Henri Bergson, and the psychologist William James, for example.[33] (Although today's scientific psychologists often consider James the father of their science, they choose to overlook his interest in psychical phenomena and his anti-materialistic views on consciousness.) The novelist Aldous Huxley later used the metaphor of the brain as a "reducing valve" for consciousness or what he called "Mind at Large."[34] The position that consciousness is actually fundamental and irreducible in nature is not unrelated to this idea. Panpsychism, for instance, is the position that matter is just a manifestation of mind—an idea with deep roots in Eastern philosophy and advanced in different ways by prominent 20th-century thinkers like Bergson, philosopher Alfred North Whitehead, and Carl Jung.[35] A good argument can also be made that consciousness is really an ill-defined term that marks the breakdown of language and symbolization at certain boundaries and margins of knowledge, rather than a well-formed problem that either the sciences or philosophy could ever hope to solve definitively on their own.[36]

Whatever the case—whether the material brain produces consciousness or merely receives or filters it—there is much less debate over the importance of the brain in shaping experience, controlling the body, and even in encoding an individual's personality and memory, all the forms of information that we find meaningful in defining our selves and in helping us act successfully in the world. Damage to specific brain areas produces very predictable and often catastrophic deficits in functioning and impairments in meaning-making, as Oliver Sacks showed in his prolific writings. The brain as described by contemporary neuroscience is a jaw-droppingly complex mechanism of interacting parts and functions—a vast, hyperfast system coordinating sensory inputs, motor responses, and involuntary processes throughout the body from heartbeat to breathing to digestion as well as preserving or "storing" a record of experiences (although the old computer metaphor for the brain, with its storage and retrieval operations, has largely given way to new metaphors drawn from weather and other chaotic systems). As discussed previously, it is also an imaging system with unbelievable resolution, able to generate realistic pictures and sounds and words in the inner workbench of thought—images based on real-life experiences as well as ones that are wholly new and original. It makes sense that if a full-on quantum computer exists in nature, the brain (or components of it) would be the most exciting and promising place to look.

Cognition is increasingly recognized to be "quantum-like" in numerous ways. For instance, when viewing an ambiguous image like a Necker cube or a duck/rabbit, the viewer only sees one aspect at a time, not both—an either/or that oscillates from moment to moment.[37] Words or other items learned in memory experiments have multiple potential links to other cues—akin to superposition—until a test is administered, which effectively forecloses nonrelevant associative links.[38] Various fallacies and heuristics in probability judgment also seem best modeled quantumly. For instance, the order in which information is presented to a test subject constrains the outcome of that person's decision.[39] Thus the latest thing in cognitive psychology is the framework of "quantum cognition," describing the processes of perception, memory, or judgment in quantum computer terms, along with a bold disclaimer that "quantum" is just a convenient and suggestive metaphor. But plenty of researchers have been keen to prove that the metaphor is more than a metaphor.

In the 1980s, physicist Roger Penrose argued that the brain must literally be a quantum computer after pondering mathematician Kurt Gödel's *incompleteness theorems*: Any formal mathematical system will contain statements that are unprovable within the system, and no such system can prove its own consistency internally. Penrose reasoned that only a quantum computer could arrive at the idea that computation can never be complete, and thus the brain—or at least Kurt Gödel's brain—must be such a device.[40] His reasoning was analogous to Hinton's argument that only a brain with "molecules" that reached across the fourth dimension could think in four-dimensional terms. Like Hinton, Penrose was clearly ahead of his time. Since Stuart Hameroff had already identified a likely quantum culprit with his microtubules, Penrose collaborated with the anesthesiologist to formulate what they call the "orchestrated objective-reduction" (Orch-OR) hypothesis, in which neuronal microtubules create consciousness through brain-wide entanglement.[41]

The narrow channels in neuronal walls that control the movement of ions into and out of the cell—and thus the cell's *action potential* (the electrical charge that passes down it when it fires)—have also attracted attention, as these are potentially sites where particles are protected from environmental interference long enough that they could become entangled.[42] Already in the 1970s, physicist Evan Harris Walker had proposed that consciousness depended on quantum tunneling at the synaptic cleft, the narrow gaps where molecules carry signals from neuron to neuron.[43] There is no reason why more than one mechanism could not play a role, or that there may be others that no one has even imagined yet. The brain's quantum computation could take multiple forms. The problem with existing theories, however, is that there is no known way that quantum entanglement could be preserved throughout or across the whole brain, which intuitively might seem to be a requirement for "quantum consciousness."[44]

Again, though, it may be that the search for the physical roots of consciousness per se, even in quantum biology, is a hopeless task, simply because of the rift I mentioned earlier between the necessarily reductive methods of objective science and subjective descriptions of experience. No matter how fine-grained neuroscientists' understanding of the brain becomes, it may never map convincingly onto *qualia*, or "what it feels like" to be a conscious entity. This is what philosopher David Chalmers called the "hard problem" of consciousness.[45] Nevertheless, as a Mac-Guffin spurring competitive efforts from various researchers in different fields, a byproduct of efforts to discover the roots of consciousness in the brain may be the discovery of quantum processes in or between neurons that might enable the brain to process information across its timeline.

In the spirit of Charles Howard Hinton, here's a sketch of what a brain-based account of precognition *might* look like in the coming era of quantum hyperthought.

We can start with what is already generally agreed upon about how memory works in the brain. "Memories" do not exist whole and discrete, like fossils of past experience tucked in the brain's folds. Different experiences activate, and thus can share, many of the same neurons and connections, across many areas of the brain. Although it is a simplistic (even simple-minded) metaphor, individual neurons could be thought of as "pixels" in our mental life and experience; just as a TV screen re-uses the same pixels in different ways from instant to instant to create sequential still images in a changing picture, the brain reuses the same cells and circuits in different configurations from moment to moment to generate the flow of our thoughts and experiences. What seems to distinguish one memory from another, or one experience from another, is a unique spatial and temporal *pattern* of neuronal activation across the brain. That pattern is determined by the variable strengths of synaptic connections among all those linked neurons.

Memory is made possible by the brain's plasticity, its ability to change from day to day, minute to minute, even moment to moment.

The strengths of those trillions of synaptic connections are continually being updated based on our experience. Although different types of learning have been identified in different brain circuits, the most basic principle operative throughout the brain is what is known as *Hebbian learning*, captured by the phrase "neurons that fire together, wire together." When a neuron sends a chemical signal to another neuron, the synapse where they link up is strengthened, so that future signals at that synapse will be easier—called *long-term potentiation*. Through this process, our experiences are self-reinforcing, like a trickle of water wearing a deeper and deeper rivulet in the soil to become a stream. By the same token, connections that are not reinforced decay or weaken over time—called *long-term depression*.

If there is a brain-based theory of precognition forthcoming in science's future, it will likely involve these same processes of memory and learning, specifically the ability of synapses to update their facility of signaling. Lo and behold, the cytoskeleton of neurons—including the aforementioned microtubules—controls this process.[46]

When the axon of an "upstream" neuron sends neurotransmitters to the dendritic spine of a "downstream" neuron, that dendritic spine enlarges and in other ways makes itself more receptive to future signals, as well as sending retrograde messengers to the upstream neuron that initiate similar changes in the axon terminal. These structural changes that enhance the ability to send and receive signals at a synapse are controlled by the shape-changing of microtubules—a process governed by a kind of chemical dance of proteins that continually disassemble and reassemble these structures, shortening and lengthening them at either end.[47] (Among the microtubule-associated proteins governing this shape-changing is tau; dysregulation of tau proteins is associated with the devastating impairments in Alzheimer's disease.) Microtubules also transmit electrical signals through the cell and serve as tracks for the transport of cellular raw materials. In reshaping the synapse and controlling synaptic efficiency, microtubules act in concert with other cytoskeletal structures called *actin filaments*, which are also currently being studied as biological computational devices.[48]

So, one hypothesis would be that these structures of the neuronal cytoskeleton may be behaving like tiny molecular versions of the apparatus in the Rochester experiment described in the last chapter: devices that somehow "weakly measure" the behavior of entangled qubits within them at time point A and then, after some regular, predictable length of time (probably rhythmically), perform a subsequent measurement—post-selection in other words. Post-selection might even be a function of the ever-shifting length of a microtubule, as its ends disassemble and reassemble. Via arrays of microtubular time eyes controlling the shape of axon terminals and dendrites, signaling at synapses may be potentiated or enhanced if they are going to be signaling in the future (and vice versa if they won't be).

Remember that, according to the Dunnean view, precognition would not be a preview of future events out in the world, as is often assumed (negatively assumed, for those who reject precognition on principle); it is instead a presponsivity of the brain to its own future states and behavior (thoughts, emotions, perceptions). If quantum computation in the cytoskeleton enables synaptic connections to be conditioned by their future signaling, this would scale up in complex networks of interlinked neurons, enabling whole "pre-presentations" of thoughts and emotions to be projected into the past, albeit imperfectly and imprecisely, in roughly the same way that salient experiences "project" into the future as memories. There is no question in this model of the brain somehow "receiving" information directly from future events; it is simply communicating with itself across time.[49]

This is by no means the first brain-based model for precognition to be proposed. I already mentioned Gerald Feinberg, who suggested in the mid-1970s that precognition is just memory in reverse. Speculating on a possible mechanism, he proposed that brain oscillatory patterns thought to play a role in short-term memory might have both an "advanced" and "retarded" component to them, in the manner of time-symmetric quantum-mechanical models.[50] More recently, Jon Taylor has suggested that similar patterns of neural activation at different points in time may resonate with each other across the brain's timeline.[51] His proposal resembles Rupert Sheldrake's argument that memory may be a function of informational patterns resonating across spacetime. But again, formative causation arguments (like Platonic models more generally) seem to put the cart of meaning (as "form") before the horse of causation. Current retrocausal paradigms in quantum physics offer an interesting alternative way of thinking about informational reflux from the Not Yet, since they apply the same principle to information that Darwin, Wallace, and their contemporaries did for natural forms: *selection*. Post-selection is really just causal Darwinism.

At its most basic level, a "signal sent back from the future" via post-selection would be one that necessarily indicates a course of action that survived long enough to send that message back—like a little breadcrumb trail from the organism's future self, or a note at a crossroads weirdly in its own handwriting, saying "come this way." Part of what post-selection entails is predictability, and thus the recognizability of that handwriting. The more the mechanism can anticipate its state in a few milliseconds or seconds or longer, the more information from its future can have coherence and context, making it meaningful or useful in guiding behavior. Here, in the organism's relationship to itself across time, is where a kind of "resonance" may come into play, although it must be understood metaphorically. When scaled up in a complex animal nervous system like that of a human being, it may be something like habit or conditioning—a kind of self-trust that the state of the individual performing a measurement now will be more or less the same as the state of individual in a millisecond, a second, or a minute (or a decade)—that acts as a kind of post-selection, providing the cipher key of back-flowing information, enabling it to usefully guide behavior (i.e., be meaningful rather than noise).[52]

Other possibilities should also be kept on the table. For example, could there even be neurons in the body that fire *in advance* of incoming signals, kind of like Asimov's thiotimoline molecule?[53] If a single neuron could get even a one-millisecond head start on firing, a chain of hundreds of such neurons (like a chain of Asimov's endochronometers) could amplify that head start enough to explain the findings of Dean Radin, Daryl Bem, and other presentiment researchers. It is already known that quantum processes accelerate the transmission of electricity within neurons[54], but for a downstream neuron to actually fire in advance of signals from the upstream neuron would seemingly require some kind of entanglement between molecules in separate neurons, across the synapse. Again, this kind of wider entanglement in the brain remains the holy grail for those trying to solve the problem of quantum consciousness, and it also remains the big stumbling block to those efforts, given the problem that entanglement tends to be lost in warm, wet environments. But researchers are rapidly learning about more and more ways quantum coherence can be sustained in biological systems over distances and across time spans that would have been thought impossible even a decade ago.[55] One puzzling phenomenon that is at least suggestive in this context is *spontaneous neurotransmission*—neurons firing without being triggered by any input from neighboring cells. Initially thought to be just "noise" in the brain (sound familiar?), it is now thought to play a role in reshaping synapses during learning.[56] Could it be evidence of thiotimoline-like neuronal behavior?

There is much we still don't know, obviously. But the bottom line is that if synaptic plasticity or other aspects of neurons' behavior or signaling are controlled or influenced by molecular computers capable of harnessing time-defying quantum principles, then it is likely here that an answer to "how can this be?"—that is, how can the brain get information about its future responses to the world?—will be found. The biological basis of precognition would be learning processes in which the brain's connectivity and signaling in the present are influenced not only by the individual's past experience but also, to some as-yet-uncertain degree, by that individual's future experience. It would enable that individual to "post-select" on rewards ahead and to be influenced by, if not intentionally access, information the individual will conventionally acquire down the road.[57]

Such a proposal is, of course, still speculative, only slightly less hand-wavy than the various alternatives. It remains a hypothesis to be tested. But it does not fly in the face of what we are learning about quantum computational processes in biological systems and what some physicists are arguing (and discovering in the laboratory) about retrocausation. Thus, it should not be unpalatable even to materialists, at least in principle.

Libet's Golem

It sometimes happens in science that new discoveries are made based on old data that were misinterpreted at the time they were collected because existing theories made no place for them. New species are often discovered in old museum collections, for example, when specimens are found to have been misidentified or just ignored, awaiting some shift in taxonomic or evolutionary paradigms. It may be that direct evidence of the nervous system's time-defying behavior has been staring researchers in the face for nearly four decades. Famous perplexities having to do with the synchronization of sensation, action, and decisions would make more sense in a nervous system capable of computing four-dimensionally across its timeline than in any purely Newtonian information processor.

Older readers will remember drive-in movies—often badly projected and frequently the picture and sound were a few frames out of sync. If the nervous system is a purely classical, mechanical information processor, our everyday experience ought to be a little bit like an out-of-sync drive-in movie … but it isn't, and why it's not is a bit of a mystery. If you step on a sharp tack with your bare foot, the pain signal takes roughly a half second to travel 1.5-2 meters between your foot and your brain and for you to become aware of it. Each nerve cell in a long chain has to receive a chemical signal, fire, release its own neurotransmitters, and so on. However, other signals, such as the sight of your foot hitting the floor, have a much shorter "flight time" since light travels much faster from your foot to your eye than that chemical-electric pain signal traveling up your whole body. But if you watch your right foot as you are walking, you feel the sensation of your big toe touch the floor at exactly the same time as you see it visually. Why?

Neuroscientist Benjamin Libet discovered this contradiction between sensory out-of-sync-ness and the subjective experience of our harmoniously orchestrated bodily movements and decisions in a series of landmark experiments in the late 1970s and 1980s. To explain how we don't experience life like a drive-in movie, he argued that some process in the brain "antedates" our conscious experience relative to the stimulus so that multiple sensations can match up and be felt as synchronous—sort of like taking separate video and audio tracks in a video editing program and sliding one to the side so the visual component synchs up with the audio. But since, it was assumed, you can't slide the slower of those components (e.g., the pain sensation) to the right in your timeline, synching things up meant sliding all the faster signals to the left or holding them in some sort of buffer while the slower ones caught up. Libet concluded that the coherence of our experience, the fact that it is all synchronized, reflects the remarkable fact that we are really living always *about a half second in the past.*[58]

It gets even stranger, though, when you include our feeling of conscious will in this fictitious synchronization. In 1983, Libet conducted a now-famous experiment that compared the subjective timing of participants' decisions to move a finger with their motor nerves' preparation to fire. He found that neurons begin to build up a charge a fifth of a second (200 milliseconds) *before* the decision to move is consciously made. This discrepancy between what is called the nerve's *readiness potential* and the subjective sense of conscious will flies in the face of our ordinary experience of deciding to act and then acting, the intuitive sense that our will causes our actions and is not merely a spectator.[59] For a certain faction in psychology and neuroscience, Libet's work was the last nail in Descartes' coffin, the final death blow to the idea that consciousness is something over and above (and prior to) the mechanical operating of the brain's circuits. Psychologist Daniel Wegner, for instance, expanded on Libet's research and built an interesting (and troubling) case that our subjective experience of being the masters in our own house is altogether an illusion.[60] Libet himself did not go so far; he felt his discovery did not eliminate conscious will but altered its essential character. Instead of exerting free will, he said, we exert a veto power over pre-initiated actions. V. S. Ramachandran has called this "free won't."[61] Our conscious will can intercede within that 200-millisecond window to say "no" to an impulsive action initiated by the brain.

Much research in psychology and cognitive science over the past few decades has identified two systems that guide our behavior in parallel: a fast, largely unconscious, emotional system (sometimes called "System 1"), and a slower, more deliberate, more reasoned system that ideally hovers over and says "no" ("System 2"). It makes sense from an adaptive standpoint that, when making quick responses to real threats—such as swerving to avoid an oncoming car or changing your foot position to avoid a tack—we wouldn't want our slower deliberative conscious will to get in the way and delay a response that the unconscious mind and body can handle more efficiently and swiftly. Yet even in the absence of such an impediment, how does a large animal like a human manage to survive when sensory signals take a measurable fraction of a second to reach the brain, where they must then be processed and interpreted, before a set of responses can then be sent back down parallel nerve channels to make a motion? It ought to make us very clumsy and easily defeated by sudden threats and by smaller animals with simpler nervous systems. And just imagine if you were an elephant, or a swift 10-ton T-Rex whose sensory and motor signals needed to travel many times that distance.

An emerging paradigm in psychology and neuroscience emphasizes the brain's role as a *predictive processor*, meeting these challenges by generating constant simulations or forecasts that are able to guide the body toward anticipated outcomes.[62] A baseball player is able to swing at a point in space where he perceives the ball will be, rather than base his actions on constantly updated, but necessarily slow, moment-to-moment input from his eyes. It happens outside of conscious awareness—and it goes along with many "superpowers" that neuroscientists have attributed to our fast, unconscious processing, in a largely unacknowledged debt to Sigmund Freud and his generation of Victorian psychiatrists who were perplexed at humans' seeming supernormal abilities (more on which later). But another possibility is that some of what gets labeled unconscious or implicit processing may really be the time-defying possibilities that have been revealed in the experiments of Bem, Radin, and their colleagues. Physicist Fred Alan Wolf proposed in the late 1980s that John Cramer's transactional interpretation of quantum mechanics could explain Libet's findings and may also help explain consciousness.[63] Quantum-biologically mediated presentiment, in other words, could be the real reason, or part of the reason, why our lives don't feel like a drive-in movie.

If the brain really is a quantum future detector—or perhaps, trillions of quantum future detectors networked classically—then effective motor action might be initiated partly from a position displaced slightly ahead in an organism's timeline, when the success of the action is already confirmed. Such a model would offer another way of thinking about skillful performance in sports or martial arts, for example, not to mention intuition, creative insight, and inspiration. I like to think of this possibility as "Libet's golem," an ironic, science-fictional perversion of the lumbering clay robot of Jewish folklore. It is conceivable that we are not after all mere automatons, spectators of our bodies, as Wegner argued, but could be pulling our meat puppets' strings from a position offset from the "now" of sensation, or perhaps even from multiple temporal vantage points distributed across time. This would be especially the case when engaged in a skilled activity, and it might account for the dissociated feeling that accompanies states of peak engagement and creativity. Could temporally displaced action-initiation even account for the "mental replay" that often follows a successful high-stakes action? In other words, when we mentally relive a successful action in its immediate aftermath, might we in fact be *initiating* that action, from that action's future?

It is in this respect that gaining greater understanding of what happens in quantum computers, including biological quantum computers and the role they play in the nervous system, really could provide an important missing piece of the consciousness puzzle. Rather than being simply tantamount to coherence or entanglement across spatially separate parts of the brain, consciousness could instead (or also) have something to do with cognition being distributed across time. With its trillions of classical connections (i.e., chemical signals) mediating the actions of many more trillions of molecular quantum computers, the brain might turn out to be an exquisitely tuned device extracting and synthesizing relevant information from across some indefinite time window and bringing it to bear on an immediate situation or problem. Although our awareness remains tied to a single synchronized (yet in fact, fictitious[64]) instant of stimuli coordinated among our five senses, we might in fact be "thinking with" a wider swath of our future as well as past history. In which case, the brain really would be a kind of informational tesseract, a 4-D meaning-machine.

This would not make the mind "infinite," the implicit and sometimes even explicit promise of those who claim psi phenomena must rule out a reductive, materialistic explanation for consciousness.[65] But even within a materialist framework, the mind would be vastly bigger, vastly *longer*, than we ordinarily suppose—and thus, indeed "transcendent."[66]

What are the possibilities? How "long" could our minds really be? Might we even sometimes draw on the *entirety* of our brain's computing power across our lifespan? We veer very far into speculation here, obviously, but some capacity to compute across long swathes of time would make sense of baffling experiences like dreams and artworks that seem prophetic of events years or decades in the individual's future. It would also help clear up yet another mystery in the cognitive sciences: the oft-noted correlation between intelligence and longevity. There are some commonsensical explanations why smarter individuals tend to live longer, such as being better able to avoid dangers, as well as possible confounding factors like education and affluence. Yet these confounds have never been able to fully account for the correlation, and cognitive epidemiologists have argued that there must therefore be a strong genetic underpinning to this association.[67] But as yet, no specific gene variants have been identified that produce both smarts and long life. Obviously, as they say, "more research is needed." But the idea that the brain could be a quantum computer drawing on its computing power over its whole history, or at least over significant swathes of that history, raises the intriguing possibility that longer lifespan might to some extent *cause* higher intelligence, by increasing the four-dimensional computing resources of the individual's brain.

It would be easy to test this hypothesis, in principle. One would simply test the intelligence or problem-solving ability of a group of identical animals (cloned mice reared in the same conditions, say) who are of the same age, and then subsequently "sacrifice" (as they euphemistically say in laboratories) a randomly selected half of the animals, allowing the remainder to live a full life—a kind of post-selection, in other words. If their brains are making computations drawing on the computing power of a whole mouse lifetime, the long-lived mice would be expected to have performed better on the problem-solving task than the short-lived ones. I only offer this as a *Gedanken*-animal-experiment, and assuredly no animals have been harmed in the creation of this book. But it is possible to go partway toward such an experiment simply by comparing the performance of mice who engage in learning or practice *after* they perform the assessed task with mice who don't ... but in that case, why use mice? The retroactive-facilitation-of-recall experiments conducted by Daryl Bem are precisely such a study in humans, and the results point to a real effect of *subsequent* learning on *prior* performance.[68]

In a 1974 meeting of physicists and parapsychologists in Geneva, Switzerland, the French physicist Olivier Costa de Beauregard—the one who first proposed that quantum entanglement might be explained retrocausally—described the train of thought that led to his own ultimate acceptance of the probable existence of something like precognition:

> My starting point ... occurred in 1951 when I suddenly said to myself: If *you* truly believe in Minkowski's space-time—and *you* know you have to—then you *must* think of the relationship between mind and matter not at one universal or Newtonian instant but *in space-time*. If, by the very necessity of relativistic covariance, matter is time extended as it is space extended, then, again by necessity, awareness in a broad sense must also be time extended.[69]

It is very much like an updated version of Charles Howard Hinton's reasoning about the brain's capacity for four-dimensional thought: Our brains are four-dimensional, so our awareness must be as well.

If our awareness is four-dimensional, the mystery becomes: Why do we experience our experience as confined to that narrow cursor in our life's timeline—the "single Newtonian instant," as Costa de Beauregard puts it? It may have a lot to do with the mystery raised earlier: Why is it that efficient causes (the ones the "push" from the past) are so much more obvious and intuitively understood than final (teleological) ones? Does it boil down to some biologically determined preferential weighting of past experience over future ones in updating synaptic connections? Could it be partly a function of our cultural beliefs and expectations about causality and free will, acting as a kind of "restraining bolt" on our natural precognitive abilities? Could it even have to do with something as simple as the way sentences in our language unfold in a single direction (the premise of the movie *Arrival*—more on which later)? We'll explore these and other possibilities, although I make no promises we'll get to the bottom of it—plenty of greater minds than mine have tried and failed to crack the nut of time and its relation to consciousness.[70] But the tesseract brain offers, I think, an exciting new way of thinking about (or perhaps, hyperthinking about) these problems, as well helping explain why there are so many situations in which, despite our tendency to consciously inhabit that Newtonian instant, our unconscious seems to "know" more than it ought to be able to in a purely Newtonian, mechanistic world. Experiences like precognitive dreams point to a whole unknown part of our lives—our whole future—that we are interacting with, subtly and obliquely, and that is exerting an influence over our thoughts and behavior now, here in our future's past.

Some of the prophylaxis against knowing more about that future (instead of just feeling it) may have to do with the difficulties of source monitoring mentioned earlier. We might picture the 4-D tesseract brain as a long hall in a hotel, with information passing up and down it in both directions like guests—some are familiar faces from our past, whom we will greet and engage with, but there are also lots of unfamiliar faces, total strangers. We'll tend to ignore, avoid, or even be suspicious of the latter, not having any reason to suspect that they may be from our own future. We may even make up untrue stories about their origins. Meanwhile, along the whole length of that hall, there is just a single window that opens onto the world beyond the body. This narrow temporal aperture of coordinated sensory experience serves as the singular focus of our engagement with external reality, and it gradually moves from one end of the hall to the other, as we move from childhood to old age. Given that even mainstream cognitive science agrees that this "now" is a fiction, then no matter how compellingly it arrests our attention, we should pay greater heed to those strangers coming down the hall—that is, pay more attention to the unfamiliar parts of what we may think of as our "inner" experience. Perhaps that way we can learn something about our 4-D nature, the shape of our cosmic wormlike life as it wends and twists its way through the glass block of Minkowski spacetime. It could really be that the now of our conscious experience bears a similar relationship to the entirety of our thought over life that a point of light from a magnifying glass bears to the sun projecting that light.

As we bring this obligatory "nuts and bolts" section of the book to a close and leave behind all the physical and biological hand-waving, let me reiterate and underscore just the following idea, the controlling theme for the second half of this book: Whatever physical (or even non-physical) mechanisms will eventually be found to explain our ability to access and be influenced by our future, much of what has been called "the unconscious" may instead be *consciousness displaced in (or distributed across) time.* Without at all realizing it, Freudian psychoanalysis may have always been a science of the truly weird, time-looping effects precognition produces in our lives.

PART THREE

Time's Taboos

Like Oedipus, we live in ignorance of these wishes,
repugnant to morality, which have been forced upon us
by Nature, and after their revelation we may all of us
well seek to close our eyes to the scenes of our childhood.

— Sigmund Freud, *The Interpretation of Dreams*
(1899)

8

Sometimes a Causal Arrow Isn't Just a Causal Arrow — Oedipus, Freud, and the Repression of Prophecy

Of all the frameworks in which the need to magically manipulate time can be discerned, the oedipal situation stands in a class by itself. The fixed, irreversible generation gap separating mother from son, father from daughter, becomes the symbol of all that is cruel and unalterable about fate.

— Jule Eisenbud, *Paranormal Foreknowledge* (1982)

The thin membrane of the present, which seals off the knowable past from a future that by definition isn't knowable (yet), is one of our most important conceptual boundaries. The anthropologist Mary Douglas showed in her classic 1966 study *Purity and Danger* that objects and phenomena that violate conceptual boundaries are not only distasteful but are even regarded as threatening.[1] Life-giving *soil* from out-of-doors (Nature), for instance, becomes *dirt* when tracked into the home (Culture), and especially neurotic souls may devote their lives to abolishing the latter. The ancient Hebrews regarded pigs as unclean because they had hooves, like ungulates, yet did not chew a cud—another category violation, around which a whole, notoriously fussy system of dietary regulations (the Book of Leviticus) was constructed. But every culture has such rules, and such fussiness, about its categories. And the rules governing where our knowledge comes from—or epistemology—matter as much to us as the rules governing what we can put on our plates.

Any kind of retrocausation or precognition throws an epistemology founded totally on memory and inference into disarray, a bit like tracking the dirt of the future into the clean home of the present. (Boundary crossing, or *liminality*, characterizes most paranormal phenomena, in fact.[2]) Consequently, skeptics who have not really looked at the evidence for precognition, who assume (because they do not know better) that physics regards it as impossible, or who feel especially threatened by epistemic violations, are quick to ridicule or ostracize those who try to fairly consider the topic. While there are good reasons to be skeptical of unusual or extraordinary claims, purely closed-minded reactions may have everything to do with deep-seated *taboos* about things that penetrate other things in a culturally non-sanctioned fashion.

I'm speaking delicately here. We are about to dive headlong into the interesting messes time loops make of our lives, as well as into our strange psychodynamic investments in linear causality. We will see that heightened expression of precognitive ability is sometimes weirdly entangled with transgressions of sex, gender, and desire. It may be no accident that the shrill reactions of skeptics to ESP are so similar to the shrill reactions of cultural conservatives to alternative sexual practices and identities. Personalities who take comfort in a neat, orderly, well-defined world are bound to be threatened by causal arrows that pierce time in the wrong direction, or information that leaks in ways it shouldn't. But the fact is, causality, like Nature herself, is not tidy. It does not obey our personal preferences, however fussy and prudish they may be.

No story better displays the entanglement of sexual taboos and retrocausation than Sophocles' *Oedipus the King*, the great tragedy about a royal heir who brings a curse on his city because he has accidentally usurped his father's throne and married his own mother (oops!). How is this about retrocausation? The ancients reckoned historical time through generations—the ever-forward-moving structure of marriage and reproduction and royal succession. Kinship and kingship were for the Greeks more or less equivalent to the second law of thermodynamics for us: inexorable and irreversible, moving in a single direction, never flowing backwards, and always basically getting worse. Thus, Sophocles' tragedy is really about a kind of time travel and the kind of calamity that could result from upsetting the usual causal order. You might say Sophocles was ancient Greece's Ray Bradbury (or Philip K. Dick).

Although the play itself centers on Oedipus's downfall, the prophetic backstory would have been well-known to Sophocles' audience, since it was based on an older myth. An oracle had warned King Laius of Thebes that he must not have a son, or he would die by his son's hand and his son would marry his wife. So, when his wife Jocasta gave birth to a boy, he ordered her to kill the baby. Unable to do the deed herself, the queen had a servant take the infant to the wilderness and stake him out on the ground to die of exposure. Of course, when you delegate a grim task like that, it always fails, and in this case the infant was found by a shepherd and adopted and raised by the King of Corinth. And like father, like son: When the Delphic oracle prophesied that Oedipus would kill his father and marry his mother, the young man fled from the city where he grew up, Corinth, to make sure no harm came to his parents. He didn't know they weren't his real parents and that Corinth wasn't his real hometown. In a chance encounter at a crossroads, Oedipus killed Laius, not knowing who the guy was, and then answered a Sphinx's riddle to become king of Thebes … and husband of his real mother, Jocasta.

The Greeks were way ahead of us in grasping that prophetic foresight is allowable and even expected in the tragic (read: thermodynamic) universe—it just needs to be oblique, and to operate in the shadows of our self-ignorance. And it inevitably produces what I have called time loops as a result. The fact that Oedipus's transgression was prophesied and that he fulfilled the prophecy precisely by trying to evade it makes the events of the story a causal tautology. Tautologies are the ultimate no-nos for pedantic gatekeepers of classical logic—you don't support a premise by appealing to the conclusion you've drawn from it. But this offense in the world of term papers and rhetoric is the *opposite* of the grandfather paradox that stands in the way of people seriously considering precognition. As I've argued previously, there is no rule that says we need to allow self-*defeating* prophecies in our picture of precognition. The common assumption that people could (and would) "use" precognitive information to create an alternative future flies in the face of the way precognition seems to work in the real world. It is largely unconscious (thus evades our "free will"), and it is oblique and invariably misrecognized or misinterpreted until after events have made sense of it. Laius and his son both fulfill the dark prophecies about them in their attempts to evade what was foretold; their attempts backfire *precisely because of things they don't know* (Laius, that his wife failed to kill his son, as ordered; Oedipus, that his adopted family in Corinth was not his real family). The Greeks called these obliquely foreseen outcomes, unavoidable because of our self-ignorance, our *fate*.

Any mention of Oedipus naturally calls to mind Sigmund Freud, whom I am recruiting as a kind of ambivalent guide in my examination of the time-looping structure of human fate. Making a central place for Freud in a book on precognition may perplex readers given (a) his reputed disinterest in psychic phenomena, and (b) the fact that psychological science long since tossed psychoanalysis and its founder into the dustbin. In fact, (a) is a myth, as we'll see, and (b) partly reflects the "unreason" of psychological science around questions of meaning. Although deeply flawed and occasionally off-the-mark, the psychoanalytic tradition—including numerous course-corrections by later thinkers who tweaked and nuanced Freud's core insights—represents a sincere and sustained effort to bring the objective and subjective into suspension, to include the knower in the known without reducing either pole to the other.

More to the point, it was Freud, more than probably any other thinker of the modern age, who took seriously and mapped precisely the forms of self-deception and self-ignorance that make precognition possible in a post-selected universe. The obliquity of the unconscious—the rules Freud assigned to what he called "primary process" thinking—reflect the associative and indirect way in which information from the future has to reach us. We couldn't just appear to ourselves bearing explicit messages from the future; those messages can *only* be obscure, hinting, and rich in metaphor, more like a game of charades, and they will almost always lack a clear origin—like unsigned postcards or letters with no return address. Their import, or their meaning, will never be fully grasped, or will be wrongly interpreted, until events come to pass that reveal how the experiencer, perhaps inadvertently, fulfilled the premonition. It may be no coincidence that Freud's theory maps so well onto an understanding of precognition if the unconscious is really, as I suggested, something like consciousness displaced in time. It so happens that Freud's clinical writings are full of likely "Dunne dreams" as well as other precognitive anomalies that have gone largely or totally unnoticed for over a century because he was so successful at reframing these occurrences in other, less causally repugnant terms.

I called Freud an ambivalent guide. Freud was open to paranormal phenomena, but he strictly rejected the possibility of precognition. Some seemingly precognitive phenomena he explained away as false memory— still the standard resort of modern skeptics—and some he explained by attributing extraordinary but not physically unthinkable sensory and in- ferential abilities to the unconscious. When those explanations wouldn't work, Freud appealed to the psychical (but still non-time-defying) main- stay, telepathy. I suggest that all of these tactics were ways to deny, evade, or just paper over a possibility that was deeply threatening to him: that our fate may not be written in our past—the basic premise of his entire theory of human nature—so much as in our future.

What adds an even more fascinating dimension to this is that Freud himself shows striking evidence of having been a "precog," foreseeing/ foretelling some of the most significant moments in his later life in his dreams and neurotic symptoms. Thus, we cannot mine psychoanalysis for guidance in exploring precognition and time loops without simulta- neously examining and deconstructing Freud's own defenses against— or you might say *repression of*—the whole possibility of information refluxing from our future. *Repression of prophecy* was intrinsic to Freud's own "Oedipus complex" and is a side of one of the most influential men of the 20th century that has gone largely unexamined.

The Medallion

Oedipus the King was Freud's favorite ancient drama long before psy- choanalysis or the mysteries of infantile sexuality were even glimmers in his eye. When he was a medical student at the University of Vienna, the young Freud would stroll among the busts of great scholars who had taught at the institution and fantasize that his own bust would one day be among them, inscribed with a line from Sophocles' tragedy: "Who divined the famed riddle and was a man most mighty." Even as a young man, Freud had tremendous ambition and a sense of his own greatness.

Over three decades later, in 1906, on the occasion of his 50th birth- day, the increasingly well-known explorer of human self-ignorance was presented with a medallion by a small group of his Viennese followers. On one side it showed his face in profile; on the other, it showed Oedi- pus standing before the Sphinx and was inscribed with that exact line from Sophocles ... even though the honoree had never told anyone of the quote's significance to him.

Freud's friend and official biographer, the English Psychoanalyst Ernest Jones, recorded that when the father of psychoanalysis read the inscription, he "became pale and agitated and in a strangled voice demanded to know who had thought of it. He behaved as if he had encountered a *revenant...*"[3]

Peter J. Rudnytsky, reflecting on the importance of that moment for Freud, writes that "Freud's loss of composure upon being honored by his followers is attributable to the blurring of the boundary between inner and outer worlds, as fantasy unexpectedly becomes reality."[4] Standard psychoanalytic thinking holds that our desires for success are linked with early childhood ideas of taking the father's place, which are retained in the unconscious like ancient bugs trapped in amber. Like Oedipus himself, Freud unexpectedly got the forbidden thing he had wished for—or was well on the way to getting it—and he suddenly felt great trepidation at the realization. The cost of getting our deepest wishes is punishment for our crimes: for a boy, castration; for a man, death.[5] A man's 50th birthday is never really a happy milestone anyway; it merely highlights the inevitability of aging and mortality. As a student, he had wished for fame and honor like those inscribed busts, but now, did he really want to be a dead man memorialized by the living?

The possibility that Freud's youthful "fantasy" had really been a premonition, and that realizing *that fact* is what really threatened Freud so deeply at his birthday celebration, is never even suggested by Freud scholars, because Freud himself effectively banished any whiff of prophecy from psychoanalysis. When he homed in on the Oedipus story and elevated it to the key archetype of the human psyche in his masterpiece *The Interpretation of Dreams*, it was enough for him that children fall in love with their opposite-sex parent, feel jealous of their same-sex parent, and never quite resolve these feelings. He consciously disregarded the fact that Oedipus's killing his father had been prophesied and that it was precisely in trying to avoid fulfilling the prophecy that the Theban prince did end up committing those acts. Freud assured his readers that it was only the universality of the incestuous desires depicted in Sophocles' tragedy that made the work so enduring. Myriad other ancient stories about fate and the prophecies it makes possible have been forgotten, he asserted, because they just offend our modern, less superstitious sensibilities.[6]

In a brief paper called "A Premonitory Dream Fulfilled" written in 1899, the same year J. W. Dunne dreamed about his stopped watch in a Sussex hotel room,[7] Freud devoted his considerable forensic intellect to debunking an ostensibly precognitive dream of one of his female patients, "Frau B." Her dream was a typical Dunne dream, but pretty vanilla stuff. This "estimable woman who moreover possesses a critical sense" told Dr. Freud that she once, years earlier, dreamed she encountered her old family doctor and friend, "Dr. K.," in a specific spot ("in the Kärntnerstrasse in front of Hiess's shop"), and the next day she ran into Herr K. at the precise spot she had dreamed. [8]

It was convenient for Freud that the alleged incident had happened well in the past, that Frau B. had not written down her dream, and that she said she had not actually recalled having the dream until after she had her real-life encounter with Dr. K. Treating her notion that she'd had a premonitory dream instead as a fantasy, Freud delved into the patient's past for a psychoanalytic reason, a "justification," for confabulating her dream-memory *after* her encounter with Dr. K. It was easy for him to come up with a plausible-enough story—at least, if you accept the sometimes-Byzantine inner-world soap operas that characterize Freudian interpretations.

It turned out that 25 years before this event, when pining for a gentleman with whom Frau B. had been having an extramarital affair—also coincidentally a "Dr. K."—the object of her secret affections paid her a visit at her home, and this at the time seemed to her uncannily coincidental. (Freud correctly remarks here that the fact that she was always thinking of the man, and that he was always visiting her, made it inevitable that one of his visits would coincide with her thoughts of him; "accidents which seem preconcerted like this are to be found in every love story.") Fast-forward to the time of the dream, when the now-twice-widowed Frau B. was able to see her still-paramour Dr. K. openly. Based on the past history, Freud argued that his patient's encounter with the other Dr. K. on the street *triggered a fantasy that she had already dreamed about it*, and that this effectively masked a wish related to her lover. Freud needed a lot of "frog DNA" to justify his reframing. "Let us suppose," he writes,

> that during the few days before the dream she had been expecting a visit from [Dr. K.], but that this had not taken place—he was no longer so pressing as he used to be. She may then have quite well had a nostalgic dream one night which took her back to the old days. Her dream was probably of a rendez-vous at the time

of her love affair, and the chain of her dream-thoughts carried her back to the occasion when, without any pre-arrangement, he had come in at the very moment at which she had been longing for him. She probably had dreams of this kind quite often now; they were a part of the belated punishment with which a woman pays for her youthful cruelty.[9]

Frau B. then ran into the other Dr. K, whom "we may suppose … had been used in her thoughts, and perhaps in her dreams as well, as a screen figure behind which she concealed the better-loved figure of the other Dr. K."[10] This would have jogged a vague memory of the nostalgic dream Freud supposed she really had had, which was then mostly forgotten. Since the present situation (a "rendez-vous") was similar to that supposed real dream, she substituted the present Dr. K., and the place where she ran into him, in place of the other Dr. K. and their romantic dream-rendezvous.

"*Let us suppose … She must have … She may have …*" As a spokesman for the unconscious, Dr. Freud spun a nice just-so story, one that is supported by nothing Frau B. actually told him about her dream. It is a tapestry of supposition, not unlike Martin Gardner's "explanation" of how Morgan Robertson might have come by the name *Titan* for his fictional doomed ocean liner. Nevertheless, Freud writes that Frau B. "was obliged to accept [his] account of what happened, which seems to me more plausible, without raising any objection to it."[11] He concludes, confidently, that "the creation of a dream after the event, which alone makes prophetic dreams possible, is nothing other than a form of censoring, thanks to which the dream is able to make its way through into consciousness."[12]

Are Freud's strained "must haves" and "probablys" really more plausible than the far simpler notion that Frau B. did in fact dream of Dr. K. the night before she met him, just as she reported?

Collecting the Bricks

Freud's objection to the possibility that Frau B.'s dream was really precognitive was not out of a rejection of psychical mechanisms operative in human life. Over the course of his career he became increasingly open to other "occult" phenomena like telepathy (or what he called "thought transference"). But in 1899, the familiar folkloric notion that people sometimes have prophetic dreams could only be an unwelcome gnat, distracting attention from his bold new theory that *all* dreams, whatever their surface appearance, are really *disguised fulfillments of repressed wishes*, often wishes of a sexual nature. It did not occur to Freud, in 1899 or ever, that dreams could *both* show us our wishes and show us the future, or that they could even do the one in service of the other. It did not occur to him, for example, that Frau B.'s wish to encounter her lover might have *primed* her to precognize running into his namesake in the street on the night before it happened.

Dunne was well aware of Freud's theories about dreams, and unlike Freud he saw no conflict between the wish-fulfillment theory and the idea that dreams can also predict the future. In fact, it seemed plain to him that dreams may reach into the future for the props and characters and stage sets to create tableaux that serve whatever purpose dreams serve, as much as they reach into our past.

> Many people, I hear, suppose that there is some clash between serialism and the 'wish-fulfillment' theory of dreams. There is none. 'Wish-fulfillment' theories are concerned with explaining why the dreamer builds a particular dream edifice: I am interested in the quite different question of whence he collects the bricks.[13]

A famous dream that opens Chapter 7 of *The Interpretation of Dreams* is a concise and heartbreaking example of the wish-fulfillment idea, and perhaps because of that, no one seems to notice that it was also a very typical Dunne dream about an alarming discovery in the dreamer's imminent future:

> A father had been watching beside his child's sick-bed for days and nights on end. After the child had died, he went into the next room to lie down, but left the door open so that he could see from his bedroom into the room in which his child's body was laid out, with tall candles standing round it. An old man had been engaged to keep watch over it, and sat beside the body murmuring prayers. After a few hours' sleep, the father had a dream that *his child was standing beside his bed, caught him by the arm and whispered to him*

reproachfully: 'Father, don't you see I'm burning?' He woke up, noticed a bright glare of light from the next room, hurried into it and found that the old watchman had dropped off to sleep and that the wrappings and one of the arms of his beloved child's dead body had been burned by a lighted candle that had fallen on them.[14]

Freud argued—sensibly, as far as it goes—that the dream enabled the father to continue sleeping for a few precious seconds with this dream image of his beloved child rather than make him rise immediately to put out the fire that had started in the next room:

> The dead child behaved in the dream like a living one: he himself warned his father, came to his bed, and caught him by the arm, just as he had probably done on the occasion from the memory of which the first part of the child's words in the dream were derived. For the sake of the fulfillment of this wish the father prolonged his sleep by one moment. The dream was preferred to a waking reflection because it was able to show the child as once more alive. If the father had woken up first and then made the inference that led him to go into the next room, he would, as it were, have shortened his child's life by that moment of time.[15]

But when we ignore the precognitive possibility, other aspects of the dream become hard to explain. If dreams are wish fulfillments that help us prolong sleep, as Freud contended, what actually woke the sleeping man, catapulting him back into the terrible reality of his grief and a fire he needed to put out? This dream has proven a favorite head-scratcher for Freud's later commentators, and among the mysteries is how exactly the man's sleeping mind "knew" what was happening in the next room. Even assuming he was able to tell there was a fire (i.e., perhaps from glare detected through his shut eyelids or a subtle smell of cloth burning), how would his unconscious have determined that it was his child's sleeve that had caught fire and not something else in the room? Why did the smell of smoke not wake the man sitting watch right next to the child, if it was able to wake the father? We are simply to accept from Freud's account that the grieving father's super-sensitive and superintelligent unconscious drew a remarkably correct inference based on sense data received while asleep in another room.

The unconscious has been regarded since Freud, and even before, as far more sensitive than our conscious mind; it somehow "knows" more and can infer more from available information. In his 1901 book *The Psychopathology of Everyday Life*, Freud deployed the super-abilities of the unconscious to explain away many familiar superstitions and the kinds of meaningful coincidences Jung later called "synchronicity," such as the familiar experience of thinking about some random person just before running into them. For instance, Freud reports having had a sudden fantasy, while walking along a Vienna street, about a couple who had rejected his services for their daughter months earlier—the fantasy was that they would now respect his authority since he had just been named Professor. Just then he heard himself addressed, "Good day to you, Professor!" It was the very couple he had just been thinking of, coming down the street. To explain this coincidence, Freud supposes that he had looked up to the street ahead just before his fantasy and unconsciously recognized their approach but blotted out the conscious awareness through "negative hallucination" while his mind could prepare his little wish-scene—analogous to the notion that the sleeping father's mind preferred to remain with the fantasy of his son for a few seconds rather than respond to a fire in the next room.[16] Again, his explanation substitutes a rather elaborate and convoluted cognitive mechanism for the more parsimonious idea that he simply "pre-sensed" an encounter with the couple just before it happened. Freud's explanation has the advantage, however, that it does not fly in the face of our commonsense understanding of causal order.

The super-sensitivity of the unconscious was not original to Freud. By the time he wrote *The Interpretation of Dreams*, Victorian psychiatrists had long been wrestling with the paradoxically enhanced perception, memory, and intelligence sometimes displayed by hysterics when under hypnosis and, especially, displayed by hysterical patients with secondary, split-off personalities (a common symptom seen in the last quarter of the 19th century, an early form of what is today called multiple personality disorder).[17] Interestingly, psychical researchers of the day played an important role in the evolving psychiatric and psychoanalytic conception of the unconscious mind as super-sensitive and, in its own way, superintelligent. Like hypnotized hysterics, spiritualist mediums in their self-induced trances were often able to access seemingly impossible information, even when trickery was ruled out through careful observation. It was explained that their subliminal sensitivities were so acute that they could "read" a sitter and extract cues that appeared to most witnesses like accessing information from some occult source.[18] Already in 1886, Charles Richet had proposed the existence of an unconscious part of the intellect sequestered from conscious awareness, and he made his proposal specifically in the context of providing a physiological explanation for table turning and other feats of spiritualists. Because unconscious thoughts and muscle movements originate outside of conscious awareness, he argued, they *feel* alien and are readily interpreted as originating with spirits or other entities.[19]

The unconscious, as an "other" inside, is, when you think about it, really a very "occult" idea. Freud's "hermeneutics of suspicion"[20] naturally invited a suspicious rationalist skepticism in return. The philosopher Jean-Paul Sartre, for one, could not abide an unconscious formation in the psyche. To him, it smacked of *bad faith*, inauthenticity, the failure to take responsibility for our actions. For instance, he pointed out the contradiction inherent in the idea of a "censor" in the mind that could be aware enough of what it was censoring to form a judgment yet also be completely alien to our conscious experience. The "resistance" that impedes patients from developing self-insight implies a similar non-aware awareness: "the patient shows defiance, refuses to speak, gives fantastic accounts of his dreams, sometimes even removes himself completely from the psychoanalytic treatment. It is a fair question to ask what part of himself can resist."[21] There is no unconscious, Sartre argued, just the avoidance of responsibility.

Claims of an unconscious mind that could only be explored through a highly subjective process of interpretation also offended the philosopher of science Karl Popper, one of Freud's harshest critics. How would you test claims about an unconscious? Psychoanalysis is not a science, Popper contended, not only because its claims cannot be falsified but also because the clinical situation, with suggestible patients in a kind of trance-like thrall to their doctor, is an echo chamber—a machine for producing evidence in support of its premises (the usual meaning of "self-fulfilling prophecy").[22]

Although 20th-century psychological science and neuroscience rejected Freud (and ignored Freud's contemporaries in psychical research), it ultimately came around to embracing some notion of an unconscious—or what came to be called "implicit processing"—as a domain of cognitive functioning that is hypersensitive to subliminal signals and much quicker at making inferences and judgments than the conscious mind. Abundant experimental evidence shows implicit processing's overriding dominance over anything like conscious will. A large school of thought, much of it inspired by Benjamin Libet's work described in the preceding chapter, holds that we are mere spectators of our lives and that conscious will is an illusion, a kind of overlay. If the unconscious was for Freud the submerged majority of the iceberg, for some contemporary cognitive scientists and neuroscientists, it is *all* submerged—the tip is a mirage. We are unaware of the bulk of what seems to occur in our heads—there is thinking, sensing, and feeling that is not thought, sensed, or felt, and our non-experience of this huge domain is much more than a matter of bad faith (although there is that also). As with Freud's unconscious, you can only probe the implicit domain indirectly, obliquely, via tools and paradigms such as priming tasks, like the ones Daryl Bem inverted in some of his "feeling the future" experiments.

The super-abilities of memory are another problematic, even paradoxical inheritance of Victorian psychology. In 1900, the French psychiatrist Theodore Flournoy coined the term *cryptomnesia* to describe the ability of the mind to retain intact, and in detail, information that a person may have even briefly encountered earlier in life.[23] A medium Flournoy worked with named Hélène Smith claimed to travel to Mars during her trances and even wrote in the Martian language; it became clear to Flournoy that much of what Smith said about the Red Planet came from material she had read in popular books about Mars when she was a child (and that "Martian" was strangely similar to French). It was central to Freud's theory too that everything we experience in our lives, even in our early childhoods, remains preserved whole and intact in our memory. He wrote in *Civilization and Its Discontents,* for instance, that "in mental life nothing which has once been formed can perish."[24]

Even if the unconscious is no longer scientific no-man's land, the idea of a memory that preserves all our experiences has been firmly and roundly debunked by a century of solid research. Memory is extremely fragmentary, and it is constantly morphing and shifting. Little or nothing from the first few years of life is preserved, and even later "memories" are mostly constructs or fictions. Yet strangely, scientist-skeptics like Martin Gardner will nevertheless unhesitatingly invoke something like cryptomnesia when it suits them to debunk ostensible psychic claims—a paradoxical and untenable, "bad faith" position. Since any notion of precognition or presentiment is scientifically heretical, though, such a mechanism is seldom proposed to help resolve questions of how people know things they shouldn't be able to, even on the stigmatized fringes ("para-") of psychology. But reconceiving the unconscious as the way behavior and experience are perturbed or shaped by future *conscious* experience has greater parsimony than the orthodox Freudian picture, or even the picture painted by some mainstream neuroscience and psychology. For one thing, it would unburden the unconscious of needing to be so "super." Much of the extraordinary sensitivity and inferential ability of the unconscious (or the sleeping brain), as described by Victorian psychiatry and as assumed in today's behavior and brain sciences, would simply be an illusion produced by our nonawareness of the brain's ability to be influenced by its future states and to draw on its processing power over larger swathes of time.

For instance, in the "father can't you see I'm burning" example, we could simply say that the grieving patient was awakened by a Dunne dream—one that fulfilled a wish, to be sure, that his son was still alive—but that also alerted him to a situation he was *about to discover* in the next room: that his child's sleeve had caught fire. Although the occasion was far sadder, this dream is in other respects very similar to Dunne's dream of his stopped watch. The very common experience of elaborately plotted dreams that culminate in an event corresponding to some sudden noise or shock that wakes the dreamer—and thus seem "temporally impossible" (because the whole "plot" of the dream is built around that terminal event)—would be examples of the same "presponding" to imminent shocks.[25] We would no longer need to posit some kind of retroactive memory distortion, as has always been assumed to be operative, along with all the other convolutions Freud invoked. The dreaming brain would simply be feeling its future.

Although it can only be a hypothesis until it is tested, some of the knee-jerk inhibitions against taking such an idea seriously are easily dispensed with. One is that it remains hard not to think of precognition as somehow difficult or strenuous—perhaps like climbing up some impossibly steep temporal or thermodynamic hill. To someone trying to grapple with the mind-bending implications of retrocausation, "computing over the brain's timeline" will seem vaguely like a big "ask" of an already overwhelmingly busy organ. But if precognition is based on anything like the quantum biological mechanisms proposed in the last chapter, it should not be thought of as something added to our cognitive load but as something basic to its functioning. In fact, precognition, as something like James Carpenter's "first sight,"[26] would really make things easier on the brain than the effortful picture painted by Newtonian cognitive psychology, with its superpowers of implicit processing and the like. Rapid, instinctive predictive processing, for instance, would seemingly be hugely resource-demanding if that processing is limited to the present moment; drawing on wider temporal swathes of brain activity, and post-selecting on optimal outcomes ahead, would simplify things. Similarly, how much of our resource-intensive memory "storage" might instead be the ongoing ability to orient toward needed information our experience is soon to supply? It would enhance our picture of ecological cognition, the offloading of cognitive tasks onto our physical, social, and cultural environment. At this point, there is no telling where mundane memory, inference, and other basic psychological processes end and precognition begins—again, it remains for future researchers to examine the question with an open mind and design experiments to test this hypothesis. But precognition would allow the mind to be "flatter," not deeper, than in most other psychological frameworks.[27]

The bottom line is: Let us not confuse how difficult precognition is to wrap our heads around with how difficult the brain actually finds accomplishing it. If it is at all within the nervous system's capabilities, there's no reason not to think that it might be the easiest thing in the world, and maybe even the very basis for our spontaneous, improvisational, yet amazingly successful (most of the time) engagement with reality.

Mister Foresight

Freud is sometimes simplistically contrasted with Carl Jung as a resolute skeptic on matters psychical. This was not the case. Although he was cautious of writing publicly about these topics lest it taint the reputation of psychoanalysis in its early years, he privately was curious and open-minded about occult phenomena his whole life. He was aware of superstitions of his own and was even fond of quoting Shakespeare's "there are more things in heaven and earth than are dreamt of in your philosophy" (from *Hamlet*) to his more skeptical friends. In the 1910s, Freud attended séances with a somewhat open mind. Much to the horror of his skeptical friend Ernest Jones, Freud engaged in telepathy experiments with his daughter Anna and the Hungarian psychoanalyst Sandor Ferenczi, the results of which persuaded him that there was a "kernel of truth" to the phenomenon described three decades earlier by

Frederic Myers, the ability of people to transmit and receive thoughts.[28] And throughout his career, he also could not fail to observe coincidences in his patients' dreams and symptoms that were unexplainable even through the super-functioning of the unconscious as he had described it in his earlier writings.

In the 1920s, when Freud felt more secure about the status of his new psychiatric approach, he felt safer to reflect on these topics in public than he had earlier, and did so in a handful of papers and lectures.[29] In a 1932 piece called "Dreams and Occultism," he described several cases of apparent telepathy—or what he called "thought transference"—in his patients.[30] One concerns an "obviously intelligent man ... not in the least 'inclined toward occultism'"[31] who wrote to him that he dreamed on the night of November 16-17 that his wife had given birth to twins. In reality, his wife (his second) was not pregnant and the patient had no intention or desire of having children with her, finding her unsuitable for raising children; the couple no longer had sexual relations, in fact. But a day later, on the 18th, the man received a telegram informing him that his daughter, who lived in another city, had given birth to twins on the same night he had had his dream. He had known she was pregnant but also knew she was not due to give birth for another month. So it seemed to Freud a case of possible dream telepathy. What clinched it was the man's feelings for the two women who seem conflated in the dream:

> I feel sure, ladies and gentlemen, that you have been able to explain this dream already and understand too why I have told it to you. Here was a man who was dissatisfied with his second wife and who would prefer his wife to be like the daughter of his first marriage. The 'like' dropped out, of course, so far as the unconscious was concerned. And now the telepathic message arrived during the night to say that his daughter had given birth to twins. The dream-work took control of the news, allowed the unconscious wish to operate on it—the wish that he could put his daughter in the place of his second wife—and thus arose the puzzling manifest dream, which disguised the wish and distorted the message. We must admit that it is only the interpretation of the dream that has shown us that it was a telepathic one; psychoanalysis has revealed a telepathic event which we should not otherwise have discovered.[32]

Freud notes that his patient merely thought his dream's correspondence to the news of his daughter's delivery was coincidental—he did not suspect that it was a telepathic dream. But Freud says this man would not have been surprised to find it was telepathic. He was devoted to this daughter, and he even felt certain she "would have thought particularly of him during her labour."[33] We have no evidence of how Freud's patient reacted to the news of his daughter's delivery, but there is no reason not to think this was in fact a *precognitive* dream of getting the telegram announcing the birth, rather than a telepathic message sent across space by his daughter—a daughter who her father liked to think was thinking only of her dad during the pains of giving birth. (The man clearly needed Freud's help.)

Another, even more striking case described in the same piece concerns a male patient in his forties, identified as "Herr P.," who had been seeing Freud on a temporary basis in the summer of 1919 to address unspecified sexual difficulties.[34] The men shared a mutual interest in things English, including English literature, and this served as a touchstone in their conversations. Late in the summer, P. lent Freud a copy of a new book in John Galsworthy's series of stories collectively known as *The Forsyte Saga*, which Freud enjoyed and they discussed. A few days later, Freud was visited in the morning for the first time by an eminent London psychiatrist, Dr. David Forsyth, freshly arrived from England to begin a period of training in psychoanalytic technique. P. did not yet know anything about Forsyth or his visit, but it was a high priority for Freud, who was eager to spread his technique to England. In fact, it was partly Dr. Forsyth's training that would require Freud to terminate his analysis of P. soon thereafter. His patient then arrived at 10:45 for his session, during which he discussed his inhibitions about sex with a woman he was courting, who was a virgin. Freud writes,

> He had often talked of her before but that day he told me for the first time that, though of course she had no notion of the true grounds of his impediment, she used to call him 'Herr von Vorsicht' [Mr. Foresight].[35] I was struck by this information; Dr. Forsyth's visiting card lay beside me, and I showed it to him.[36]

Freud then provides background on his and his patient's shared literary interests and the Galsworthy novel P. had just shared with him. Then Freud explains:

Now the name 'Forsyte' in these novels differs little from that of my visitor 'Forsyth' and, as pronounced by a German, the two can scarcely be distinguished; and there is an English word with a meaning—'foresight'—which we should also pronounce in the same way and which would be translated 'Voraussicht' or 'Vorsicht'. Thus P. had in fact selected from his personal concerns the very name with which I was occupied at the same time as a result of an occurrence of which he was unaware.[37]

Freud then adds two other previous coincidences in P.'s therapy, which also centered on visiting Englishpersons, and proceeds to unpack the psychoanalytic meaning of his patient's uncannily timed disclosure. Freud had warned P. at the outset that the analysis would have to terminate when his regular patients returned to Vienna in the aftermath of the First World War and foreign students (like Dr. Forsyth) arrived, but P. naturally felt jealous, owing to the *transference*, the powerful and possessive attachment a patient may develop toward the doctor (the latter having been put in the role of a parent or other important figure in the patient's life). Freud interprets P.'s coincidental mention of being called "Mr. Foresight" by his girlfriend as a message addressed to him by P.'s unconscious:

The remarkable fact was that he brought the name into the analysis unheralded, only the briefest time after it had become significant to me in another sense owing to a new event—the London doctor's arrival. But the manner in which the name emerged in his analytic session is perhaps not less interesting than the fact itself. He did not say, for instance: 'The name "Forsyte", out of the novels you are familiar with, has just occurred to me.' He was able, without any conscious relation to that source, to weave the name into his own experiences and to produce it thence—a thing that might have happened long before but had not happened till then. What he did say now was: 'I'm a Forsyth too: that's what the girl calls me.' It is hard to mistake the mixture of jealous demand and melancholy self-deprecation which finds its expression in this remark. We shall not be going astray if we complete it in some such way as this: 'It's mortifying to me that your thoughts should be so intensely occupied with this new arrival. Do come back to me; after all I'm a Forsyth too—though it's true I'm only a Herr von Vorsicht [gentleman of foresight], as the girl says.' And thereupon his train of thought, passing along the associative threads of the element 'English' went back to two earlier events, which were able to stir up the same feelings of jealousy.[38]

Here, the unwillingness and/or inability to countenance real prophetic foresight prevented Freud from seeing what might have been obvious to J. W. Dunne: the fact that just after P. made his utterance, Freud expressed surprise and showed him Dr. Forsyth's calling card. In other words, rather than telepathically mucking about in his doctor's Forsyth-obsessed brain, P. could just as easily have been "pre-sponding" to that imminent rewarding (but also unsettling) disclosure and reaction by his doctor.[39] Dunne's friend J. B. Priestley would have called this a clear instance of the future-influencing-present effect. Had Freud omitted this little, crucial detail, it might have been hard to deconstruct his thought-transference argument, and indeed most case descriptions of ostensible telepathy (or clairvoyance for that matter) leave such details out. Writers on these topics think it is enough to state whether or not a psychic subject correctly produced veridical information without clarifying *how the psychic found out* he or she was correct. I am arguing that the latter element of feedback is the crucial piece of the story.

Interpreting P.'s case in terms of precognition has the advantage of making sense of his whole prior history of book-lending to Freud, which preceded Dr. Forsyth's visit and Dr. Freud's preoccupation with the Englishman.[40] We might indeed call all of P.'s behavior leading up to the divulgence of Dr. Forsyth's calling card a kind of *precognitive symptom* taking the form of a time loop. Freud would not have shown P. Dr. Forsyth's card (or expressed gratifying amazement at the coincidence) had P. not spoken of being called "Mr. Foresight."

One wonders whether P.'s girlfriend gave him the nickname "Mr. Foresight" because he had some kind of natural precognitive habit. There is no way of knowing, as Freud provides no other information about this patient. But Freud's omission of any mention of the meaning of the nickname is telling. The girl did not call him "Herr von

Telepathie," after all. Herr P.—or at least, his unconscious—was announcing quite loudly the psychical modality that was operative, but Freud ignored this, reframing the events to better suit his theory.

The "No" of Father Time

Like the Theban King he so identified with, Freud was blind to prophecy—even tragically so, as we will see in the next chapter. But the clinical setting has also provided other, more open-minded psychotherapists with ample evidence of psychic functioning on the part of their patients, including ample evidence of precognition.[41]

No Freudian psychoanalyst has considered the question of precognition and its role in psychotherapy more fully than Jule Eisenbud, who keenly noted in his 1982 book *Paranormal Foreknowledge* that the two issues Freud was so intent to keep segregated—the precognitive habit and Oedipal sexual issues—actually go hand in hand. Eisenbud argued that whatever else they do, episodes of precognition, such as a precognitive dream, fulfill a wish to transgress time; for some of his patients, this need to defeat time was distinctly related to a wish to cross the generation gap. Securing some vision of the future provided, by implication, an ability to surmount that generational barrier—which constitutes, he wrote, a "symbol of all that is cruel and unalterable about fate."[42]

Note that the man "untainted by the occult" who dreamed of his wife giving birth to twins a day before his beloved daughter did that very thing precisely fits such a template. There is also an interesting Oedipal dimension to the "Mr. Foresight" story, not explicitly elaborated by Freud but readily inferred from the details he gives us. A classic symptom of unresolved Oedipal issues is falling in love with or marrying partners very different in age—in either direction.[43] From the fact of Herr P.'s age ("between forty and fifty") and the fact that the "pretty, piquant, penniless girl" he wanted to sleep with but couldn't was a virgin, there was most likely a sizeable age gap between them. And we can infer that P.'s problem (since the girl was a virgin) was his own impotence. Reluctance to deflower a virgin was a common sexual inhibition back then, and it was no doubt coupled in this case with guilt, some fear of being punished for "robbing the cradle." Did his precognitive behavior represent a gambit to transgress time but also circumvent the inhibition wrought by his guilt?

The Oedipal predicament is not only an incestuous sexual wish but also an expectation of punishment in retaliation for this wish. Consequently, those with unresolved "Oedipus complexes" elicit inhibition from their world, like a castrating father always lurking over them and their achievements. This alerts us to an added, and very important, Oedipal implication in the Herr P. episode, in connection to his nickname and its similarity to that of the arriving English doctor. Forsyth/Foresight is here, as the French psychoanalyst Jacques Lacan would later put it, the "name of the father." The arrival of "Mister Foresight's" namesake Dr. Forsyth was like the arrival of the father which, in this case, was specifically and literally going to "cut short" the patient's treatment (treatment that might have enabled his sexual relations to proceed, had it continued), and thus is every bit like the arrival of the castrating father to punish or at least say "no" to the child's Oedipal wishes.

In French, *le nom du pere*, "name of the father" sounds just like *le non du pere*, "the *no* of the father," a pun obviously lost in translation. Resolution of the Oedipal phase of development, according to Lacanian thinking, entails internalizing this "no" as part of identification with one's surname, the otherwise arbitrary signifier that establishes one's identity or place in the system of cultural symbols he called the Symbolic order. While on the one hand acceptance of this "no" buys us normative mental health, the relatively neurosis-free life, it also tends to inhibit us from even imagining anything other than ordinary, billiard-ball causality. By submitting to the rules of language, we submit ourselves also to its (linear) grammar. By the same token, failure to fully identify with one's name (and the limiting refusal it entails) is tantamount to coming unstuck in the linear-causal signifying chain of language, thus in some at least figurative sense, unstuck in time. In short, you might even say that the expression of precognition reflects an active, unresolved Oedipus complex, while denial of precognition represents the "healthy," non-neurotic internalization of, or identification with, the phallic-patriarchal Symbolic order.

Given this, isn't it interesting that the ultimate argument generally deployed against the existence of precognition by skeptical guardians of Enlightenment rationalism is the famous *grandfather* paradox—effectively, a variant of the Oedipus myth that emphasizes how impossible it is to transgress time because it would mean negating in some fashion one's own forefathers?

Consider the following case of one of Eisenbud's patients—a typical Dunne dream in which the man seems to have precognized a comic strip he was about to read in his newspaper:

A patient dreams that he is shooting arrows with or at a childhood playmate in a scene reminiscent of his childhood. His father is present. The only affect experienced by the dreamer is a sense of frustration because his aim is not accurate and he cannot control his shots.

On the following day the patient is surprised to see that a character in one of the comic strips he is in the habit of reading insures the accuracy of his aim by shooting an arrow and afterward painting the target circles around the spot where it had struck to give the impression that the shot had been a bull's-eye.[44]

Like other precognitive dreams, this one fractally involves a "time gimmick" in the form of the comic itself—Johnny Hart's then-popular strip *B.C.*:

The precognitive effect in this instance is suggested not only by the patient coming upon such a specifically fitting resolution for his dream situation *after* the dream but also by the very format of the element in question. The comic strip, titled *B.C.*, itself suggests the idea of a time gimmick, dealing as it does with the often anachronistic doings of a prehistoric people. It suggests that Time and the past, which to the patient represent threatening memories from his childhood, are only comic situations which, insofar as they are subject to this kind of re-creation and revision, are not real or really dangerous.[45]

In other words, the time gimmick, as well as the very precognitive "format" of the dream, enable the dreamer to retroactively defeat the Oedipal "phallic inhibition" that is so beautifully represented right in the dream: being unable to hit a target with an arrow when in the presence of his dad. The comic strip expresses the patient's Oedipal wish: By being "before" in time, the man is able to redefine his sloppy shooting *post hoc* yet also *before* the whole psychosexual saga. Put simply, a way to "kill the father" is to be on the scene before him.

The Oedipus complex, it is becoming clear, is the flip side of the coin of the grandfather paradox. The implied threat that transgressing the causal/temporal order will negate/annihilate the would-be Oedipus is the threat hanging over his head, the "no" that "cuts off" any speculation about foresight. But as I argued earlier in this book, the grandfather paradox is really an empty scarecrow. There is nothing requiring retrocausation to lead to a self-cancelling paradox; in fact, paradoxes are prevented by physical law.[46] As the Greeks knew, all prophecies are self-fulfilling. They operate outside of conscious awareness (in other words, "in the unconscious"), and thus we only become aware of a prophecy when the prophesied event has come to pass. Precognition and other forms of "time travel," and thoughts of the grandfather paradox that they invite, are perhaps ways of fulfilling that wish of eliminating competition with the father, the ultimate way of having one's cake and eating it too. Even by calling that scarecrow the "grandfather paradox," we miss the target by one generation, overshooting into the past the real aim, which is the safe elimination of the father while still existing.

An arrow, of course, is not only a standard phallic symbol; it is also our most basic cultural symbol of causality. The above example from Eisenbud expresses recursively, within itself, the doubts about causality and coincidence that hover over all precognitive dream reports. Drawing a bullseye around wherever one's arrow happens to hit is precisely the selection bias accusation that is used to "shoot down" (so to speak) most psi claims; it was the precise metaphor used by Richard Wiseman to debunk the Aberfan dreams (Chapter 1), for instance.[47] It is also the number-one criticism that will be aimed at many of the dreams and other ostensibly prophetic phenomena discussed in this book, and not without some justification. Precognition is only visible in hindsight, since it must be confirmed as such by events. Thus, in many cases it is very hard to distinguish it from simple hindsight bias, the adjustment of our perception of the past based on new data.

But the dreaded coin (or medallion) of hindsight has a welcome flip side: It is the same thing as *post-selection*, the very principle that allows time travel—including time-traveling information—to exist without producing causality-offending paradoxes. Post-selection just means we live in a possible universe, the *only possible* universe, and again reflects a kind of causal-informational Darwinism. The only information that "survives" being sent into the past is information that does not contribute to its own foreclosure in the future. For instance, you are never going to have a completely accurate and clear dream about a future outcome you would or could intercede to prevent. It's not necessarily that the causality police will swoop down in their flying saucers to stop you (although Igor Novikov's self-consistency principle and quantum-mechanical theories of closed-timelike curves do predict that improbable events may occur to prevent paradoxes[48]). It's mainly that, from a future vantage point farther along your world-line in the block universe, *it didn't happen*. No amount of searching in hindsight will find spent causal arrows for an impossible event. Thus all "prophecies" can be included somehow, if only very obliquely, in the backstory of what was foreseen.

In a sense, Wiseman is right. Precognition *is* a matter of drawing bullseyes around where our arrows happen to hit; what we are precognizing is ourselves drawing those bullseyes in the future. What could be a better depiction of this, and the concept of post-selection, than the arrow dream of Eisenbud's patient and the *B.C.* comic it seems to have precognitively "targeted"?

After Dunne's *An Experiment with Time*, Eisenbud's *Paranormal Foreknowledge* may be the most thoughtful and interesting book ever written on precognition. Yet even this bold para-psychoanalyst, who had gone out on several limbs in his career writing about other psi phenomena, was hesitant and cautious in his traverse of the epistemological quagmire created by this one. Although he had written and circulated the bulk of his book privately to colleagues as early as 1953, "Cartesian doubt"[49] made him delay publication for almost three decades (until 1982). And even then, he only recognized precognition as a possible explanation for coincidental phenomena in the clinic when less causally taboo explanations like telepathy, clairvoyance, or PK would not suffice. The arrow dream, for instance, did not for him meet the stringent criteria of true precognition, simply because the comic strip "was already in print at the time the patient had his dream and it required nothing more than ordinary (that is, telepathic or clairvoyant) psi percipience for him to apprehend it."[50]

But is it really easier to imagine that the patient's sleeping mind somehow scanned the still-folded newspaper outside on his driveway (or in the delivery truck, or in the print warehouse) and located within it a comic strip suiting his particular psychodynamic purposes than to suggest his brain could simply have reached into its own (near) future to find a reading experience suiting the same need? Let's pause on this question, as the exact impediment to precognitive thinking and theorizing displayed here by Eisenbud is encountered again and again in the literature, and various fallacies lie at the heart of it. It is another of those bugbears that it is time to slay, once and for all.

To Eisenbud, as to many parapsychologists open-minded to other psi phenomena, precognition is so unnatural to our common-sense way of thinking that nature, too, must somehow find it difficult—the problem I mentioned earlier in this chapter. But if his patient's brain (or consciousness, if you prefer) could search across space as well as time for a suitable "brick" to build his dream edifice, how coincidental that it happened to be one that he was going to physically read in an hour or so anyway! The clairvoyant explanation thus still rests on foreknowledge that he would read the comic when he woke up, so "ordinary psi percipience" really simplifies nothing. The precognitive hypothesis is vastly more parsimonious, cutting out an unnecessary explanatory middleman.

Let me reiterate: *We should not confuse how difficult we find imagining a thing with how difficult nature finds accomplishing it.* Were we to do that, we would make the mistake of seeing quantum mechanics itself, with its famously "spooky" characteristics, as applying only to a few subatomic particles here and there, rather than being the very substrate of our physical existence. If precognition exists at all, there is every reason to think that it is not only common but probably a constant in our lives. It would not have evolved just to be used as a rare trump card by a few especially gifted (or cursed) individuals in a few remarkable circumstances, or just by neurotics oppressed and inhibited by their Oedipal complexes. It is far more likely that we are, all of us, fully four-dimensional, precognitive creatures and that our time-binding capabilities simply have found many interesting ways to fly under the radar—partly because of all those cultural no-sayers, the "castrating fathers" who take every opportunity to explain away our anomalous experiences in some chaste, unoffensively Newtonian way. If there is any "ordinary psi percipience" we should default to, it is more likely to be precognition, not any of the other commonly invoked modalities like telepathy or clairvoyance.[51]

Denial and condescension are the default reaction of those castrating cultural fathers to reports of anomalous experience. But when this tactic doesn't work or is not really believed, our attention will be redirected instead in culturally safe directions, including toward the past, making us assume that those experiences represent some sublimely strange deviation of memory and desire. This is one reason why the psychoanalytic tradition is so interesting: It has always represented a kind of halfway house to the acceptance of anomalies that the rest of science rejects out of hand. Instead of rejecting, it reframes.

The entire construct of the unconscious may really be a kind of re-framing, a compromise formation between Enlightenment mechanistic psychology with its manly world of linear causation—picture a bunch of *fathers* hanging out at the pool hall *playing billiards*—and a converse awareness that something about us is transcendent. Instead of allowing a rich *temporal* transcendence, which would be the ultimate Oedipal scandal, Freud offered the world a less causally perverse compromise: "Here, you can have the mind's spread-outness in *space*, and even a few superpowers. Just don't look in *that other direction* (the future) for the causes of your dreams and your inexplicable actions."

The closing lines of Freud's landmark work, *The Interpretation of Dreams*, sound almost desperately insistent, when read in this light:

> And the value of dreams for giving us knowledge of the future? There is of course no question of that. It would be truer to say instead that they give us knowledge of the past. For dreams are derived from the past in every sense. Nevertheless the ancient belief that dreams fore-tell the future is not wholly devoid of truth. By pictur-ing our wishes as fulfilled, dreams are after all leading us into the future. But this future, which the dreamer pictures as the present, has been moulded by his in-destructible wish into a perfect likeness of the past.[52]

Note how Freud keeps rerouting our attention to the past, almost like he is afraid of something in that other direction. There was indeed a lot to be afraid of, as we will see. But I am arguing that it is precisely there, that taboo direction, the future, that might contain many of the answers to the deeply weird behavior of humans and the anomalous situations we experience. Dreams offer the key.

9

Wyrd and Wishes — Metabolizing the Future in Dreams

*Let us learn to dream, gentlemen, and then perhaps we
shall find the truth . . . but let us beware of publishing
our dreams before they have been put to the proof by the
waking understanding.*

— Friedrich August Kekulé von Stradonitz, speech on his
dream-discovery of the ring structure of benzene (1890)

The inevitability of things prophesied is one factor that has always made prophecy so taboo, something not to be toyed with, and thus somewhat fearful. After all, it is from the future that death and downfall ultimately arrive—nothing good. Thus in a world gripped by fate's time-looping iron law, writers of tragedies did not depict the ability to see the future as a possible "superpower" or as a way of improving an individual's fortunes, the way modern writers about "developing your ESP powers" or "honing your intuition" might. Stories like that of Oedipus highlight the tragic folly of trying to evade or avoid something foreseen by an oracle, and those prophecies are generally ominous. Getting a preview of the future, like meddling in the past (for instance, tampering with royal succession), comes at a cost, or else is a consolation prize for some grave loss. It cannot liberate us from our fate because there is always something we don't know about ourselves, and that thing is bound to be our undoing.

The Anglo-Saxons of Northern Europe had their own word for a fate or destiny that can only be seen in hindsight because of the obliquity of foresight. *Wyrd* is one of a large and fascinating family of *w-r* words still found in our language connoting change and exchange, turning and turning-into, but also (along with this) the *twisting* both of objects and of minds and souls. *Wyrd* comes from *weorthan*, "to become," but with a sense of turning or spinning—as in the "spinning" of the thread of our life. Thus it embeds a fan of connotations ranging from a man's *worth* to the *writhing* and *wriggling* of *worms*, and the *wrath* of *wraiths*. Wyrd, as becoming and as turning, represents "what has turned out" or "what will have turned out" or "what you will have turned into." It is a kind of future-perfect tense, a retrospective view from a future vantage point that can turn, look back, and survey the ironic (or even *warped*) paths a life has taken. Hindsight, in other words. *Post-selection* by another name.

Other than through a common appearance in fantasy novels, including the *Discworld* series of Terry Pratchett, the word *wyrd* survives now in English solely via the wonderful word *weird*, and this is thanks entirely to Shakespeare's *Macbeth*. The "weird sisters" whose prophecies captured the mind of an ambitious young Scottish general and his wife were three witches living alone in the wilderness. They were inspired by the Norns of Norse mythology, the three sister-goddesses—analogous to the Greek Fates—who together wove a man's destiny and could thus foretell it. Even up to Shakespeare's day, *weird* didn't simply mean "strange" as it does now; it meant more the inevitability of things prophesied as well as prophecy's cunning misdirection. It is always one step ahead of us and speaks a deceptive language that, by luring us with our wishes, tricks us into fulfilling it.[1]

The weird sisters' first prophecy that Macbeth would be made king seems like a good thing, but weirdly, neurotically even, instead of just letting it come to pass in whatever way the world wills, Macbeth actively pursues this outcome—goaded by his even-more-ambitious wife—and finds that the "positive outcome" foreseen is fraught with paranoia and guilt. The later prophecies conjured for Macbeth by the sisters are far more oblique—that Macbeth will be safe until Birnam Wood marches on Dunsinane and that he will not be harmed by anyone "of woman born." These Macbeth takes as reassurances. But clearly, when outcomes are dark, "weird" (i.e., *wyrd*) speaks a figurative language similar to dream, and the prophecies about Macbeth's downfall come to pass: Malcolm's army attacks Dunsinane Castle under cover of boughs cut from Birnam Wood; and Macduff, who fights and kills Macbeth at the end, turns out to have been "untimely ripp'd" from his mother's womb (Caesarean section, in other words), not birthed in the usual way. Here, just as in the Oedipus story, foresight operates in the shadow realm of our self-ignorance.

The necessary obliquity of prophecy in a post-selected (i.e., possible) universe is one of the reasons why, despite Sigmund Freud's strong resistances to the subject, we must enlist his aid, recruit him over his own dead body as it were, in our study of it. Specifically, any theory of the oblique language spoken by prophecy and the time-looping way it shapes our lives must bring Freud's theory of dreams as symbolically disguised wish-fulfillments into dialogue with J. W. Dunne's observations about precognitive dreams and the pragmatic impediments to observing them, along with recent developments in the neuroscience of sleep and memory. The tropes and detours Freud identified as the symbolic language of the unconscious turn out to be none other than the associative laws that govern how the brain stores and retrieves information, the rules by which new experiences in our lives are linked with older ones. We are now learning that it is precisely in dreaming that these associations are forged, making dreams the "royal road" not only to memory but, I argue, to "premory" as well. Yet ironically, because Freud, the great dream pioneer, rejected the possibility of prophecy, it ruled his fate in a tragically wyrd way—not unlike Macbeth, or indeed Oedipus.

The Invisible Key to Dreams

The dream that started it all, the one that revealed to Freud the answer to the Sphinx's riddle, centered on a close friend named Anna Hammerschlag, whom Freud had treated for hysteria briefly in spring of 1895. He had the dream one night the following July, while on vacation, and gave Hammerschlag the name "Irma" in his description:

> *A large hall—numerous guests, whom we were receiving. —Among them was Irma. I at once took her to one*

side, as though to answer her letter and to reproach her for not having accepted my 'solution' yet. I said to her: 'If you still get pains, it's really only your fault.' She replies: 'If you only knew what pains I've got now in my throat and stomach and abdomen—it's choking me.' —I was alarmed and looked at her. She looked pale and puffy. I thought to myself that after all I must be missing some organic trouble. I took her to the window and looked down her throat, and she showed signs of recalcitrance, like women with artificial dentures. I thought to myself that there was really no need for her to do that. She then opened her mouth properly and on the right I found a big white patch; at another place I saw extensive whitish grey scabs upon some remarkable curly structures which were evidently modelled on the turbinal bones of the nose. [2]

At this point, Freud summons a trio of medical friends in the dream to get their opinion. "Dr. M," his friend "Otto," and another friend "Leopold" examine Irma. Dr. M confirms what the dreamer has seen in Irma's mouth, and the men poke and prod Irma's shoulder and abdomen. They agree she has some sort of infection, which her dysentery should eliminate from her body.

We were directly aware, too, of the origin of the infection. Not long before, when she was feeling unwell, my friend Otto had given her an injection of a preparation of propyl, propyls ... propionic acid ... trimethylamin (and I saw before me the formula for this printed in heavy type). ... Injections of this sort ought not to be given so thoughtlessly ... And probably the syringe had not been clean. [3]

The method Freud hit on was to *free associate* on each separate element of the dream—that is, reflect honestly and spontaneously on what each figure, each object, each noticed element reminded him of, and follow the trains of association where they led. The force of this method was like splitting the atom: A dream that may fill a paragraph or less of description (the "manifest content") mushrooms into pages and pages of associations that, in many cases—Freud argued *all* cases—present in multiple ways a single coherent latent (or unconscious) thought or a nexus of closely related thoughts.

Freud's free association on each of the elements of the Irma dream runs to some 14 pages in his 1899 masterpiece *The Interpretation of Dreams*, and he admits that even then he has not exhausted the dream's many possible layers of meaning. He begins by identifying the "day residues," obvious points of contact with the previous day's activities and preoccupations. Most dreams have one or two, and here there were several. Freud had this dream while summering at an open spacious house called Bellevue, near a resort outside of Vienna. While not as vast as the drawing room in the dream, the house did have a similar expansive quality. The day before the dream, Freud had received a visit from the family pediatrician, Dr. Oskar Rie, who appears in the dream as Otto. Although Rie was a friend, Freud felt ambivalently toward Rie and disliked his habit of bringing gifts whenever he visited. On this occasion, Rie specifically annoyed Freud by bringing two things: a bottle of spoiled *Ananas* or pineapple brandy that, when opened, smelled like fusel oil (similar to the smell of the chemicals in the dream injection); Rie also brought news that their mutual friend Anna (dream Irma) was "better, but not fully recovered." It happened that she was going to be invited to a party at the Freuds' a few days hence, for which preparations were already being made. And on the evening prior to the dream, to clear his conscience about her treatment, Freud had spent time writing up a report on her case. It is worth emphasizing that Anna Hammerschlag's "condition" was hysteria that had emerged in the aftermath of the loss of her husband, nothing like the organic disease that was displayed in the dream.

It is impossible to adequately summarize in a few sentences, but most of the associations in the dream, including the figures present, pointed to professional worries Freud was then having. He was feeling vulnerable firstly because of his support for his best friend, Wilhelm Fliess, a quack ear, nose, and throat doctor who had recently seriously botched a nose operation on a mutual friend and who had recommended a questionable course of treatment for one of Freud's patients that had caused serious complications. Major and minor medical malpractice was going around in Freud's medical circle, and Freud himself bore his share of guilt. In addition to the patient he had seriously injured following Fliess's advice, his treatment of another, psychotic patient a few years earlier with an injection of the dangerous drugs chloral hydrate and sulfonal had led to the patient's death. Another friend and patient of Freud had died after injecting himself with cocaine that Freud had prescribed to be used only orally. As he was venturing into brand-new territory in his psychiatric work with hysterics, he could not have been without a measure of doubt about his new "talking cure" and would have been eager for any news of his treatment successes.[4] Instead, hearing from Dr. Rie, dream Otto, that their friend Anna was "better, but not fully recovered" was not what he wanted to hear.

Despite the air of anxiety and guilt that seemed to oppress his waking professional life at this period, the conclusions he was able to draw from this one dream analysis, as far as it went, excited him greatly:

> If we adopt the method of interpreting dreams which I have indicated here, we shall find that dreams really have a meaning and are far from being the expression of a fragmentary activity of the brain, as the authorities have claimed. *When the work of interpretation has been completed, we perceive that a dream is the fulfillment of a wish.*[5]

What was the wish in this case? There are many layers to it, but briefly, it boiled down to *Freud not being responsible for Anna/Irma's condition* but that Dr. Rie/Otto instead should be responsible. (Remember that dream Otto had "thoughtlessly" given Irma the injection that caused her infection, and the syringe he had used had not been clean.) It was a wish that Freud be beyond any kind of professional or personal reproach in Anna's case.[6]

Five years later, Freud revisited the house in Bellevue, and wrote to Fliess:

> Do you suppose that some day a marble tablet will be placed on the house, inscribed with these words?—

> In This House, on July 24, 1895
> the Secret of Dreams was Revealed
> to Dr. Sigm. Freud.[7]

We see here again Freud's obsession with commemorating his real or imagined accomplishments—first marble busts, now marble tablets. But his achievement here was indeed groundbreaking. Nobody in history had given so much detailed attention to a single dream and in the process divulged so many personal vulnerabilities, private sources of guilt, and deep desires in a public forum. Freud's book goes on to subject several other dreams of his own and those of his patients to similarly close scrutiny, in some cases to more convincing effect. More than any other single exploit in Freud's work, though, this one dream interpretation catapulted him to ultimate immortality and fame. It was a milestone in psychology that some have compared to Darwin's contributions to biology a few decades earlier or Einstein's contributions to physics a few years later.

The dream itself seemed to "know" how scientifically significant it was. Its culminating image, the formula for the organic compound trimethylamine in bold type, would naturally have called to mind August Kekulé's famous discovery of the hexagonal structure of the benzene molecule after a dream of a snake biting its own tail. Although the Czech-Austrian chemist alleged he had had his dream in 1861, it was only in 1890, five years before Freud's dream, that Kekulé told the story for the first time at a Berlin conference to honor the discovery. "I was sitting writing at my textbook," Kekulé said, "but the work did not progress; my thoughts were elsewhere"—

> I turned my chair to the fire and dozed. Again the atoms were gambolling before my eyes. This time the smaller groups kept modestly in the background. My mental eyes, rendered more acute by repeated visions of this kind, could now distinguish larger structures of manifold conformations; long rows, sometimes more closely fitted together; all twisting and turning in snake-like motion. But look! What was that? One of the snakes had seized hold of its own tail, and the form whirled mockingly before my eyes. As if by a flash of lightning I awoke; and this time also I spent the rest of the night working out the consequences of the hypothesis.[8]

It quickly became a famous, proud moment in Austrian science, and to this day no discussion of dreams in the context of genius, creativity, or scientific discovery fails to cite it. It would have provided Freud with a template for his own making of a milestone scientific discovery in a dream—in his case, a discovery *about* dreams.[9] You can't get more snake-biting-its-tail-ish (or fractal) than that.

Freud's interpretation of his dream was a cultural watershed, leading to the post-Victorian epoch of self-inquiry and self-scrutiny, a kind of novelistic approach to the soul. Freud's writings made psychological causation complex and mysterious, and through them he got Westerners to see themselves and their lives as having infinite, perhaps unplumbable depths. After Freud, it was no longer easy to see humans as simple creatures with clear-cut, straightforward motives and needs—even if certain root principles, such as a drive for satisfaction or pleasure, could be discerned at the root of it all. The twists and turns through which our desires flow, in Freud's picture, have the sublime complexity of a weather system or a butterfly, not a simple steam engine. As we will see later, there are also more than a few similarities between the invisible, warring motives in the unconscious as Freud depicted it and the obscure "superposition" of unmeasured particles in the emerging science of quantum physics; the latter lent an almost "psychodynamic" mystery and inscrutability to the world of material interactions.

Many Freudian constructs are easily parodied for sure. The single-minded obsession with sex and childhood incestuous desires, as well as constructs like "penis envy," can be bracketed or set aside (or, some argue, thrown out like bathwater). But the Freudian big picture has retained its power. Humans are complex, conflicted, inconsistent creatures with warring impulses, contradictory emotions, and divided aims. Our conscious self or ego is a construct and a compromise, a treaty appeasing these various sides of ourselves, weaving them into a somewhat coherent and productive whole that at best accommodates cultural expectations while giving us sufficient leeway to satisfy most of our needs and desires. Calling our attention to the dimension of ambivalence in our mental life has probably been the most important, basic, and enduring contribution of Freudian psychoanalysis, even if the precise nature and "location" of the unconscious, where these divided aims lurk, is debatable.

Freud's wish-fulfillment theory of dreams has fared less well than some of his other ideas. Although it was long popular with the wider public, it was highly controversial in psychology even at the time he proposed it, and it was later rejected out of hand by most scientists. Popperian science rests on the ability to falsify hypotheses with evidence and repeat an experiment to gain better confidence in one's conclusions, but there is no way to falsify an interpretation of a dream. Indeed, there is really no objective basis from which to assess any claim related to meaning. For example, how can we ever know that Freud's many, sometimes brilliant, sometimes strained interpretations of his and his patients' dreams in *The Interpretation of Dreams* do not reflect *his own* "wish" to prove his theory correct? We will see later, in fact, that Freud's own wishes about his dream theory may have been precisely—and fractally—part of his (mis)interpretation of the Irma dream, causing him to miss a stunning precognitive dimension.

As I argued earlier, the "schizophrenia" of dreams—being amenable either to biological or hermeneutic study—reflects their unstable position on the fault line between C. P. Snow's "two worlds" of the sciences and the humanities. The humanities all in one way or another address meaning as it comes to be encoded in language or other cultural forms, but meaning always boils down the value of a thing to or for an individual. There is no way really to get at meaning without losing our grip on objectivity, and vice versa. It is directly analogous in fact to basic tradeoffs of knowledge that define quantum physics. Niels Bohr showed that an experimenter is prohibited from gaining knowledge of both the position and momentum of a particle because the tools necessary to gain one type of information are actually antithetical to the tools necessary to gain the other, complementary type.[10] The philosopher Slavoj Žižek uses the term "parallax" to describe dual-aspect phenomena that cannot be apprehended other than in a kind of alternating gestalt, like the famous duck-rabbit of psychological research on perception.[11] Dreams are perfect examples of objects that need to be approached obliquely, flickeringly, from multiple, non-integral perspectives, in a kind of "parallax view."

To acknowledge the inability to scientifically adjudicate the "correct" meaning of a dream, precognitive or not, is *not* equivalent to saying that there can be no meaning in the dream. It is only to concede that such meaning (or its absence) is not something that can be readily evaluated solely through the usual scientific tools of quantification and replication, since the dreamer is an *n* of 1. Yet Freud-bashers in scientific psychology and neuroscience have historically committed the oddly superstitious mistake of thinking that if the scientific tools do not exist to verify a dream's meaning, then dreams are therefore not meaningful. It is not just like searching under the proverbial streetlight for one's lost keys just because the light is better there, even though you know you probably dropped them in the dark alley nearby. It is more like saying the keys *must* be somewhere in this pool of light because that is where light exists to detect them, denying the existence of the alley altogether. When you cannot find the keys you remember you once had, you will end up either with a theory of invisible keys or a theory that your memory of ever having had keys in the first place is false.

Until recently, much of the neuroscience of dreaming has read like a theory of invisible or nonexistent keys. J. Allan Hobson, the most outspoken contemporary dream neuroscientist and the most vocal and persistent critic of the Freudian wish-fulfillment theory, argued in 1977 that dreaming represents chaotic hyper-activation of the brainstem during sleep.[12] Dreams contain no symbolic meaning, he insisted; the conscious mind simply imposes meaningful order on that chaos, sort of the way a patient will see suggestive pictures in a Rorschach inkblot. Nobel Prize-winning biologist Francis Crick, one of the co-discoverers of DNA, lent fuel and the weight of authority to the anti-Freudians in a 1983 paper arguing that dreams are the discharging of mental static, random and meaningless associations, a way the brain gets rid of un-wanted or unneeded information.[13] Other functional theories have also found some support in the peculiarities of nocturnal brain activation, such as the theory that dreams prepare us to face threats or emotional challenges in waking life.[14] The common theme in these accounts is: Dreams may be interesting neurological phenomena, but they do not contain any hidden or obscure meaning or represent any covert, "off-stage" portion of our meaning-making mind.

In recent years, however, cognitive science and neuroscience have made greater peace with Freud, having been "obliged" by mounting evidence to acknowledge that his core theory of the unconscious ac-curately characterizes many dimensions of cognition. Again, Freud's terminology is often replaced by the less baggage-laden term implicit processing. Research has also started to vindicate some of Freud's ideas about dreams, albeit with some key modifications.

Evidence from sleep science over the past few decades has pointed to a role for dreaming in the solidification or consolidation of memories and the forming of new associations to events that occurred in recent waking life. Newly learned material is better remembered after being "slept on," and complex material is simplified during sleep, or reduced to its gist.[15] If you are exposed to material in a morning lesson, you will do better on a quiz the following morning, after a night of sleep, than you will on a quiz the preceding afternoon. There is an evolutionary correlation between REM sleep, when the brain is most active at night, and learning. Altricial animals (those most dependent at birth, like hu-mans and birds and some mammals, such as dogs and cats) show much more REM sleep than precocial animals (those born able to function). In other words, the more an animal needs to learn in order to survive and function, the more its brain is active at night, and the more it seems to dream.[16] Rodent studies have shown that brain areas activated during daytime exploration and learning are reactivated during sleep (compared to control animals that haven't engaged in learning). And the hippocampus, which can be likened to the brain's librarian or archivist, is extremely active during sleep.[17]

But while dreams contain tantalizing bits of our recent daily life—Freud's "day residues"—they seldom if ever replay experiences of the previous day in any literal fashion, and their surreal quality (or "bizarreness") has always frustrated scientists' attempt to link the *content* of dreams to the formation of new memories. But in 2013, a psychologist named Sue Llewellyn hit on a colorful and inspiring answer. She did so by venturing out of the science stacks into the alien world of the humanities and ancient history, unifying the available neurobiology of sleep and memory with insights drawn from the study of the ancient "art of memory" used by orators in pre-Gutenberg and pre-literate times.[18] To link to-be-remembered new information to older contents of their memory, practitioners of this art playfully used puns, analogies, and substitution to create bizarre and memorable mnemonic images. Llewellyn suggested that dreams are essentially the ancient art of memory operating automatically while we sleep.[19]

Memory seems to work on multiple levels in the brain. The circuit level (multiple interlinked neurons and circuits, involvement of distinct brain areas like the hippocampus, amygdala, and so on) is best understood because it unfolds at a scale that puts it within the granularity of existing research tools. On this level, we can see how "memories" are encoded in the brain physically as the readiness of dispersed groups of neurons to fire together again having fired together in the past (i.e., Hebbian learning—"neurons that fire together, wire together"). Again, long-term potentiation (and its opposite, long-term depression) reflects the constant forging of new connections between neurons and the updating of the weights of existing connections—the readiness of synapses to transmit signals, based on their (prior) history of signal transmission.

According to the mnemonic theory, dreams are the *experience* of this nightly re-updating of neural connectivity via the triggering of associations around recent experiences in waking life—Hebbian learning at work. Specifically, Llewellyn argues that a dream scene represents a junction retained in the hippocampus, drawing together disparate associations to encode an autobiographical (episodic) memory. Instead of a "junction," a dream could also be thought of as an *associative halo* around a salient experience from your day. The experience itself generally will not be represented because the brain does not need to replay that. What it needs to do is connect that experience to other experiences and themes so that it is accessible later via multiple associative pathways, and thus better integrated into long-term memory.

It makes beautiful sense of the weird characteristic of dreams that has long beguiled dreamers: that they seem so closely related to profound concerns and experiences in our waking lives, yet leave those concerns and experiences precisely unrepresented, like a blank at their heart. It is what naturally led the suspicious Freud to think that dreams were specifically hiding something, like spies smuggling letters past checkpoint guards, cloaking their "true meaning" in symbolism. He was probably incorrect in this assumption, but at the same time, the mnemonic theory explains why Freud's innovative method of free association—saying the first thing or two that a given dream element reminds the dreamer of—is helpful when interpreting a dream. Free associating on a dream's elements, as Freud showed with his Irma example, quickly produces a wealth of coherent references to recent experiences and concerns in the dreamer's life, and often the disparate elements in a single dream "point" to the same window or timeframe in waking life, as though the dream is indeed an "art of memory"-style bundle of associations to that narrow window of time.[20] Waking experiences that feed into a dream are seldom more than one degree removed from the bizarre narrative a dreamer will remember on waking. But unless it occurs to the dreamer to free associate on each dream element—unpacking the various puns and other substitutions—that "latent content" will remain mostly or wholly obscure, and the dream will just seem like some baffling and inscrutable message from God-knows-where.

The correspondence between the mnemonic hypothesis and Freud's theory is close in other ways too. The techniques used by ancient orators to remember speeches and books—puns, absurd juxtapositions and substitutions, vivid and dramatic narratives, and so on—happen to precisely match the tropes that Freud described under his rubrics of "condensation," "displacement," and "dramatization." If dreams are art-of-memory-style associative halos around waking events, it makes sense of why these should be so prevalent in dreams. It also makes sense of why dreams so often contain sexual imagery. One of the trade secrets of medieval and modern mnemonists was making memory images as dirty as possible, because sexy images are easily remembered.[21]

Dreaming could thus really be described as the nightly metabolism of waking experience by the brain, analogous to the metabolism of food by the digestive system. What Freud thought were symbolic disguises hiding some deep dark secret were really the associative connective tissue of long-term memory, the way recent events are made more accessible and findable by connecting both logically and illogically to things they remind us of. Without knowing it, Freud was really a pioneer in memory research, mapping out the illogical, poetic tropes our brain uses to file and retrieve information. [22] The idea that dreams often represent some satisfying situation or wish is not incompatible with such a view, although even Freud came to admit this was not a universal rule. The mnemonic view, however, omits any need for a "censor" to "repress" unwanted thoughts.

Llewellyn's mnemonic hypothesis is the most satisfying functional account of dreaming yet offered by a mainstream scientist. It restores color and meaning to dreaming without losing sight of the neurobiological mechanisms. One dream researcher, commenting in *Psychology Today*, remarked on the irony that it took an outsider to the field of sleep and dream research (Llewellyn teaches at the University of Manchester's Business School) to weave together those disparate threads from C. P. Snow's sundered worlds into such a compelling account of dreaming. [23] But the sour jingle of those invisible keys was also to be heard. The eminent Hobson, in one of numerous professional responses published with her article, praised the elegance and originality of her hypothesis but challenged her to design an experiment that could actually be used to test it, adding that he himself could not imagine one. He specifically forbade any form of "anecdotal self-analysis"—providing examples of one's own dreams and demonstrating how they support the theory (the standard move in psychoanalytic writing)—and declared that "we must not tolerate neo-Freudianism, no matter how brilliant." [24]

As long as one-sided authorities like Hobson control the playing field, the study of dreams will remain at an impasse. If meaning's sinews are as idiosyncratic and private as Freudian psychoanalysis presumes (and as working experience with mnemonic techniques also affirms), it would indeed be virtually impossible to design a rigorous experiment to adequately test Llewellyn's hypothesis. So, unless and until psychological scientists can bring themselves to trust individuals' meaning-claims, they may be doomed to forever circle that streetlight when it comes to dreams, which are among the most personal and private experiences in our lives. If precognition centers on meaningful personal experiences, it faces the same challenge. We cannot make progress without trusting—however cautiously and critically—those dreaded anecdotes.

Symbolism Versus Obliquity

All of which leads to the obvious—and at this point, obviously rhetorical—question: If dreams do represent a process of recent experiences being accessioned by the brain, could they be doing the same thing with *future* experiences? If we trust even some of the evidence for precognitive dreaming provided by Dunne and many other writers, the answer seems to be yes. It looks very much like neuronal networks might be being reinforced and conditioned not only by their past history of signaling but also, to some as-yet-undetermined degree, by their future history. Viewing this as a normal function of the brain—the brain's nightly metabolism of future as well as past time—suggests why precognitive dreaming may potentially be much more common than even Dunne thought. If the function of a dream is to update our memory-search system by triggering associations to "new" material, it could be that, as often as not, it is future experiences that are the "absent center" of a dream.[25]

This is where the analogy to the digestive system breaks down, of course. As far as we know, the stomach at night is not digesting tomorrow's breakfast, let alone a breakfast I might eat several years from now. The brain may be far, far weirder (or wyrd-er) than the stomach.

Although Dunne did not see any conflict between precognition and wish-fulfillment in dreams, he largely ignored the Freudian idea that a dream's surface content consists mainly of symbols and substitutions and compromises among warring desires—an idea that is readily carried over into the mnemonic theory. Nor did Dunne bother to scratch below the surface of his dreams in search of thoughts or feelings in relation to future events that may have been represented obliquely in them. He was content to look for obvious resemblances of dream motifs to waking experiences, and he imagined, like many laypeople, that free association is a difficult or esoteric exercise. Consequently, he noted that people are unlikely to recognize most precognitive content (or any kind of meaningful content for that matter) because of dreams' associative logic:

> The difficulty of remembering is easily overcome; but the difficulty of associating proves in some cases insurmountable. It is always hard to discover in the average dream any incident which is clearly related to a *chronologically definite* past waking event, and some people's

dreams are far too complex to allow such connections to be traced. It is obvious that persons thus handicapped would find it equally impossible to discover in their dreams any clear suggestion of precognition.[26]

More recent investigators of precognitive dreaming have also typically not gone beyond the level of manifest content (as Freud termed the dream's surface-level narrative and images), focusing instead on immediately obvious relations of dream elements to things seen or encountered later in waking life. In their experiments with precognitive dreaming, Stanley Krippner, Montague Ullman, and Charles Honorton had independent judges assess the similarity of their psychic subject's dream descriptions to target scenarios (based on randomly selected paintings) without delving into the dreamer's private and personal associations or attending to possible symbols or Freudian tropes.[27] Dale E. Graff, who directed the U.S. military's Star Gate remote viewing program, went on to write two very interesting memoirs about his experiences as well as his personal experiments in precognitive dreaming; in his experiments, he routinely obtained many close matches between dream scenes and newspaper photographs or cartoons—although, since he focuses mainly on visual forms (per standard remote-viewing methods), he has not ventured too deeply into dream symbolism.[28] In an effort to scientifically analyze a huge database of 11,850 of his own dream scenes, many of which he identified as precognitive, film and video game CG artist Andrew Paquette claimed to find a relative *in*frequency of unambiguous symbols in his dreams, especially those that had veridical precognitive content.[29] On the other hand, a recent writer named Bruce Siegel, replicating Dunne's experiment in his own life and finding that just over a quarter of his 241-dream sample appeared to be precognitive, noted that his dreams very often used the same tropes—metaphor, substitution, wordplay, etc.—that would be familiar to a psychoanalyst (and that can be glossed, for convenience, as symbolism).[30]

Psychoanalytically informed parapsychologists have demonstrated that apparent precognitive dreams not only may be subject to the same kinds of contortions and distortions Freud described but may express the same types of divided feeling and emotional complexity.[31] In his 1982 book *Paranormal Foreknowledge*, Jule Eisenbud provides many examples of what could be called typical Dunne dreams, appearing to match something the patient was about to read in the newspaper or encounter the next day, along with the kind of richly layered (sometimes uncomfortably detailed) commentary that is typical of Freudian case studies. Eisenbud regarded precognitive elements in such dreams as serving the dream's purpose: fulfilling a repressed wish. But it is easy to reframe the cases he presents in terms of the newer mnemonic hypothesis. What seems like a dream "collecting precognitive bricks" to fulfill a wish can generally be redescribed as a dream about the complex thoughts and emotions that will be triggered by a later, unsettling learning experience in the dreamer's life. There is not too big a gap between the two theories: If precognition focuses on a person's future conscious thoughts in response to some experience, those future thoughts may still often be "wishful."

For example, a female patient with a distinctly "Oedipal" pattern of self-inhibition and frustrating relationships with older men had a dream involving her roommate, who had just become engaged to a man the patient herself had previously dated.

> Shortly after the engagement was announced, the roommate, who had been visiting her parents' home in the east, took a plane to join her fiancé in the Midwest. On the eve of her flight the patient dreamed that the plane crashed and that her roommate was killed. The roommate's plane did not crash, but a later one out of the same city the next day did, and many lives were lost. The crash occurred several hours after my patient reported her dream to me.[32]

Following standard Freudian theory, this dream appears to Eisenbud as the use of psi-acquired information (an imminent fatal plane crash out of the same city her roommate was in) to help represent an unconscious wish about the death of the roommate, who was a rival for a man's affections. In light of the mnemonic theory, we might flip this and say that the dream was *pre*-presenting a "what if" that would naturally have occurred to the dreamer upon learning of a fatal plane crash out of that city. Note that whereas Eisenbud would assume the death wish to be a thought that already existed (but was repressed) in the patient's unconscious, and that seized on a convenient future brick to represent itself in the dream, I am proposing that the dreamer simply precognized a thought or mental image she would consciously, albeit perhaps fleetingly, have the next day on hearing of the disaster.

Another of Eisenbud's patients reported a dream of being smothered in a landslide, "a vast roaring avalanche of mud and rock,"[33] from which he awoke in terror, quickly realizing to his relief that the dream had been triggered by his wife flushing the toilet. First thing the next morning, though, he read in the paper about a man and boy tragically being buried alive under 20 tons of coal in a coal hopper accident. Eisenbud suggests that the patient was using this bit of psi-acquired data to represent his "anal" anxieties, his wife's flushing of the toilet acting as a kind of nucleus "attracting" information appearing in the next day's news to help express those anxieties. But it could just as easily be supposed that the toilet flush "preminded" him of the disturbing reading experience the next morning about people being buried in black muck—a kind of *prime* in reverse (like in the temporally inverted priming experiments of Daryl Bem). The real source and subject of the dream might have been relief that this muck-burial happened to someone else and not him. As we will see in the next chapter, the main message "sent back" from future learning experiences about disasters and deaths seems to be the rewarding thought "but I survived." Another possibility for the previous dream about the plane crash, too, is that it was not really about a death wish for the roommate so much as thoughts of *personal survival* provoked by news of a disaster befalling or "nearly" befalling someone close to the dreamer.

I propose that Dunne, in his comment about dreams collecting future bricks to build a wish-fulfilling edifice, was *nearly* right, but that we should reverse his formulation: A precognitive dream uses *past and present bricks* to pre-present (or, per the mnemonic hypothesis, simply associate to or perhaps "encode") *a future thought*. That is to say, a dream should be interpreted from the temporal vantage point not of the dream itself but from the future point at which the dreamer will have those thoughts consciously, in waking life (as well as, in rare cases, realize that those thoughts/experiences supply the meaning of that remembered dream). Often there isn't too much time delay—a matter of hours or minutes, or even seconds in some cases[34]—but there are plenty of examples in which years or decades pass before the experience that "makes sense" of an old dream. Vladimir Nabokov's dream of "Harry and Kuvyrkin" comes to mind, and we will see further examples. Once again, what Freud naturally took as evidence of an off-stage or submerged unconscious agency, harboring secret thoughts that must take nightly symbolic form to escape a censor, may really just be future conscious thoughts associatively pre-presented at some earlier point in time.

Let's apply this idea to some well-documented dreams that we have already encountered in this book, to see how it adds to our understanding.

Less Guilty by a Factor of 10

First, we can revisit Dunne's most well-known disaster dream, about the eruption of Mont Pelée. Commentators naturally tend to focus on the eruption (which, we should note, does not actually happen in the dream) and his death toll closely matching the headline but not the reality. They seldom comment on the "bureaucratic nightmare" sequence, in which Dunne's dream-self tried to save all those lives but could get no one to believe his warnings. This part of the dream may have related to thoughts the soldier would naturally have had in response to the strange experience of reading about the eruption in the newspaper, having just dreamed of it.

Having uncannily "foreseen" the imminent death of "4,000" people on a French island volcano in a dream, Dunne could not have read the bold *Daily Telegraph* headline about 40,000 dead in Martinique with idle detachment. Besides the usual shock people feel learning of some disaster that claims the lives of many innocent (though anonymous) people far away, he would have also felt excitement that he had just dreamed about such an event—including, he thought, the exact same number dead; he notes that he misread the estimated death toll in the headline as "4,000" (and remembered it that way for several years thereafter). But tempering such excitement (or at least curiosity), how could he not have also had the thought as he read the news story that, if he'd dreamed about it, there *ought* (pun intended) to have been some way of using this foreknowledge to intervene and save those lives?

There is no way to get inside Dunne's head and know for certain that this thought process went through his mind when he read the *Daily Telegraph* article. It didn't occur to him to record his reactions in greater detail, and why would he? So to some degree we are playing a game of suppositions here. But the whole second part of the dream appears to represent anguished frustration at being unable to avert a catastrophe that *only he* knew was imminent. This part of the dream is particularly interesting because it seems to represent a set of emotions that many people do report upon learning that something tragic or sad that they have dreamed about has come true.

Physician Larry Dossey, in his book *The Power of Premonitions*, cites several examples of people who failed or were unable to act on a premonition of death or disaster and then were stricken by guilt. One, a patient of Dossey's, was a radio dispatcher at a police station who had a history of accurate premonitions. At work one morning he had a distinct sense that a toddler was walking near a pool and was about to fall in. It had a vividness that he had learned to trust over the years, but because he had no way of knowing when or where the event was going to occur, what could he do about it? Less than an hour later, a police unit reported finding a child who had drowned in a nearby apartment complex; the dispatcher was devastated, requiring counseling over the following months.[35] Elizabeth Krohn, the Houston woman who began experiencing accurate precognitive dreams of plane crashes following a near-death experience (Chapter 1), initially felt her new ability was a curse rather than a gift, because these depressing previews of death and catastrophe seemed to be without purpose—or, at least, the purpose was not to avert those catastrophes or save lives.[36]

If vaguely guilty thoughts did cross Dunne's mind upon reading the *Daily Telegraph* article, reason would quickly have stepped in to absolve the young soldier of too much hand-wringing. Even if he had not been camped out far from civilization or communication, "warning someone" would never have occurred to him at the time he actually had the dream, since until he read the headline he had no idea the dream was actually a premonition. And even if he had had some sense of the dream's premonitory nature, he could not possibly have known where and when the eruption might occur, and thus whom to warn. But if Freud's work has taught us anything, it is that humans are not rational creatures, and that the unconscious has no sense of time and logic. Thoughts of using prophecy to improve our outcomes or save others, and a guilt when others fall victim to outcomes we have seen in our dreams, may be—indeed, must be—inevitable. This is a big part of the confusion and taboo that surrounds the whole topic of precognition and part of what deflects most people away from thinking too deeply about the subject.

Dunne's dream seems to have represented precisely this emotional mélange. In other words, it does not seem to have been merely a dream about a news story; it seems to have been a dream about a very particular *train of thought* as well as associated emotions (a sense of frustration and even guilt) that would have arisen in him *because of the fact that he had dreamed about it beforehand.* This time loop would also make sense of the matter of the missing "nought." A less prophecy-averse Freud would certainly have insisted that Dunne's misreading of the terrible death toll of 40,000 as the less terrible (by a factor of 10) 4,000 would have reflected a bit of wish-fulfillment to offset his guilt, or at least cut it down to a slightly more manageable size.

The more we scrutinize cases of precognitive dreaming, the more we find this self-similar or fractal structure, including sometimes even a representation of the shock at having dreamed of the event, or of the value of the dream to the dreamer, within the body of the dream itself. (We will see a particularly striking example of this later—the famous "scarab dream" of one of Carl Jung's patients.)

The Wyrd of the Air Marshal

Another example of a precognitive dream that seems to contain fractal spirals of self-reference and onion-like layers of possible psychodynamic significance is Captain Gladstone's dream about Victor Goddard's plane crash.

Remember that it was Goddard's letter to Gladstone, and not the crash itself, that would have been the source of Gladstone's dream, setting the whole time loop in motion. Presumably the contents of Goddard's letter consisted of an abbreviated version of what he wrote nearly a decade after the incident in his *Saturday Evening Post* article. Our only direct evidence of how Gladstone reacted to the story—his "reader response"—is the testimony of his cordial reply, reproduced at the end of that article (Chapter 2). It is all very "how do" and "cheerio"—very British and very polite ... and also very brief, even curt (in contrast to what Goddard said was a lengthy letter). Again, it expresses regret at the incident and relief that no one was hurt—what one would expect him to say. But when he received Goddard's letter, how could Gladstone not have also felt a mix of complex emotions, not unlike what Dunne would have experienced upon reading about Mont Pelée in the newspaper?

Freud enlightened us to the dark side of human feelings where the lives of others are concerned, especially others who aren't close to us. Apart from the ordinary and expected sentiments expressed in the letter, Gladstone would also, and probably even mainly, have felt *excited* to learn that the event had happened, because it meant he really had had a Dunne dream. That confirmation would also have effectively undone some of his embarrassment at the party months earlier, when he had assumed that its honoree, Goddard, was dead and then was immediately proved wrong and subtly shamed by the revenant Goddard himself.

Goddard's narrative in *The Saturday Evening Post* does not at all flatter "Dewing" (the pseudonym given to Gladstone)[37]—it makes him out to be a bit of a fool, albeit a fool surreally vindicated by fate. Goddard very thinly conceals his lack of respect for the bold but evidently not-too-bright naval officer—first because of the man's absurd confidence that he, Goddard, was actually dead, based solely on a dream he couldn't even place in time (when pressed, he didn't know if he'd had the dream the previous night versus that afternoon), but also for what turned out to be Gladstone's somewhat limited grasp of Dunne's book. Clearly irritated, not to mention slightly unsettled, Goddard admits he was inclined to argue with Gladstone about how Dunne meant readers to conduct his "experiment with time" in their own lives.[38] So, added to his embarrassment at his mistake, Gladstone would have felt chagrined at how this eminent RAF hero so coolly and condescendingly schooled him on the finer points of the book that he himself had just been enthusiastically reading.

It is thus irresistible to psychoanalyze Gladstone's dream and the one discrepancy from the real outcome that is evident in it: that in his dream it had been a *fatal* crash. Freud, even if he would have found some way to deny the whole matter of dream prophecy (let alone time loops), would eagerly point out that this error was a death wish. At least as Goddard reports it, there is a bit of glee in Gladstone's certain pronouncement to the other unnamed man at the party that Goddard was dead. Gladstone's slip-of-the-tongue reaction to seeing Goddard alive, again if accurately reported, is telling: "I'm terribly sorry! I mean I'm terribly glad …"

Like Dunne's presumed guilt upon reading the headline about Mont Pelée, such ill will on Gladstone's part would have been temporally "impossible." It could not have come from any *prior* experience of Gladstone's, since at the time he had his dream he had not yet met Air Marshal Goddard let alone been talked down to by him. Thus, such a death wish (if true) would have been based on ill will he would only feel later, *after* their conversation at the party, thus adding further twists to the time-looping nature of the whole weird—or, wyrd—affair.

So much for Gladstone's being "sorry." "I'm terribly *glad*" could additionally be Goddard's subtle, clever hint to the reader about the real identity of "Dewing." And this raises the further interesting question: Was Gladstone's dream based only on Goddard's letter, or could it have been based also, or instead, on a future reading of the *Saturday Evening Post* article itself?

The Saturday Evening Post was an American magazine, but it is not impossible that Gladstone would have read it, and this is made much more likely by the fact that the article was made into an acclaimed 1956 British film, *The Night My Number Came Up*, starring Michael Redgrave as the air marshal. If Gladstone saw the film, its depiction of the harrowing flight and the crash in a snowy valley near the Japanese beach, in which the plane ends up nearly face down in the snow, could have supplied his precognitive imagination with the vivid images in his dream and the sense that it had been a fatal crash. The film depicts his character ("Commander Lindsay," portrayed by Michael Hordern) as amiable and innocent. It is not insulting toward his intelligence and even adds the embellishment that his dream helps the authorities locate the crash at the end. But Gladstone might well have also sought out the article to see how he had been portrayed by Goddard there, and if so, he would easily have taken offense at Goddard's portrayal of him, for the reasons given above. This would have added insult to the injury of his embarrassment at the party and perhaps compounded his retroactive "death wish" for the RAF hero.

Here, again, we veer very far into speculation, as all this is would be impossible to verify without actually putting Gladstone on the couch or knowing whether and when he read Goddard's article and/or saw the film based on it. But when we add the possibility of time loops to the Freudian picture—or when we add Freud to the Dunnean theory of precognition—it alerts us to the possibility that people may be subject to conflicted feelings and guilt about situations that haven't occurred yet in the flow of time, as well as pre-experience feelings that will arise later *because of* their premonitory experiences. More basically, it also underscores that what dreamers are precognizing, when they precognize, is neither events per se nor even the way they hear about them, for instance in the media. What they are precognizing are *their own thoughts and emotions* triggered by those learning experiences. They even seem to *precognize their memories*, again in a true fractal spiral.

Close but No Cigar

Lastly, we come full circle. There is no more stunning and ironic example of the fractal nature of dream precognition than the very dream that started it all, Freud's "specimen dream" about "Irma" (Anna Hammer-schlag) on the night of July 23-24, 1895—the dream that, he believed and asserted, had given him the precious key to dreams. Freud claimed that this dream concealed, through various tropes (substitutions, puns, etc.), a wish that he be blameless in his patient's treatment. He had quite naturally assumed it reflected wishes relevant to his life at the time he had his dream; indeed, what else did he have to go on but his own memories? But the benefit of time and hindsight reveals a very different, premonitory interpretation, one that Freud himself could hardly have failed to detect but that he nevertheless kept silent about.

In early 1923, Freud found that he had leukoplakia, a patch of pre-cancerous white tissue inside his mouth, on his right cheek and spreading to his palate. It was the result of a life of indulging in his famous cigars, which his friend Wilhelm Fliess had already advised him to quit smoking at the time of the dream. Though his doctors in 1923 were not fully frank with him, it was plain that they were concerned that the tissue had already become cancerous. After handwringing and frank consideration of suicide, Freud grudgingly subjected himself to a series of awful and life-changing surgeries. First the affected tissue was removed. Then, after a few months, when his doctors determined the cancer was more invasive than previously thought, a surgeon removed a large section of Freud's upper jaw and palate with a chisel—with the patient only under local anesthetic—leaving a gaping hole between his mouth and his nasal cavity that had to be fitted with a prosthetic. Afterwards, scabs formed where the tissue had been cut away. Several courses of radiation therapy also followed, along with several more surgeries over the remainder of his life—16 more years—and the contraction of tissue inside his mouth left Freud with limited ability to open his mouth or talk.[39]

In 1982, an Argentinean psychoanalyst and cancer surgeon named José Schavelzon, who studied the histopathology of Freud's cancer, noticed that the description of the lesion in "Irma's" mouth in Freud's dream strikingly matched the course of Freud's own disease and the complications from its treatment. It begins with his leukoplakia (the white patches), then the scabs produced by the surgery, then the nasal cavity visible inside his mouth upon removal of the palate (i.e., a feature in the mouth reminding Freud of the turbinal bones in the nose, which in fact are just over the palate), as well as the reluctance or inability to open the mouth due to a prosthesis (i.e., the notion that Irma was like a woman shy to open her mouth because of dentures).[40]

It is a startling discovery, and deeply ironic—indeed, deeply *wyrd*. How strange that of all his dreams, this one dream, his number-one "smoking gun" for the wish-fulfillment theory—what could be considered Freud's equivalent of Darwin's famous finches—would match so closely the illness that, Freud believed, and his doctors believed, was going to take his life three decades hence.[41]

Was the dream a "warning unheeded"? Robert Moss (and following Moss, Larry Dossey) reads it that way and contrasts Freud with Carl Jung, who allegedly gave up smoking after a dream.[42] Moss, perhaps reluctant to countenance precognition in the sense being advocated here, proposes that a single cancer cell already lurking in 1895 might have sent some kind of chemical alert to Freud's brain that manifested as a specific and uncannily correct dream-warning. Such a notion seems like another evasion of prophecy by granting inferential superpowers to the unconscious (and in this case, the body's tissues), although the question of any intentionality in the unconscious is somewhat paradoxical in any case. The precognitive hypothesis proposed here assumes no "intent" to send messages to oneself backward in time—the postcards we get from our future selves are sent automatically, even if the thoughts they represent are conscious ones. Rather than warning his younger self, it seems very much as though Freud's dreaming brain used various elements of his life in 1895 as "bricks" to pre-present significant thoughts—including wishes—he was going to have 28 years later.

What would Freud's thoughts and wishes have been in 1923?

It's not hard to answer this question. Firstly, and most obviously, Freud would undoubtedly have wished that he had heeded his friend Fliess's warnings to him all those years ago about his cigar use. Freud notes in his own interpretation of the dream that some anxiety about his health was already on his mind in 1895, yet it clearly had not been enough to break him of his smoking habit. The doctors—both the rhinologist who performed the initial surgery and his personal physician, Felix Deutsch—kept Freud in the dark about the true, dire extent of his cancer, per standard medical practice at the time, but they both made it clear to him that his cigar smoking was the cause.[43] Recall that his first reaction to Irma's complaint in the dream is that "*it's really only your fault.*"

Freud noted that dreams often swap and transpose attributes of people and situations, and they often disavow undesired qualities of the dreamer, or undesired situations, by giving them to other figures. It very much seems like his specimen dream transposed his own medical condition in 1923 to his friend and patient Anna Hammerschlag in 1895 and that his telling her it was her own fault was really a kind of self-reproach. Interestingly, all the other symptoms displayed by dream Irma or identified by the dream doctors examining her have been identified as Freud's own illnesses prior to or at the time of the dream—including intestinal symptoms (Irma's "dysentery") and rheumatism (a "dull area" the doctor's note on Irma's left side). Freud biographer Didier Anzieu notes that the examination performed by the trio of doctors mirrored Fliess's recent examination of Freud's chest for heart trouble, which Fliess had attributed to Freud's nicotine addiction. "Freud is the patient he himself examines in the dream," Anzieu asserts.[44]

Very significantly, at the time of the dream, Freud had just resumed smoking after a period of abstinence, and he was specifically worried about what Fliess would think of that lapse. Did this specific concern resonate with his situation in 1923, sparking a kind of temporal short-circuit?

When interpreting the dream, Freud had unsurprisingly attached sexual meaning to the "injection" that he surmised was somehow responsible for Anna/Irma's condition. In life, Freud was feeling anxious about his advice to Anna that she seek some sexual release—the "solution" that he initially blames her for not accepting. Freud attributed Anna's hysteria to her (by then) nine years of widowhood; she had evidently become reclusive and depressed following her husband's death in 1886, just a year after her marriage. It is likely Freud also felt some anxiety about his own attraction to her. Freud had known her since they had been teenagers, as she was the daughter of his Hebrew teacher, and she had been a great beauty in her youth. Freud's fondness for her continued through his life, and he always used the intimate *du* form of address with her (instead of the more usual *Sie*).[45] The "probably not clean" syringe he imagined had caused her disease in the dream is easily seen, among other things, as a phallic symbol standing in either for his own desires or at least for his own advice that she seek some sexual outlet—advice that he was now forced to doubt (since as Dr. Rie had pointed out, she was "better but not fully recovered").[46] But in hindsight, from the vantage point of his 1923 realization that his smoking habit really had been fatally toxic to his health, does the unclean syringe not take on an even more compelling and also straightforward, totally un-Freudian meaning as ... *just a cigar*?

Thoughts of mortality were at the forefront of Freud's thoughts in 1923, and not only because of his cancer. Freud had lost his daughter

Sophie to Spanish Flu in 1920, shortly after writing his famous book about death and trauma, *Beyond the Pleasure Principle*. Even more crushingly for Freud, not long after his initial surgery, Sophie's four-year-old son, Heinerle, Freud's favorite grandson, died of a fever. Freud was devastated, and the depression he endured for the rest of his life was as much over this loss as about his own greatly diminished quality of life as a result of his illness. In short, Freud was thinking about death, and he was specifically thinking about pediatric illness and the death of children. (Freud really lost two grandchildren since Sophie had been pregnant at the time of her death.) The pediatrician "Otto" (Dr. Rie), who had cared for Sophie and his other children decades earlier, would thus also have made sense as an association to the tragedies he was enduring in 1923, if only as a figure standing in for a general theme.

Through the catastrophe of Freud's initial diagnosis and surgeries, and for the remainder of his life, his youngest child, Anna, was a nearly constant companion, acting as his nurse in addition to being his psychoanalytic protégé (the one individual among his followers who could literally carry forward "the name of the father" of the psychoanalytic movement). Freud's biographer, Ernest Jones, writes that Freud "made a pact with [Anna] at the beginning [of his illness] that no sentiment was to be displayed; all that was necessary had to be performed in a cool, matter-of-fact fashion with the absence of emotion characteristic of a surgeon. This attitude, her courage and firmness, enabled her to adhere to the pact even in the most agonizing of situations."[47] So Anna too would have been much on Freud's mind in this period, and it is conceivable that Anna Hammerschlag was, in addition to standing in for Freud himself, also a kind of precognitive dream stand-in for his daughter, her namesake. Anna Freud was born five months after the "Irma" dream and may even have been consciously named after its central figure, perhaps as a kind of commemoration of Hammerschlag's importance in Freud's life as a result of that dream. Hammerschlag, who as Gerhard Fichtner puts it, was the "*secret godmother* of *The Interpretation of Dreams*,"[48] was also godmother to young Anna.

While it would be difficult, even in a life so thoroughly documented as Freud's, to identify a single experience in 1923 or after that might definitively have been the target/source of Freud's dream, one episode in Jones' biography highlights Freud's dependency on his daughter and the nature of his infirmity, and it readily calls to mind the dream scene of trying to get "Irma" to open her mouth and calling for the assistance of another physician:

The huge prosthesis, a sort of magnified denture or obdurator, designed to shut off the mouth from the nasal cavity, was a horror; it was labeled "the monster." In the first place it was very difficult to take out or replace because it was impossible for him to open his mouth at all widely. On one occasion, for instance, the combined efforts of Freud and his daughter failed to insert it after struggling for half an hour, and the surgeon had to be fetched for the purpose.[49]

Most importantly, I suggest that in 1923 and after, Freud would have been reminded of the role of his specimen dream in his life and career. How could he not have been struck, precisely as he had been on receiving the medallion in 1906, by the uncanny closeness of a significant, ominous turn of events in his own life to something he had dreamed/fantasized years earlier? Would he have secretly recognized that dream in hindsight as a premonition? I find it hard to imagine he would not have at least harbored some thoughts on this coincidence, although admitting them would have been unthinkable at that point. It would have been, so to speak, *hard to open his mouth* about any private doubts he may have had about the adequacy of his dream theory in hindsight.[50]

Let's suppose for a moment that, on some level, Freud did recognize that the dream had been premonitory and thus that his wish-fulfillment theory—at least as he had formulated it in the book that put him on the scientific map—was not, after all, a complete theory of dreams. The dream would have caught him in a Catch-22. He would have recognized his theory was inadequate, that it missed a whole prophetic dimension of dreaming, but he would have nevertheless reflected that, had it not been for his *premature* interpretation of the dream as fulfilling various wishes he had had at the time of the dream, he would not enjoy the stature he was coming to enjoy late in life. His fame—in fact, nothing less than his *immortality*—rested in no small part on the confidence that this one dream interpretation had given him. The sentiment Freud had conveyed to Fliess, that a marble tablet should commemorate the house outside of Vienna where "the secret of dreams was revealed" to him, was thus quite appropriate in the context of his life and career. But reflecting on it after the fact, from hindsight dominated by the encroaching reality of his death, how can there not have been a sense of hubris followed by nemesis, the law that governed the Greek tragedies?

Maybe he *didn't* answer the sphinx's riddle, as he so confidently claimed to have done. Was his whole theory thus a kind of *malpractice*?

Remember that the famous "snake eating its tail" dream of August Kekulé seems to have provided a kind of precedent and template for the role the Irma dream was set to play in Freud's life.[51] Although Freud did not pick up on it in his own analysis, the Kekulé story seems to be vividly indexed in his dream by terminating in the formula for an organic molecule, highlighted in bold type as though for special emphasis. But this indexing of the Kekulé story may also take on a more equivocal meaning if we view the dream from the standpoint of hindsight.

In the published text of Kekulé's speech at the 1890 *Benzolfeier* event, the chemist followed his dream narrative with an admonition: "Let us learn to dream, gentlemen, and then perhaps we shall find the truth . . . *but let us beware of publishing our dreams before they have been put to the proof by the waking understanding*" (my emphasis).[52] Freud would not have been in a position, either in 1895 or later in his life, to know that Kekulé probably had an ulterior motive in telling his dream story: to shore up his own priority in making the discovery of benzene's ring structure in light of the uncomfortable fact that three other chemists had actually published on it as much as three years before he did.[53] Belatedly saying "it came to me in a dream" at a fest in his honor was a way of asserting he had not plagiarized[54] ... and implying that through great scientific caution he had not rushed to publish his insight until he was sure it was true was a way of accounting for the strange discrepancy in publication dates. But to the 67-year-old Freud, Kekulé's famous words about not rushing to publish on the meaning of our dreams before we really know what they are about might have taken a different meaning: an admonishment for his hubris and prematurity in publishing his thesis that dreams are *only* the fulfillments of repressed wishes—in other words, an admonishment for "not waiting for the sugar to melt."

So, I suggest that it may have been exactly Freud's belated ambivalence or doubt about the nature of dreams as wish fulfillments (versus premonitions), *in light of the Irma dream seeming premonitory*, that could be the most important latent "meaning" of his Irma dream. If there was a single overriding wish in Freud's life during the terrible year 1923, it would have been precisely that the dream *had* in fact been (just) a wish fulfillment, just as he had asserted all those years ago. *It was a wish that he had been right about dreams being (just) wishes.* Talk about fractal spirals of self-reference—or snakes eating their own tails!

It would not only "wish away" his cancer but reinforce his own correctness about his own great dream "discovery," putting him beyond any professional reproach. Displacing his own illnesses—all of them, past as well as future—onto another figure (Anna/Irma) not only fulfilled his wish but also made it possible to disavow the dream as a premonition, creating the ambiguity that necessarily typifies refluxing information in a post-selected universe. The dream's choice of this particular patient as a "brick" to represent these future thoughts also enabled him to deflect his deeper anxieties over prophecy onto something more acceptably "Freudian"—that is, sexual—in nature.

Freud's dreaming brain might have seen a "transference" of his illnesses onto Anna Hammerschlag as an acceptable compromise. Committing the malpractice of failing to notice an organic lesion in a patient (and friend)—perhaps symbolically his own daughter/nurse—was "less than" having to endure it himself. Maybe some guilt for overlooking the illness of a patient—exactly the kind of guilt that was "going around" at that point in his circle of medical men—would have been preferable to the depression he was now suffering, and also preferable to the malpractice of getting the world to believe (wrongly) that dreams never referred to future events other than in the straightforward Newtonian way that they may point us in a certain direction (i.e., "By picturing our wishes as fulfilled, dreams are after all leading us into the future."[55]). And, placing the blame for his patient's treatment on the family pediatrician (who in the dream delivered a bottle of pineapple brandy, *Ananas*—remember that *Anna* would be born a few months later) would have been a kind of reproach against fate, and perhaps the limits of medicine, for the death of his grandson and Sophie, whom Rie had treated as a child. (Sophie would have been two years old when Freud had the Irma dream.) Later commentators like Didier Anzieu argue we must consider Freud's dream-interpretation to be part of the dream-work,[56] so we might see not just the dream itself but the whole complex of interpretation surrounding it as premonitory.

What is so striking is how very like Oedipus Freud really seems to have been. As a young man he treaded boldly into a fresh new kingdom ready for a leader, the kingdom of dreams and the unconscious, all the while batting away the buzzing gnats of experiences that seemed prophetic, using various evasions, denials, and rationalizations why *that* can't possibly be true. And his most famous dream, the dream that launched his career and for which he imagined a marble monument in his honor—equivalent to his answer to the sphinx—turned out to have a vastly different meaning than he had claimed. In hindsight, that dream became like the blind prophet Tiresias at the end of Sophocles' tragedy, pronouncing Oedipus's guilt. It leveled a guilty pointing finger.

This is what makes Freud's medallion episode also so deeply wyrd. The denial of prophecy by the hapless prince-cum-king was the real meaning of the Oedipus story that Freud had so centralized in his personal myth and the theory that immortalized him, and he reenacted this denial and displacement (i.e., "focus on the incest") in his own life and works. More than that, he himself seems to have been a precog—if only because he paid more attention to his dreams and parapraxes than most people. The truth of prophecy, and the truth of *his own* prophecies, was staring him in his face his whole life, but he could not squarely face it.

The belated doubt I am suggesting Freud must have felt about his dream theory may also provide a new light in which to see his late "conversion" to telepathy, which his skeptical friend Ernest Jones found so baffling and regrettable. This softening toward the occult may have been a kind of compromise formation, a concession protecting himself against cognitive dissonance. Telepathy enabled him to navigate cunningly between the possibility he could not face—that the unconscious could be prophetic—and a humbler idea he could more easily accept, and indeed that had motivated him even as a young psychiatrist developing a radical new theory of the psyche: the idea that there *are* more things in heaven and earth than are dreamed of in our philosophy.

Where All Royal Roads Lead

In his late masterpiece *Civilization and Its Discontents*, Freud metaphorically likened the unconscious to the Eternal City, Rome, in the way that it preserves the past layers of its history. A visitor to Rome, Freud wrote, would see traces of the earliest stages of the city's history still in the landscape, and shaping the modern city that has grown amid the ruins. "Except for a few gaps, he will find the wall of Aurelian almost unchanged. In some places, he will be able to find sections of the Servian wall where they have been excavated and brought to light."[57] Some periods are represented by ruins, "not ... ruins of themselves but of later restorations made after fires or destruction. ... There is certainly not a little that is ancient still buried in the soil of the city or beneath its modern buildings."[58]

This resolutely, even desperately past-oriented psychological pioneer wanted to believe—indeed needed to believe, for his theory to work—that the human psyche goes well beyond this level of preservation, that "nothing that has once come into existence will have passed away and all the earlier phases of development continue to exist alongside the latest one."[59] He thus conjured a remarkable image of the psychological Rome almost as a kind of augmented-reality or virtual-reality experience, with every period flickeringly superimposed: "Where the Coliseum now stands we could at the same time admire Nero's vanished Golden House. On the Piazza of the Pantheon we should find not only the Pantheon of to-day, as it was bequeathed to us by Hadrian, but, on the same site, the original edifice erected by Agrippa; indeed, the same piece of ground would be supporting the church of Santa sopra Minerva and the ancient temple over which it was built. ..."[60]

But even if the universe can be characterized as a glass block where everything in the past still exists and everything in the future already exists, such a picture does not reflect how information is retained in our heads. Science has long since demolished Freud's picture of human memory as a place where everything is preserved whole and intact. The brain's preservation of information is in a constant tension with its need to revise and update itself; thus memory, it is now argued, is much more like the real Rome, with bits and pieces of the past here and there but mostly ruins that, while they look authentic, are in fact reconstructions made at some later date. Most of the past is gone, the stones and bricks of old experiences having long since been reappropriated and rearranged to make edifices serving more recent needs. Dreaming, as it is coming to be characterized by today's neuroscience and psychology, is the nightly activity of modernizing this old city, making facelifts and repairs and building new structures, slowly obliterating the more distant past to make way for episodes and concerns that are more contemporary and pertinent.

But if anything like the hypothesis I am developing in this book is true, one's personal Rome may be even stranger than this, and stranger than Freud's flickering virtual-reality tour through perfectly preserved layers of the past. Some of those ruins that seem like they belong to the past are really *future* temples, *future* Coliseums, belonging to a kind of science-fictional Rome where buildings are constructed for purposes that can't be anticipated or imagined yet, but confusingly using the "bricks" of our past experience. How much of the "symbolism" of our dreams really reflects our as-yet-unfathomable future purposes and future thoughts remains an open question. And what about our inscrutable neurotic behavior and parapraxes—might those also issue just as often from our future as from our past? How many of the *traumas* that shape our lives might really be, as in Freud's own case, catastrophes that lie ahead of us?

10

Prophetic *Jouissance* — Trauma, Survival, and the Precognitive Sublime

It is right it should be so:
Man was made for joy and woe;
And when this we rightly know
Through the world we safely go.
Joy and woe are woven fine,
A clothing for the soul divine.
Under every grief and pine
Runs a joy with silken twine.

— William Blake, *Auguries of Innocence* (1803)

It was September 23, 1955, and the actor Alec Guinness had just arrived in Hollywood to film the movie *The Swan*. He was 41, and
it was more than two decades before he would become a household
name in America for his portrayal of the wise Jedi Knight Obi Wan
Kenobi in *Star Wars*, and still four years before being real-life knighted
by Queen Elizabeth II for his achievements on the British stage and
screen. And it was the very first time he had set foot in California. Unfortunately, the 16-hour flight from London had made the famously

cranky actor doubly cranky, and events of the evening—including the gender-bending attire of his dinner companion—conspired to magnify his displeasure.

An American screenwriter, Thelma Moss, wanted to buy Guinness a meal, but she was wearing trousers—something women didn't often do in those days. After being turned away from three different respectable establishments as a result of this unfortunate wardrobe choice, Moss drove her increasingly hungry and grumpy companion to a more liberal Italian place, Villa Capri, that she knew would admit them. Except, she had no reservation ... and there were no available tables.[1]

By this time, Guinness was desperate: "I don't care where we eat or what," he told Moss. "Just something, somewhere." Guinness wrote in his 1985 memoir *Blessings in Disguise* that as they left the restaurant to continue their search for food, he "became aware of running, sneakered feat" chasing them down, and turned to face a handsome young man in a sweat-shirt and jeans.

"You want a table?" the man offered. "Join me. My name is James Dean."

Before going back into the restaurant, the young star of *East of Eden* (and the forthcoming *Rebel Without a Cause*) wanted to show Guinness a shiny parcel in the parking lot: a new silver Porsche Spyder 550 he had just received from the mechanic who customized it. It was wrapped in cellophane, with flowers and a bow on the hood. "It's just been delivered," he announced full of pride. "I haven't even driven it yet." Dean, a car collector and racer when he wasn't acting, had nicknamed the car "Little Bastard."

"The sports car looked sinister to me, although it had a large bunch of red carnations resting on its bonnet," Guinness wrote. "How fast is it?"

"She'll do a hundred and fifty," Dean answered.

At that moment, a grave expression passed over Guinness's face, and he warned his new friend, in a voice he says he could hardly recognize as his own: "Please, never get in it." He looked at his watch. "It is now ten o'clock, Friday the 23rd of September, 1955. If you get in that car you will be found dead in it by this time next week."

Dean just laughed at his warning: "Oh, shucks! Don't be so mean!"[2]

Guinness apologized for his strange utterance, explaining that it was due to hunger and lack of sleep. He and Moss then joined Dean and his entourage for a lovely dinner, at which no further mention was made of Dean's new car or Guinness's distressing premonition. Yet Guinness recalled that, despite the gaiety of the evening, he felt uneasy through the whole meal. And indeed, a week later, at 4:00 PM on Friday, September 30, Dean's neck was broken when he slammed into another car while speeding through an intersection near Paso Robles, California, going twice the speed limit.

Skeptics will whip out their "law of large numbers" and "selection bias" arguments to debunk Guinness's story, of course. Guinness no doubt knew or could guess of his young dinner companion's reckless lifestyle, shared by many young celebrities. One might guess that many of Dean's friends and acquaintances uttered similar warnings to Dean all the time, sort of the way we imagine young celebrities constantly getting concerned warnings about their drug abuse and other self-destructive behavior. In a certain small percentage of cases, the warnings come true soon thereafter, and these are the ones remembered after the fact and retold as part of the survivor's life story. This one instance, because it happened to nearly coincide with Dean's (perhaps likely or even inevitable) death in an automobile, could have taken on a numinous quality for Guinness in hindsight, as he rehearsed and retold the event to himself and others over the subsequent years.

But such a just-so story is subverted (if not undercut) by its repressed ghost. There is a coincidence in Guinness's story that most readers, both skeptical and credulous, will miss simply because it is so obvious: The fact that the premonition was not about some random death, or the death of just any famous celebrity, or of just any acquaintance of Guinness. It was the death of a person Guinness had just met and formed a bond with. While this fact can be used to support the "law of large numbers" argument, it also lends itself to the opposite argument on the quite rational consistency of premonitions as centering on personally meaningful events and relationships. We will see later in this chapter that, on at least one other occasion in the early 1950s, Guinness had another premonition about the death of an artist with whom he had recently formed a kind of connection.

Even if Guinness claimed he couldn't recognize the oracular voice that came from his mouth when warning Dean of his imminent death, most moviegoers can imagine that voice readily, for it uttered a similarly grave pronouncement aboard the Millennium Falcon en route to Princess Leia's home planet Alderaan in *Star Wars*. "I felt a great disturbance in the force," Obi Wan Kenobi famously says, clutching his chest just after (the audience knows) Alderaan has fallen victim to the Death Star, "as if millions of voices suddenly cried out in terror, and were suddenly silenced. I fear something gravely terrible has happened." Afterward he sits clutching his head with a pained expression.

The fact that audiences can so readily understand this scene, and relate to a "force" that connects people across time and space during a crisis, attests to the lasting power of Frederic Myers' telepathy theory, which had dominated people's thinking about psychic phenomena for nearly a century by the time *Star Wars* was released. Indeed, other than the role played by an automobile that could travel 150 miles per hour, practically hyperspace to a Victorian, Guinness's premonition about James Dean would not have been out of place in *Phantasms of the Living*, the compendious 1886 volume Myers wrote with psychologist Edmund Gurney and skeptical writer Frank Podmore. Because ostensibly telepathic phenomena so often center on death, sickness, or other crises, Myers argued that it is strong emotion that overcomes the distances that usually separate people from their friends and loved ones, both in time and space. *Trauma* is the energy that powers telepathic broadcasts.[3]

The notion of a person in crisis as a telepathic broadcast tower has given way to newer metaphors for anomalous experiences that seem to involve some remote connection, such as entanglement—even though quantum mechanics as we currently understand it does not even allow entanglements between two people's brains on the basis of shared genes, let alone a shared dinner. But the link to powerful, especially negative emotions remains an overriding theme in accounts of ESP phenomena. Precognitive experiences frequently take the form of apparent "warnings" of death or disaster, as we've seen, even though as often as not it is in trying to evade foreseen outcomes that people end up fulfilling them. It raises interesting questions about how precognition may work as an orienting function, especially if, as I have argued, its adaptive purpose is fundamentally to orient us toward rewards.

We can get some clues to a possible answer by considering Freud's writings on trauma, as well as subsequent psychoanalytic thinking about the paradoxical motivating power of emotions that lie, as Freud famously put it, "beyond the pleasure principle."

Psychological trauma was a new concept at the time Freud was constructing his theory of the unconscious in the late 1800s. The industrial age and its railways had created a widespread phenomenon that until then only soldiers had been confronted with: grievous injuries, mutilation, and close calls such as the witnessing of horrific accidents befalling others. When the insurance companies were forced to assess claims related to psychological injuries that seemed to set in after a person's physical injuries, if any, had healed, psychiatry was forced to confront a new class of illnesses, what one later writer called "pension hysterias."[4] Trauma, which originally meant a physical wound, came in Freud's writings to refer to events that, because of their suddenness or horror, left some kind of lasting scar on the psyche.

Freud's innovation in the medicalization of trauma was twofold. First, he extended the conception of trauma to the sexual domain—namely, child sexual abuse. In the 1890s, because of repeated stories from his patients that seemed to point to sexually traumatic events in their childhoods, he formulated his famous "seduction theory." Child abuse and pre-pubertal sexual experiences were, it seemed to him, much more pervasive than anyone had yet recognized and were the driver of adult hysterias and neuroses. However, when he "discovered"—many would say *invented*—what he later called the Oedipus complex, or lingering incestuous wishes from childhood, he abandoned his seduction theory in favor of a much more far-reaching idea: that many of these traumatic, neurosis-inducing "memories" were actually fictions woven from the threads of real, poorly understood experiences and a much larger component of fantasy, all abetted by childhood confusions about sexuality. The trauma, in many cases, was not some actual molestation that had occurred, but a nexus of ideas and fantasies inarticulately preserved in memory. Psychoanalysis came to mean enabling the patient to put into words those hitherto inarticulate ideas and fantasies, not simply recovering some buried memory (which is the simplistic idea still found in pop-culture parodies of the Freudian couch).[5]

Long after Freud's death, Freud's abandonment of the seduction theory was seen by many feminists and other critics as a betrayal of his patients who may really have been abused by their fathers. The reassessment of memory and trauma that ensued led to an epidemic of "recovered abuse memories" in the 1980s and early 1990s. These "memories" were often the product of highly questionable therapeutic methods like hypnosis.[6] Thanks to the important research by Elizabeth Loftus and others into the fallibility of memory and the ease with which false memories can be created in therapeutic settings, the pendulum swung back in the late 1990s, away from assuming traumatic childhood memories are accurate. But Freud's cultural reputation, even in the humanities, has never really recovered from this "scandal."

Nevertheless, and whatever the extent to which Freud's reduction of trauma to sex should be bracketed, his second key innovation in this domain remains one of his most enduring and significant ideas: that trauma consists not in what happens to us, but in how we think about what happens to us. Crucially, these thoughts are displaced in time or deferred from the event as such. As the French psychoanalyst Jean Laplanche put it, "we try to track down the trauma, but the traumatic memory was only secondarily traumatic: we never manage to fix the traumatic event historically. This fact might be illustrated by the image of a Heisenberg-like 'relation of indeterminacy'."[7] The philosopher Jacques Derrida erected a whole philosophy on the notion of what he called *différance* (combining the sense of *defer* and *differ*), with its central assumption that traumas are always secondary, always "supplements": "One wishes to go back *from the supplement to the source*: one must recognize that there is *a supplement at the source*."[8] Put simply, in this school of thought, memory is an infinite regress into the past, following chains of associations among memory traces, yet may never hit the bedrock of anything traumatic "back there."

Could the inability to ever localize the origin of a trauma in the past, and the psychoanalyst's need to assemble some chain of "traumatic thoughts," signal that the search for origins has always looked in the wrong direction, for the wrong trauma, or both?

Playing Gone

Even decades after he had formulated his theory of *Nachträglichkeit*—"afterwardsness" (or as John Forrester puts it, "the deferred action specific to neurotic causality"[9])—Freud continued to be perplexed by traumatized patients behaving in compulsive and seemingly very unpleasurable ways, almost as if they wanted to relive the event that had traumatized them rather than forget it. On the one hand, conflicts between our conscious aims and our unconscious desires could go some of the way toward explaining this. People's reactions to traumatic events may be much more complex than we like to imagine, for one thing—we harbor unconscious death wishes for those close to us, as a result of sibling rivalries and the like. But ambivalence could not be the whole story. Why do war veterans obsessively relive objectively horrifying combat situations in their dreams? Why do neurotics find it so hard to "let go" of real or imagined traumas and end up staging situations that essentially repeat and reinforce them, almost as though they are trying to (re)create those traumas instead of move on? For a doctor whose whole theory of human motivation rested on the individual's pursuit of his or her wishes in dreams and of pleasure in daily life, this compulsive returning to past traumas was a conundrum.

In 1919, Freud wrote his most controversial and arguably most interesting essay, *Beyond the Pleasure Principle*, in which he attempted to formulate a solution. He said that the main clue to his answer came from watching his toddler grandson Ernst repeatedly throwing a spool over the side of his crib and exclaiming *"fort"* (gone), then pulling it back and enjoying its return, *"da"* (there); and then, when he was slightly older, doing the same thing with his own reflection in a mirror. The *fort-da* game is one of the most memorable images in Freud's writings, and those who knew Freud assumed Freud had written this after the death of his daughter Sophie, Ernst's mother, in 1920. But he hastened to correct them that he wrote it months before her death[10] (making it another possible candidate for precognition).

Staging the loss and recovery of objects and the self, Freud argued, is the child's way of beginning to think about and master (via play) the traumatic absences of the mother. By bringing loss under its own symbolic control, the child builds a capacity to endure it. Thus, it is in dealing with trauma that the child first learns to use symbols to represent things that are absent. For later writers in the Object-Relations school, such play with what D. W. Winnicott called "transitional objects" is the very roots of cultural experience, the very beginnings of symbol use.[11] But what was most interesting to Freud was the compulsive, repetitive quality of these childhood games, as well as the fact that the emphasis seems to be on the "gone" (*fort*) half of the *fort-da* game. Children, in their play, like to play gone. Freud suggested that there is in an organism's own destruction also a kind of reward, annihilation being the ultimate release of psychic tension, whose dissipation is felt as pleasure.[12] He proposed that, apart from and even surpassing the rule that we are governed in our actions by pleasure, there is a parallel urge to dispel life energy and thus tension—and that this drive can be found at the root of war neuroses and the neurotic's compulsion to repeat unpleasant situations. Specifically, he called this a "death drive," or *thanatos*. Thus, beyond pleasure lay the even more extreme reward of oblivion.[13]

Although intriguing, Freud's idea of an instinctive urge toward negation or annihilation seemed paradoxical, and never really caught on ... except as it was reformulated by the French psychoanalyst Jacques Lacan in the late 1950s. Lacan's French had an advantage that Freud's German lacked, specifically the word *jouissance*, meaning painful pleasure or pleasurable pain—literally something "beyond pleasure" that takes over and drives a neurotic or someone who has been traumatized. The simplistic examples commonly given of *jouissance* include an orgasm so extreme that it causes agony, or the erotic pleasures of sadomasochistic acts. But a better analogy would be addiction, the compulsion to repeat an act (taking a drug, for instance) that cannot be resisted yet no longer gives much pleasure because it is more about the temporary dissipation or release of unpleasure.[14] There is no equivalent word in English either. In reference to Lacan, *jouissance* is usually translated as "enjoyment," but it needs to be understood that there may be something deeply ambivalent or even repellent about this particular kind of enjoyment. It is *an enjoyment we do not want*, a weird mix of excitement and pain, reward and regret. The concept of *jouissance*, as the underlying energy driving human compulsions, including pathological compulsions and obsessions treated in psychotherapy, became so central for Lacan that late in his career he made the provocative statement that *jouissance* is the "only substance" psychoanalysis deals with.[15]

Lacan might better have said "force" and not substance. Later Lacanian thinkers have likened *jouissance* to the warping of space in a gravitational field. The contradiction between conscious aversion and unconscious reward bends our symbolic-imaginary spacetime, causing the strange tail-chasing, repetitive "orbiting" behavior of all neuroses and obsessional behavior, and on some level all behavior. One's "enjoyment" in this French sense of the word is what "turns one's crank" (recall here also the "twisting, turning" sense of the Anglo-Saxon *wyrd*). What may to an outsider appear to be a miserable or dreary compulsion (an addiction, a pattern of dating the wrong kind of person, obsessively collecting Hollywood memorabilia, whatever) conceals and also preserves or protects a vital and enlivening unconscious dimension, which it is the aim of psychoanalysis to help unbury. According to Lacanian psychoanalysis, this circular, orbital pattern is one's *symptom*.

The push-pull of *jouissance* around signs of self-destruction represented a significant advance over Freud's thinking about why traumatized people behave the way they do. Whereas Freud understood the traumatized person's "compulsion to repeat" as a way of metabolizing or exorcising the pain of traumatic events and thoughts, Lacan saw that repetitive symptoms are really an adaptation to a new regime of enjoyment, how a person reorganizes his or her life in such a way as to continue to derive enjoyment from something that, on a conscious level, may be despised and even (in its most extreme and pathological forms) possibly does harm.

Lacan was no more interested in literal precognition or prophecy than Freud was, but his revision of the Freudian theory of symptoms and their relation to trauma is highly suggestive for an understanding of precognitive phenomena, and the ways trauma may sometimes become "displaced in time." For instance, in many cases where disasters and deaths are precognized, even including deaths of loved ones or near-fatal perils in one's own future, there is an implicit reward, if only in the very primitive—and hard-to-acknowledge—sense of "but I survived." This can be a very repellant kind of reward, something appealing to a very base, "lizard-brain," survival-oriented part of us that may be at odds with our conscious, moral, social desires and sense of self.

The paradoxical connection between survival and death, which sparked Freud's thinking but which he could never resolve successfully, in some sense boils down to a matter of *semiotics*: the fact that the one value (survival) takes on its meaning or value as a signal only contrastively, when paired with its opposite (death/destruction). According to structural linguistics, which was hugely influential on Lacan, all signifiers ultimately derive their meaning from their opposition to other signifiers. In life's *semiotic* (or "sign language"), death or disaster befalling others is the foremost signifier of our own being-there, our *da-sein*. If you find yourself "traumatized" by witnessing something terrible, you have by definition survived. Dreams seem to give people dramatic and often distorted previews of those situations lurking in the foggy waters ahead. So do premonitions like Alec Guinness's vision of James Dean's death. One can imagine that Guinness would have read of the death of his fellow actor, whom he had just met a week earlier, with a mix of horror and regret, but also grim affirmation: *It wasn't me. I* didn't have the reckless need to go racing through a little California town in a flashy sports car.

We could apply this logic to interpreting one of the best-known premonitory dreams, Mark Twain's dream about his brother Henry lying dead in a metal casket. In his *Autobiography*, which he dictated to a stenographer in 1906 at the age of 70, Mark Twain recounts that when he was a young man, age 23—at that point just Samuel Clemens—he had been in training to be a Mississippi River steamboat pilot, and he persuaded his 19-year-old brother Henry to come work with him as a "mud clerk" aboard a boat called the *Pennsylvania*.[16] The writer told how one night in May 1858, while they were ashore and staying with their older sister Pamela and her husband and daughter in St. Louis, he dreamed of Henry lying in a metal casket, which was placed on two chairs. Henry wore a suit of his own (Samuel's) borrowed clothes, and on his chest was a bouquet of white flowers with a single red rose. The dream was so vivid, he recalled, that he actually arose and went outside to collect himself before viewing the body, which he expected was on display in the house. During his walk, he realized that it had only been a dream. He told Pamela about it, with her six-year-old daughter Annie present.

A few days later, the brothers shipped out in the *Pennsylvania* on its run south to New Orleans. There, Samuel had the most violent in a series of ongoing clashes with the boat's pilot and was made to stay ashore when the boat made its run back north to Memphis. Two or three days later, he received news that Henry had been badly injured in a boiler explosion that had taken the lives of many of the *Pennsylvania*'s passengers and crew. Samuel took the next boat to Memphis and sat with his severely burned brother in the hospital, but Henry ended up dying of an overdose of morphine that the inexperienced doctors administered to kill his pain. The writer recalled that the next day, when he arrived at the building where the dead were laid out in caskets, he was stunned to behold the exact scene he had seen in his dream. Henry's body was laid out in a suit he had borrowed from Samuel when they were in St. Louis. Some women volunteers, impressed by Henry's stoicism enduring burns over his whole body, had pitched in to buy him a metal casket, whereas the rest of the bodies were laid out in caskets of white pine. Just then an elderly volunteer nurse entered and placed a bouquet of white flowers, with a single red rose in it, on Henry's chest.[17] A few days later, when the coffin was brought to their sister Pamela's house in St. Louis, it was laid on two chairs, also as Samuel had seen in his dream.[18]

In a Freudian reexamination of this case, religion scholar David Halperin notes that a submerged death wish could have accounted for what only seemed in hindsight like a precognitive dream about Henry's death.[19] The young Samuel Clemens felt a good deal of resentment toward his younger but much more upstanding brother, who appears as the "goody-goody snitch" 'Sid' in *Tom Sawyer*, for example. Henry could do no wrong in their mother's eyes, Twain later recalled, whereas he himself could do no right.[20] From these clues, Halperin deduces that Clemens would have harbored unconscious murderous wishes for Henry, as siblings typically do, and thus would probably have had many dreams over the years involving his death. It thus might not actually be too strange a coincidence, Halperin argues, for Samuel, upon seeing his brother in a coffin, to recall having dreamed approximately that scene at some point and formed the notion that he had had a recent premonitory dream about it.

The testimony of Twain's niece Annie Moffett somewhat undercuts this argument, however. According to Moffett, the dream occurred while napping in daytime, when Samuel and his siblings, including Henry, were at home, and that Samuel actually came rushing into the room where they were all sitting to tell them about it.[21] It shows that his confused rising from bed to view Henry's casket could well have been a consummate storyteller's later embellishment. But the discrepancy lends some support to the basic core truth of the story: that Samuel did indeed have a dream of Henry's dead body before his death, and that it made enough of an impact on the dreamer that he shared it right away with his family. Presumably he did not go telling his family about dreams of his dead brother *all* the time—that might have stood out in Annie Moffett's memory as remarkable for different reasons. (She also noted that others in the family were amused at how seriously Samuel evidently took this dream.)

Even if we accept Samuel Clemens' dream as a bona fide case of dream precognition, Halperin has hit on an important dimension of this story that should not be ignored: the fact that there would have been more to his reaction to his brother's death than simple grief. There was guilt, first of all. Twain felt guilty the whole rest of his life for inviting Henry to work on the *Pennsylvania* and for not insisting his brother remain with him in New Orleans.[22] And there would have been even more to it, as once again, the death of another person always contains, by implication, a small but important piece of news that some basic animal part of us takes reassurance in—*I survived, I'm still here, it didn't happen to me.* Given the singular circumstances of Henry's death—dying as a result of a boiler explosion after Samuel had been made to stay on shore—how can such a sense of luck or fate favoring Samuel over his brother not have crossed the future writer's mind, leading to an unconscious sense of relief commingled with that guilt? For Samuel's unconscious, if not his conscious reflection, the meaning of this story would have been "it could just as easily have been me."[23] I suggest that it is precisely this equivocally rewarding signal that might have been "displaced in time" to spark a dream some days earlier.

Calling Samuel Clemens' dream a "dream of his brother's death" is really as inaccurate and misleading as calling Elizabeth Krohn's dreams

(Chapter 1) "plane crash premonitions." His dream was about *being alive* to witness his brother lying dead in a coffin, including the singular and significant detail of his brother wearing *his own* borrowed suit. It was a dream about the viewing of Henry's body, a kind of wake, and a wake is an event in which the living—those who have survived—pay respects to the dead. Samuel Clemens' dream was not a premonition of his brother's death, but a premonition of his own survival.

Entropy and Sublimity

The concept of *jouissance*, particularly as it relates to scenes of destruction and ruin, provides an alternative, psychodynamic explanation for the prominence of explosive, entropic occurrences in precognitive phenomena. The reader will by now have noticed that many premonitory experiences center not just on death but on chaotic and explosive events like car and plane crashes, terror attacks, calamitous sea disasters, and devastating volcanic eruptions—in other words, things moving rapidly from a state of order to a state of disorder. Physicist Edwin May noted that psychics in the U.S. military Star Gate program were much more accurate at describing "hot" targets (explosions, nuclear reactors on aircraft carriers, etc.) than other targets. The prophetic halo around 9/11 or many of J. W. Dunne's dreams would be consistent with May's hypothesis that psychically sensitive individuals may somehow, through some as-yet-undiscovered "psychic retina," be detecting large, rapid changes in entropy as bright beacons on the landscape ahead in time.[24]

May's argument makes a certain amount of sense given the classical equivalence of time's arrow with entropy. Things that are very rapidly dissipating heat, such as stars and nuclear reactors and houses on fire, or even just a living body making the ultimate transition to the state of disorder called death, could perhaps be seen as concentrated time. But steep entropy gradients also represent a category of information that is intrinsically interesting and meaningful to humans and toward which we are particularly vigilant, whatever the sensory channel through which we receive it. An attentional bias to entropy gradients has been shown for the conventional senses of sight and hearing, not just psi phenomena. Stimuli involving sudden, rapid motion, and especially fire and heat, as well as others' deaths and illness, are signals that carry important information related to our survival, so we tend to notice and remember them.[25]

Thus, an alternative explanation for the link between psi accuracy and entropy is the perverse pleasure—that is, *jouissance*—aroused in people by signs of destruction. Some vigilant part of us needs be constantly scanning the environment for indications of threats to our life and health, which means we need on some level to find that search rewarding. If we were not rewarded, we would not keep our guard up. Entropic signals like smoke from an advancing fire, or screams or cries from a nearby victim of violence or illness, or the grief of a neighbor for their family member are all signifiers, part of what could be called the "natural language of peril." We find it "enjoyable," albeit in an ambivalent or repellent way, to engage with such signifiers because, again, their meaning, their *signified*, is our own survival. The heightened accuracy toward entropic targets that May observed could reflect a heightened fascination with fire, heat, and chaotic situations more generally, an attentional bias to survival-relevant stimuli. Our particular psychic fascination with fire may also reflect its central role as perhaps the most decisive technology in our evolutionary development as well as the most dangerous, always able to turn on its user in an unlucky instant.[26]

The same primitive threat-vigilance orientation accounts for the unique allure of artworks depicting destruction or the evidence of past destruction. In the 18th century, *the sublime* entered the vocabulary of art critics and philosophers like Edmund Burke and Immanuel Kant to describe the aesthetic appeal of ruins, impenetrable wilderness, thunderstorms and storms at sea, and other visual signals of potential or past peril, including the slow entropy of erosion and decay. Another definition of the sublime would be the *semiotic of entropy*. As Kant described:

> Bold, overhanging, and, as it were, threatening rocks, thunder clouds piled up the vault of heaven, borne long with flashes and peals, volcanoes in all their violence of destruction, hurricanes leaving desolation in their track, the boundless ocean rising with rebellious force, the high waterfall of some mighty river, and the like, make our power of resistance of trifling moment in comparison with their might. But, provided our own position is secure, their aspect is all the more attractive for its fearfulness; and we readily call these objects sublime, because they raise the forces of the soul above the heights of vulgar commonplace, and discover within us a power of resistance of quite

another kind, which gives us courage to be able to measure ourselves against the seeming omnipotence of nature.[27]

Landscape paintings from the 18th and 19th centuries by artists like J. M. W. Turner and Caspar David Friedrich often display this aesthetic appreciation of violent nature, disasters, and especially ruins. If there is any one painting that has always exemplified the sublime—the painting that stands as its exemplar in many Freshman Art History textbooks—it is Friedrich's *The Sea of Ice*, also called *The Wreck of Hope*, created in 1823 or 1824. Jagged slabs of ice pile in a rough pyramid in a cold Northern ocean, and if you look carefully, the stern nameplate of a ship can be seen about to disappear in the water bearing the name HMS *Griper*. (The work was inspired by the explorer William Parry's 1819 expedition to the Pole, although in fact the *Griper* survived the expedition.) There is a remarkable similarity between this and other paintings by Friedrich and the iconic photos of the twisted wreckage of the World Trade Center towers rising from the gloom soon after their collapse on 9/11.

Originally, the sublime was elevated above the merely beautiful as something that mainly men were able to savor and enjoy (women were believed to prefer pleasant domestic scenes, flowers, and other-images that were not so existentially challenging). Today we find the sublime aesthetic dominant in disaster cinema and post-apocalyptic science fiction. Films like *Alien* or *Planet of the Apes* (with its famous final scene of the Statue of Liberty rising from a far-future beach) exemplify the mood of enjoyment-in peril as much as the bleak haunted landscapes of Friedrich or the sweeping destructive visions of Turner. The common element that links these works is that they stage the same pleasure at annihilation-and-return, losing and finding again, that Freud observed his grandson Ernst engaging in with his spool, albeit on a far grander scale. The basis of the aesthetic sublime is precisely in its reinforcement of the thought "but I survived," an enjoyment of the fact that *I'm still here, even amid these signs of ruin*. If you're able to witness and even be traumatized by some sign of destruction, then you've survived it. "Your position is secure," as Kant put it.

The aesthetic of the sublime may help us understand the many premonitory dreams and visions and artworks related to disasters like 9/11. It ought to be evident that, for most Americans, who did not live in Manhattan or Washington, DC, and who did not lose loved ones or friends in the attacks, the "trauma" of that day was really a mélange of complex and conflicting emotions that went way beyond the obvious shock and horror of the destruction. As philosopher Slavoj Žižek has noted, 9/11 fell into a fantasy space that had been prepared for it by decades of disaster cinema as well as growing social antagonisms in American society. It represented the fulfillment of a repressed wish on the part of many Americans, not only to be gripped by an unfolding cinematic disaster happening elsewhere to other people, but specifically to see massive icons of Establishment power and wealth destroyed in such a daring, David-vs.-Goliath way—this indeed was the genius of the attacks, to give Americans "what we wanted" on several unspeakable levels.

It sounds terrible to say, but the result was that Americans *enjoyed* the news coverage of 9/11. It was a spectacle, it inspired awe at its audacity, and certainly for most Americans, it provoked an enormous sense of relief that the terrorists hadn't targeted their particular place of work or that of their loved ones. If you were watching it on television, it was probably not happening to you; it thus created a nation of grateful survivors, united by love and patriotism in its aftermath, as well as survivor's guilt. This mix of guilt and gratitude, horror and relief, is the essence of *jouissance*.

Freud wrote that "if we are to be judged by our unconscious wishes, we ourselves are nothing but a band of murderers."[28] According to the logic of *jouissance*, it is more that we are vampires, deriving an unspeakable pleasure from signs of suffering and death. Žižek has likened *jouissance* to the drive that propels the undead in horror stories; it is a kind of life beyond life, an excess or surplus of life that cannot be contained in the living.[29] Again, it sounds terrible, totally amoral, but it could be said that the Lacanian framework restores a bit of our moral dignity that Freud's logic of narcissism and his talk of death drives seemed to take away. We do not really thrill to others' losses or suffering out of ill-will or malice toward our fellow humans; it is simply that *if* death and suffering are seen to befall others—*if we are in the position of witness*—then those fates are not (at least not yet) happening to *us*. In his classic study *The Denial of Death*, Ernest Becker paraphrases Aristotle: "Luck is when the guy next to you gets hit with the arrow."[30] It may be that feeling our fate most exquisitely depends on these kinds of sublime close calls. Obsessively re-watching the planes crashing into the towers, dwelling endlessly on news images and photographs for months and years afterward, re-living the destruction and our own reactions to it in our conversations was very much like a neurotic symptom, a "compulsion to repeat," and a way to enjoy our own survival. It expressed a morally unacceptable "life drive," rather than a death drive as Freud would have framed it.

What Freud seems to have overlooked in his interpretation of his grandson Ernst's *fort-da* game was the child's point of view—that even though the spool was "gone," *Ernst himself* was still there, and the spool's gone-ness may have highlighted or intensified his budding awareness of self. More than the birth of symbolism, playing gone with transitional objects might be the birth of self-consciousness in relation to void. The spool is serving as a symbol for the child, but the symbol's referent is not the mother—it is the child's own persistence in the world, his survival (again by contrastive opposition). The aesthetic love of destruction and decay is similarly a way of playing "gone" and thereby bringing our survival into sharper relief. By extension, what traumatized people may be enjoying, what they anxiously cannot get enough of (in their traumatized state), is their own being-there or *da-sein*. If our prophetic unconscious orients us toward our future survival, we might expect it to similarly focus on chaotic upheavals that serve as a backdrop for an "I survived" signal—a context in which the persistence of the post-selecting self makes sense as "good news."[31]

Whether or not it is the real or only substance addressed by psychoanalysis, as Lacan argued, *jouissance* seems to be the real substance of prophecy. We are connected to our future by a resonating string of ambivalent enjoyment. Even when they seem darkest, the oblique messages carried on that string often have to do with our own survival in the Not Yet.

"Use the Luke, Alec!"

In a 1977 interview on the BBC talk show *Parkinson*, Alec Guinness remarked that his "very spooky" premonition of James Dean's death in Little Bastard had been unique in his experience.[32] He was mistaken. We know from his memoir that it was at least the second time such a thing had occurred in his life within the span of a few years in the early 1950s. The first, because it did not involve such a long time delay and had a more "haunting" quality—and perhaps because it did not involve such a famous celebrity—did not fall for him in the same mental category. Yet, in fact, it seems very much like an example of the same future-influencing-present effect at work around learning of the untimely death of another artist with whom he had just made some connection. In this case, the death itself had taken place exactly a year *before* the experience; the connection was via one of the dead man's paintings. What Guinness failed to recognize was that it also may have been premonitory of his role in one of the most iconically entropic scenes in cinema history: the destruction of the Death Star.

The actor recounts that, four years before his trip to Hollywood, he and his wife Merula purchased a painting by the Ukrainian-English painter Bernard Meninsky called *Two Irish Girls*, which "showed two solid-looking females in shawls, confronting each other in some place of bright green bushes and withered hedgerows." Guinness writes that there was "something enigmatic" about the painting, however, and one night when he entered the room where he and Merula had hung it, he was seized by an inner voice obsessively reciting a Bible chapter and verse, "Luke, Chapter XXIII, Verse 31." He had attended a religious school in his teens, ending up at age 16 a "confirmed atheist," so he had to scour his house to get his hands on a Bible to look up that verse. Eventually successful, he read the following: "For if they do these things in a green tree what shall be done in a dry?"

"It was obvious," Guinness wrote, "that the words could be applied to the painting, which I was staring at with fascination. For the first time I noticed that the green bushes were loosely painted, round, self-satisfied faces and the twigs agonized, screaming, figures."[33]

Here, a skeptic will interrupt to point out that his years of religious schooling had given Guinness ample exposure to the Bible, and that his unconscious mind could have simply connected a subliminal perception of the faces and figures in the green foliage and twigs in Meninsky's painting with a Bible passage he had once read and whose sense he had somehow retained, along with the exact chapter and verse, despite no conscious memory of it—what Theodore Flournoy called cryptomnesia. Yet we now know that memory does not work as Freud or Flournoy believed. We do not retain every experience pristine and unaltered in our memory; in fact, quite the opposite—most memories of our past, including memories of things read or seen in books, are extremely fragmentary and inaccurate.[34] Even if that Luke passage had somehow stuck in Guinness's mind, how would he have retained the exact chapter and verse? As I suggested previously, the superpowers of the unconscious as formulated in the Victorian era really seem like a deflection away from a much simpler (but of course, temporally obscene) explanation for these kinds of experiences. Precognition simply orients us to pertinent information latent in the landscape of our near future.

In this case, the Luke passage was only part of what Guinness precognized. He writes that after his discovery of hidden, unsettling depths in the painting, he took it off the wall and replaced it with another. When Merula entered the room, she didn't notice the new painting but said immediately that the room had "regained its innocence." Then comes the kicker: "A day or two later we learned it was the anniversary of Meninsky's suicide."[35]

A day or two later we learned … While Guinness implies something spookily haunting about this picture, which had perhaps been created in one of Meninsky's bouts of depression that led to his suicide in 1950, the reality is likely much more straightforward—er, straight*backward*. Learning that it was the anniversary of Meninsky's suicide—perhaps in a newspaper or magazine retrospective on the artist (Guinness unfortunately does not say)—was clearly surprising and unsettling, precisely because Guinness and his wife had recently purchased a work by the artist. Guinness's close encounter with the painting a day or two previously under the influence of Luke XXIII:31 oriented him to this learning experience as well as amplified its uncanniness, according to the time-loop logic we have seen again and again in this book. Reading a perhaps sad or disturbing story about Meninsky and his mental illness and suicide seems to have pre-oriented Guinness toward the painting a few days earlier, via the passage in Luke, but in turn that would have primed Guinness to pay attention to information (perhaps in a magazine) about Meninsky and his death. The apparent coincidence of dates (the year anniversary) is itself nothing special. Humans, and the media, like to mark anniversaries, and in this case it was probably such a commemoration that provided the occasion for the unsettling learning experience.

The detail of the Gospel of Luke is, in a way, the most bizarre and ironic aspect of Guinness's story. The actor does not mention the coincidence in his memoir, but of course by the time he had written of this event (in 1985), he had become world famous for precisely a line in which his character, *as the spirit of a dead man*, addresses "psychically" a young rebel by that very name: "*Use the force, Luke.*" The line is delivered in the moments before Luke Skywalker destroys the Death Star, and is probably the single best-known, best-loved, and best-remembered line Guinness ever uttered on stage or screen … *and Guinness hated that fact.*

To become most famous for a role in what he regarded as a

children's film was an embarrassment to Guinness—who in 1977 was the only "movie star" in *Star Wars*—hence he barely mentions the film in his writings other than being forced to acknowledge that it had made him financially comfortable in his middle age. That blow to his artistic self-respect, while granting comfort and fame, is itself arguably a kind of equivocal "survival"—another kind of existential gain set against the backdrop of a loss, even a kind of "castration." One can only wonder whether this is why his precognitive unconscious, all the way back in 1951, fastened upon a line from Luke's gospel awaiting discovery in his library, to help represent his premonition of learning how he had, in effect, survived Bernard Meninsky's suicide. As when he learned of James Dean's death, it was the other guy who got hit by the arrow.

PART FOUR

LIVES OF THE PRECOGS

"Warry, seriously, everywhere's Jerusalem, everywhere trampled or run down. If Einstein's right, then space and time are all one thing and it's, I dunno, it's like a big glass football, an American one like a Rugby ball, with the big bang at one end and the big crunch or whatever at the other. And the moments in between, the moments making up our lives, they're there forever. Nothing's moving. Nothing's changing, like a reel of film with all the frames fixed in their place and motionless till the projector beam of our awareness plays across them, and then Charlie Chaplin doffs his bowler hat and gets the girl."

— Alan Moore, *Jerusalem* (2016)

.

11

A Precognitive Seduction –
Maggy Quarles van Ufford, Carl Jung, and the Scarab

Woman is invading man's sphere more successfully every day; but there are still certain fields in which man may consider that he is rightfully entitled to a monopoly— and the purloining of scarabs in the watches of the night is surely one of them.

— P. G. Wodehouse, *Something Fresh* (1915)

Carl Jung awoke one morning in 1920 with a crick in his neck and a realization: He had fallen in love with one of his patients.

The recognition of his feelings about Maggy Quarles van Ufford, an argumentative but alluring 25-year-old aristocratic Dutchwoman who had been seeing him for a few months in his Zurich clinic, came from a vivid dream. He had seen Maggy sitting high above him atop a temple tower, some Asian temple, so high that he had to crane his neck all the way back just to see her (hence the crick in his neck when he awoke). Although the dream had an Asian ambience—clearly referring to Maggy's childhood in the Dutch East Indies—it was a line of Christian devotion that ran through his head as he lay there thinking about her, a fragment of libretto from the composer Schenkenbach about the Virgin Mary:

She sits so high above us,
No prayer will she refuse.[1]

The "love" Jung felt for Maggy had a specific name in the business: It was the *countertransference*, a common hazard first identified by Jung's erstwhile psychoanalytic "father," Freud. It was the clinician's counterpart to the strong feelings—often sexual—that patients develop toward their therapists. The theory of this bond, the transference, remains another of Freud's enduring contributions to psychotherapy. Freud came to feel that these feelings were a crucial lever in the treatment, even the central object of analysis.[2] He even suggested that the doctor's reciprocal feelings could serve as a kind of radar, helping the doctor discern the contours of the patient's unconscious by investigating the feelings the patient aroused in himself.

Jung agreed, and he also came to feel that these feelings offered an important opportunity for the doctor's growth too, not just the patient's, so long as they were handled with proper care. Maggy's case would prove to be extremely important in the evolution of his thinking about the transference and countertransference. She also would prove influential on his thinking about other topics that came to dominate his interest during the 1920s and later, such as Eastern religion. And most importantly, it was one of Maggy's dreams, probably early in her treatment—likely also sometime in 1920—that was at the heart of what became, decades later, Jung's most famous and memorable anecdote, the specimen case of his theory of synchronicity.

During one of her sessions, Maggy told Jung that she had dreamed that someone gave her a costly piece of jewelry in the form of a golden Egyptian scarab beetle. Just as Maggy was telling him her dream, Jung heard a tapping on the window behind him. He turned to see an iridescent green-gold beetle butting its head against the glass "in the obvious effort to get into the dark room."[3] Recognizing the insect as a rose-chafer, a European relative of the Egyptian scarab or dung beetle, he opened the window, cupped the insect in his hands, and handed it to Maggy. "Here's your scarab," he said.[4] Jung described that this remarkable moment had a transforming effect on his hyperrational, closed-off patient—it "punctured the desired hole in her rationalism"[5] and enabled her therapy to make new headway.

It is the most enchanting story in Jung's writings, and probably one of the most oft-retold psychotherapeutic narratives. It is also probably the most famous Dunne dream in modern times: In the dream, someone handed the dreamer a beetle; that "someone" turned out to be her doctor the next day. Because it was the telling of the dream that led the doctor to notice and admit the beetle into his office, it was also a time loop—like so many other examples of self-fulfilling prophecy we have seen already in this book. Also, like other precognitive dreams, this one seems to have contained a representation (or pre-presentation) of the moment's significance to the dreamer: The wriggling, hapless insect in Jung's cupped hand became, in the dream the night before, a "golden … costly" piece of jewelry.

Yet precognition and time loops are not what come to most readers' minds when they read either Jung's descriptions of this event or any of its many retellings in metaphysical or parapsychological literature. There are various reasons for this, including that confusing time-looping aspect. We mistakenly suspect that tautologies are the same as paradoxes, and (to paraphrase J. R. R. Tolkien in the epigram for this book) we are especially liable to disbelieve in a prophecy when we ourselves had a hand in bringing about its fulfilment. There is also the distracting matter of the insect's apparent connection to ancient Egyptian religion—which we will examine momentarily. But it has also not helped matters that until just a few years ago, all we knew about this event or this patient was limited to a few paragraphs in Jung's published writings on synchronicity. That, fortunately, has changed.

In a 2014 paper in the *Journal of Analytical Psychology*, Vicente de Moura, a Jungian analyst and Curator of the Pictures Archive of the C. G. Jung Institute in Zurich, for the first time revealed Maggy's identity and details of her biography. He also presented correspondence between her and Jung that reveals other precognitive episodes in her therapy, as well as identified other places in Jung's writings where she appears.[6] We are now at last able to place the famous scarab episode within the larger context of the dreamer's life and treatment.[7]

The fascinating story of this once-anonymous Dutch precog can help us to formulate and apply a new, much more powerful theory of meaningful coincidence. "Synchronicities," I argue, are probably not the product of ancient archetypal patterns imprinting themselves on our lives, as Jung claimed. They appear instead to be misrecognized time loops, arising from our hitherto-unacknowledged precognitive natures. Yet, like whirlpools in the fabric of social reality, such time loops often draw the meaningful stuff of culture into their vortex, confusedly making cultural symbols—in this case, an ancient Egyptian symbol of rebirth—appear to wag the dog of physical events.

Puncturing the Desired Hole

Maggy, whose full name was Henriette Madeleine Quarles van Ufford, had moved to Zurich from her home in Holland in early 1918, along with her two younger sisters, Lizzie and Mischa.[8] Mischa, the youngest, had developed some psychological difficulty as a result of the rigid, puritanical upbringing the girls had received from their grandmother, who had raised the girls since their mother's death in 1908; so Maggy, who had read about Dr. Jung's new psychotherapeutic approach, arranged for Mischa to be treated by him.[9] For Maggy, though, it seems to have offered a chance to escape the stultifying aristocratic atmosphere she and her sisters had endured their whole lives up until that point.

According to de Moura, the Quarles girls came from a family that could trace its ancestry back as far as the Middle Ages on their father's side and had reaped enormous wealth from the spice trade with the Orient. Their grandfather had owned an indigo plantation in India. Their father, Charles Gerard Quarles van Ufford, was a former high officer in the Dutch Navy and had been a successful administrator in the Dutch East Indies, where the family had been living when Maggy was born. The family moved back to Europe in or about 1897, after the three-year-old Maggy fell ill with malaria. This is possibly an important detail, as precogs often suffer some sort of childhood illness or trauma. (J. W. Dunne, for instance, spent three years confined to a movable bed following a serious accident at age six.) In Holland, Charles Gerard became very wealthy in the stock market and continued to generously support his daughters.[10]

Maggy never fit in with her aristocratic European life. Jung mentioned in an unpublished lecture about this patient (where she also appears anonymously) that she was extremely intelligent and sensitive and did not share the interests of her peers or her culture. She insisted on behaving unconventionally and, as a young woman, refused to marry[11]—though with her wealth, her looks, her passion (Jung wrote that she played the piano with such intensity that her body temperature quickly rose above 100 degrees[12]), and her brains, she ought to have been quite a catch for any man of suitable quality. He would have to put up with her independent-mindedness and argumentativeness though, a product of her keen intelligence and education. In her conservative social world, these qualities did not contribute to her being happy.[13] But now, in Zurich, freed from the stifling atmosphere of her youth, in an intellectually exciting milieu dominated by the psychiatrist-mystic Jung, all that was changing.[14]

Her sister Mischa's treatment apparently did the trick. A year after starting treatment, she married a Swiss artist, Ignaz Epper, and followed the artistic path of many of Jung's female patients, becoming a sculptor and eventually settling with her husband in Switzerland's countercultural capital, Ascona.[15] It was in late 1919 or early 1920 that Maggy herself began treatment with Jung[16]—and it is hard not to think that this may have been part of her intention all along when she packed up and moved from Holland to Zurich with her sisters in tow. It was Maggy who had arranged Mischa's treatment, and Maggy was, in her own way, as much in need of what Jung could offer.

When she arrived in Jung's clinic, Maggy had already seen two other therapists—one for two months, another for just a week—but had, in Jung's words, "exploded" both of the poor souls.[17] Maggy told Jung that at the beginning of both of those aborted therapies, she had had the same dream: being dropped off at a frontier railway station and facing an impenetrable dark forest. Neither of the first two therapists had been up to the task of leading her through that forest—and both later gave up being analysts.[18] Maggy was a tough case. Could Jung succeed where his predecessors had failed?

Although he publicly played the scientist role his whole life, Jung was more than (although some critics would say less than) a psychologist. He wanted to be, and increasingly saw himself as, a spiritual teacher, a guru.[19] It was his increasingly subjective and mystical approach to the unconscious and its world of what he called archetypes that had precipitated his break from Freud seven years before Maggy entered his care.

Although he publicly claimed (wrongly, as we will see) that Maggy's scarab dream was unique in his experience,[20] Jung was no stranger to uncanny coincidences, as well as other experiences and events we would now call paranormal. Nearly as storied as the scarab episode are the mysterious "exteriorizations" Jung experienced in Freud's Vienna office while on a visit in 1909, during a dispute precisely over the question of psychic phenomena, acceptance of which somewhat divided the two men. (The difference was not as stark as sometimes claimed—Freud just urged greater caution.) Jung described feeling a burning sensation in his diaphragm, followed by a loud crack from Freud's bookcase. As Jung described the incident, Freud was shocked when Jung said it was about to happen second time, and it did. Freud's initial puzzlement at this experience later waned when he found that the bookcases kept making the sound even after Jung's departure.[21]

Jung also reported ghostly apparitions as well as dreams and visions that would have fit perfectly in the case files that had been amassed and studied since the late 1800s by researchers at the Society for Psychical Research. Their theoretical rubric to account for these occurrences, again, was telepathy, a kind of mental contact between people across space and, to some extent perhaps, even across time. In their 1886 volume *Phantasms of the Living*, Edmund Gurney, Frederic Myers, and Frank Podmore presented hundreds of examples, along with a catalogue of "meaningful coincidences" that they also explained via the telepathy concept.

But the telepathy theory, built on the metaphor of long-distance electronic communication that had been linking up people between countries and even between continents in the latter half of the 19th century, did not help much to explain how something like the scarab episode could occur. Telepathy implied mental contact between humans—or at least, between a human and a fairly sentient creature. A beetle hardly fits the bill as the sort of being who could be "summoned" by some unconscious telepathic call. And the comprehensive framework of ESP developed by the Rhines in the 1930s also did not seem adequate to account for the *symbolic meaningfulness* of some psychic experiences.

It would take three decades and the help of his friend and patient, the quantum physicist Wolfgang Pauli, for Jung to formulate his own theory of paranormal and coincidental phenomena, the "acausal connecting principle" he named synchronicity. This principle, he confidently claimed, could account for purported resonances between an individual's mental life and ancient mythic motifs, such as (in Maggy's case) the resonance between a therapeutic breakthrough and a scarab beetle, an ancient Egyptian symbol of metamorphosis and rebirth. The scarab story was the centerpiece of the 1951 Eranos lecture in which Jung publicly debuted his new theory, "On Synchronicity."[22] He also gave an abbreviated version of the story but expanded on aspects of its meaning in a longer 1952 monograph, *Synchronicity: An Acausal Connecting Principle*. There, he elaborates on the "archetypal" significance of the event:

The scarab is a classic example of a rebirth symbol. The ancient Egyptian Book of What Is in the Netherworld describes how the dead sun-god changes himself at the tenth station into Khepri, the scarab, and then, at the twelfth station, mounts the barge which carries the rejuvenated sun-god into the morning sky. The only difficulty here is that with educated people cryptomnesia often cannot be ruled out with certainty (although my patient did not happen to know this symbol). But this does not alter the fact that the psychologist is continually coming up against cases where the emergence of symbolic parallels cannot be explained without the hypothesis of the collective unconscious.[23]

Psychologists love to debunk synchronicities, of course, just as much as they love to debunk prophetic dreams. They point out that humans are supremely bad with statistics, underestimating the frequency with which "impossible" coincidences might occur.[24] We're also bad at being objective: The meaningfulness of an event may simply be a function of taking a particular, egocentric point of view on it. Psychologist Ruma Falk found that an egocentric bias causes us to disproportionally notice chance events that bear on our own interests and priorities. Participants in Falk's experiments at Hebrew University in Jerusalem were more surprised by coincidences that happened to them in their own lives (either in the course of an experiment or in the past) than by identical coincidences reported to have happened to another individual. A coincidence centered on another person, Falk says, seems unremarkable, just "one of many events that could have happened."[25] (It is a problem that, not accidentally, besets attributions of meaningfulness to dreams as well. Since they concern very private associations and thoughts, dreams interpreted in public are seldom as persuasive or compelling to others as they seem to the dreamer.)

Whether or not a coincidence like a scarab beetle showing up just at the moment someone is telling you their dream about such an insect is random from the point of view of an indifferent, meaningless universe, these things are meaningful in terms of the associative links in the individual witness's head, and those links bias how we perceive and interpret the world. If we take Carl Jung's concept of synchronicity simply as a description of the brain's appetite for meaningful and self-centric associations, his definition, "an acausal connecting principle," would raise few psychological or even neuroscientific eyebrows. The brain is an "acausal connecting organ," an insatiable meaning maker, with a highly self-centric bias.

But Jung meant much more by his concept. He saw synchronicity as potentially being able to account for how events in the external world actually link up and unfold. It was a new explanatory principle to complement physical causality. In his monograph, he wrote:

> [I]t is impossible, with our present resources, to explain ESP, or the fact of meaningful coincidence, as a phenomenon of energy. This makes an end of the causal explanation as well, for "effect" cannot be understood as anything except a phenomenon of energy. Therefore it cannot be a question of cause and effect, but of a falling together in time, a kind of simultaneity. Because of this quality of simultaneity, I have picked on the term "synchronicity" to designate a hypothetical factor equal in rank to causality as a principle of explanation.[26]

Jung generalized from the scarab case, as well as other clinical parallels he had observed between ancient myths and his patients' dreams and fantasies, to assert that *all* meaningful (i.e., non-random) coincidences have an archetypal basis in the collective unconscious. While in some of his writings the latter constructs may not imply anything more than a domain of shared, primitive instincts that express themselves in similar ways across cultures, his writings on synchronicity imply something like a field of shared meanings that extend beyond the individual and can directly interact with the material world. In a 1957 letter, he asked "How does it come that even inanimate objects are capable of behaving as if they were acquainted with my thoughts?"[27] Synchronicity was his answer.

Part of the concept's continued popularity may reflect the brilliant energetic suggestiveness of Jung's neologism. Despite his explicit claim that it operates outside the domain of classical energetic causes and effects, the word *synchronicity* unmistakably connotes energy, resembling as it does the word *electricity*; it implies a dynamism and a current moving and flowing among material configurations and mental forms, ideas, and symbols. It is easy to imagine synchronicity as a kind of inner vitality in individual and collective history, something in motion that, when touched, can shock, and can create short-circuits—for instance, between a moment of therapeutic epiphany and an ancient rebirth symbol. The "exteriorizations" Jung experienced in Freud's study also carry this sense of an energetic, if not transfer, then mutual arising. Had Jung written his monograph a few decades later, he might naturally have seized on the idiom of "entanglement" and "nonlocality" to describe such occurrences.

Just as it promised to mediate the psychical and the physical worlds, Jung's synchronicity theory also deftly bridged the two sides of his own self: the scientist and the mystic. The scarab incident he used to illustrate his new scientific theory became a kind of public certification of his guru role. At the moment he opens his office window and catches the beetle and hands it to the astonished young woman who has just been telling him her dream about a scarab, Jung the psychiatrist becomes Jung the magician-shaman—a wizard who, even if he has not actually conjured the animal with his powers, nevertheless has had the presence of mind, the wit, to capitalize on its fortuitous appearance in that instant and use it to effect a therapeutic epiphany. According to Jung scholar Roderick Main, in the same way his gesture "punctured the desired hole" in his patient's rationalistic resistances, he intended his new concept to puncture a hole in the rationalism of the West.[28]

Unfortunately, Jung's bold new concept has not really led to any greater understanding of meaningful coincidences. Some of Jung's readers, even those appreciative of his many other contributions to psychology, have argued that this concept actually has had the opposite effect, obscuring these phenomena and even discouraging serious study of them.[29] For one thing, calling events "acausal" effectively forecloses scientific consideration, since science deals in causes. As psychologist Charles Tart puts it, it enables one to lazily say, "Well, it's synchronistic, it's forever beyond my understanding."[30] And by implying the simultaneity or *synchrony* of such events, it encourages us to ignore important, potentially significant aspects of their unfolding in time.

The scarab incident is a perfect example of the obscuring effect of Jung's synchronistic framing. By focusing (egotistically, we might say) on the literal co-incidence Jung himself was in a position to witness in his office—the beetle appearing simultaneously with Maggy *telling him* her dream—Jung effaced the more astonishing and interesting relationship between what transpired in his office and Maggy's dream the *previous* night. The result, again, is that few readers even notice the precognitive dimension of the scarab vignette, or if they do, they are distracted by Jung's implication that the whole nexus of occurrences (the patient's dream, the arrival of the beetle while she was describing it, and his "intervention" by letting it into his office) was somehow the effect or result of timeless archetypal patterns imprinting themselves on human events, stage-managing such occurrences to edify and enlighten the people involved.

This kind of reasoning easily veers into extreme implausibility, as in Jung's suggestion that the beetle was "obviously" trying to get into his dark consulting room—he added, in a 1960 letter, "as if it had understood that it must play its mythological role as a symbol of rebirth."[31] Is Jung just waxing poetic here? Readers may not take it that way, and in his letter he goes on to add: "Even inanimate objects behave occasionally in the same way—meteorological phenomena, for instance." Plain common sense, and a moment's thought, should dispel any such notion of the insect's motives, however. The room was darker than the yard outside, and thus the insect would have seen the sky reflected in the window; its trying to "get into the room," as Jung put it, was really its confused attempt to either evade, fight, or mate with its own reflection. It happens to insects all the time. (Jung can be forgiven for not knowing that beetles with iridescent shells, like the rose chafer, have optical systems designed to respond to such surfaces in other beetles; this causes them to also be particularly drawn to the polarized light reflected off glass windowpanes.)

This may seem a pedantic quibble, but the "archetypal" significance of the beetle also dwindles considerably when we consider the cultural context of Jung and his work. In two critical studies, *The Jung Cult* and *The Aryan Christ*, psychiatry historian Richard Noll argued that much of what Jung cited as "smoking gun" evidence for the collective unconscious and archetypes could be accounted for by cryptomnesia—patients reproducing in dreams and fantasies ideas encountered in their prior reading.[32] Although we need to be cautious of cryptomnesia invoked to debunk psychic claims, for reasons discussed earlier, what makes Noll's argument compelling in Jung's case is that his world was suffused with reading material that would supply his patients with precisely the mythological symbols that so interested him. Not only were they widely available in scholarly works, since ancient symbolism and pagan religions were all the rage at that point, but they were also available in publications of the Theosophical Society. For years, the

Theosophical Publishing House had been flooding Europe and America with inexpensive, Theosophically inflected translations of ancient wisdom literature and Eastern philosophy. Spiritual and intellectual seekers of the sort who flooded to Jung's clinic were avid readers of these books, as was Jung himself.

Noll argues that Jung's strong personality and ego contributed to turning his clinic into an echo chamber that amplified the archetypal signal. He specifically sought mythological material in his patients' dreams and fantasies; patients were rewarded when they supplied it (and ignored when they didn't); and a powerful selection or file-drawer effect made ancient myths and symbols seem like some objective organizing principle in our lives when they were more likely just the doctor's own interests (and his patients' reading) writ large. To this day, it is mainly patients in Jungian analysis who report archetypal or alchemical dreams (just as it is mainly patients in Freudian analysis who produce Oedipal ones[33]). Noll thus concluded that the collective unconscious is not some transpersonal Platonic wellspring of shared symbolic motifs but, much more humbly, simply the books on Jung's own impressive bookshelf and those of his well-read patients.

Some later writers on coincidence have departed from archetypes and focused more on the role of "intention" in creating synchronistic events. In his book *Connecting with Coincidence*, psychiatrist Bernard D. Beitman argues that it was Jung's "intense desire" for something irrational to open the mind of his patient that drew the insect to the window.[34] As mentioned earlier, there is an extensive and interesting literature on mind-over-matter effects (psychokinesis or PK)[35]; and some researchers like Dean Radin have even tried to harmonize the findings on psi phenomena with the idiom of "magic."[36] Yet cases like the scarab incident, where an outcome appears complexly symbolic, make intention particularly hard to swallow as an explanation. How exactly could Jung's intense desire act as a magnet for *that precise species* of insect? What Beitman is suggesting presupposes either "superpowers" that go well beyond even the unconscious mental feats Freud and his predecessors had posited or, alternatively, some omniscient higher knower capable of aligning our intentions with the infinitely complex webs of material causation governing objectively unfolding events. Once again, the fact that we live in a world of information—including cultural information like books and symbols—does not mean the universe speaks our mental language. At best, both the archetypal and intentional explanations lack parsimony.

Fortunately, a causal (with a big asterisk beside the word) explanation for meaningful coincidences is no longer nearly as unthinkable as it was in Jung's day, thanks to advances in several fields that, as we saw earlier, seem to be converging on a plausible (and indeed even materialistic) answer to how experiences from our future may reflux into our past and inform our dreams, thoughts, and actions. It remains to test these hypotheses, deepen our understanding of physical laws and the brain with new methods and technologies, and persist in our inquiries into psychology and nature with the healthy presumption that we don't yet know everything about the physical world or how the mind/brain works. We cannot simply reject anomalous phenomena that don't fit into the current materialist paradigm, but it is also too soon to appeal to explanatory factors beyond physical causation, as the latter is turning out to be far more rich, varied, and interesting than once believed. Causation really seems to go both directions in time.

With the scarab incident, the simplest explanation is, I argue, the most powerful: Maggy's dream simply oriented her toward a highly meaningful moment, a reward, in her near future. That moment was partly brought about by her own actions, informed by that dream. The effect was its own cause.

The rewards of that moment—to both of the humans in that room, if not to the hapless beetle—would have been immense. Jung's parenthetical note that his patient "did not happen to know this symbol"[37] enables us to infer a crucial detail: that he went ahead and explained the symbolism of scarab beetles to her during the session. Moments in therapy when the doctor finds one's case particularly interesting and resonant with his particular interests, even if (or especially if) it entails a sacrifice of our prior, more limiting beliefs, feel gratifying and inspiring. Jung's ability to translate patients' mundane individual experiences into timeless mythic themes was precisely what many patients sought in his clinic. He called the process of expanding beyond our previous one-sided views "individuation," but it could also be called the *jouissance of reframing*. Destruction of our previous self-conception, replaced by a broader self-understanding, is a kind of sublimely rewarding "survival," which again is ultimately the focus of most precognitive and premonitory experiences.[38]

The rewards for Jung would have been similarly palpable. Dream symbols with ancient mythic resonance were exactly what he sought from his patients, as they seemed to validate the very construct on which he had been staking his career and reputation for a decade. And scarabs were particularly exciting to him, as he himself had had a powerful vision of a scarab in December 1913, six years before Maggy entered treatment with him. It was the very first of his visions in his "confrontation with the unconscious"—a creative, near-psychotic period of depression and soul-searching that ensued after his traumatic break from Freud. In the vision, he dropped into a cave where he saw the following scene:

> At first I could make out nothing, but then I saw that there was running water. In it a corpse floated by, a youth with blond hair and a wound in the head. He was followed by a gigantic black scarab and then by a red, newborn sun, rising up out of the depths of the water. ... I was stunned by this vision. I realized, of course, that it was a hero and solar myth, a drama of death and renewal, the rebirth symbolized by the Egyptian scarab.[39]

Jung described and painted this and other visions during the years 1913-1917 in his private journal of transformation, his "Red Book." In that book, he also described sitting in a desert, watching a black scarab beetle blindly pushing its dung-ball, "living [its] beautiful myth."[40]

As a rule, Jung was quite ready to divulge intimately personal material to his patients, and on other occasions admitted doing so with Maggy. For instance, he told her his dream about her as the Virgin Mary, and what it meant.[41] He was also known to bring out his "Red Book" and show it to his most trusted patients.[42] We have no proof, but it is reasonable to suppose that after he handed Maggy the wriggling gold-green beetle, he would not only have explained its meaning but also told her of his own scarab visions and perhaps may have even shown her his private journal. If Maggy did not already by this point feel as though she was being initiated into the ancient mysteries, this session would have been a real turning point for her—truly "golden."

The promise of intellectual as well as spiritual excitement is what drew many people like Maggy to Zurich and to Jung's clinic in the 1920s and later, and what kept them in his circle of devoted patients and students. Especially for his women followers, who at that time in history were often compelled to fill less intellectually satisfying social and domestic roles, "treatment" with Jung was really a master class in history, philosophy, and world religions, along with permission to think and express themselves in a much larger way than they had been accustomed to doing.[43] Jung's world of mythology and mysticism seems to have been precisely what Maggy longed for, so different from the supremely boring and traditional role that her life in Holland had prepared her to play.

Again, to explain the scarab incident there is no need to appeal to some transpersonal domain of electric archetypes; nor is it helpful to invoke the "intense desire" of Carl Jung. Maggy Quarles van Ufford dreamed of a scarab because the next day, her myth-obsessed doctor would hand her a rose chafer and deliver an exciting, learned discourse on the significance of the scarab in Egyptian religion—a profoundly meaningful and rewarding moment in her life. It was thus Maggy's own precognitive brain, not Jung's "very creative, very strong mind"[44] (as Beitman puts it), that created that meaningful moment ... and that gave Jung his most enchanting story. Thanks to Vicente de Moura's research, we can now give credit where credit is due.

But Beitman is correct that Jung "completed the coincidence"[45] by opening the window and handing the beetle to his astonished patient. This illustrates not only the time-looping nature of precognition but also the important fact that its rewards are very often *social* experiences, confluences of two (or more) lives that enfold and entwine in some profound and seemingly fateful way. J. B. Priestley observed how the future-influencing-present effect often manifests especially around romantic connections.[46] As Freud noted in his debunking of Frau B.'s premonitory dream, "accidents which seem preconcerted ... are to be found in every love story."[47] If precognition serves a social orienting function, we might look for it to manifest particularly strongly in situations where a desired romantic connection is impeded, either by physical separation or social taboo.[48] Therapeutic contexts, with their powerful and (usually) not-acted-upon transference and countertransference feelings, ought to be the perfect cloud chamber in which to capture time loops. And indeed, it appears that the scarab incident was just one part of a larger "precognitive seduction" of Jung by Maggy.

Cupid's Causal Arrows

De Moura revealed that Maggy was also the patient Jung described at length in "The Realities of Practical Psychotherapy," a very interesting and suggestive lecture he delivered in Bern, Switzerland in May, 1937 but never published.[49] Here as in the scarab case, Jung affected clinical detachment and pretended to find Maggy boring ... at least at first. This patient wore her rationalism like an armor, he said, parrying his efforts at opening her to the irrational, to the mysteries, with deft ripostes from Kant and Schopenhauer, all the arsenal of her extensive education and reading. He described that she had a "compulsive argumentativeness and ... fondness for philosophical hair-splitting that was quite intolerable despite her high intelligence."[50] Jung described that her unconscious world also had a somewhat impenetrable Oriental flavor, exotic and deeply out of synch with Europe, which he surmised must have been the product of her early childhood and the Malay *ayah*, or wet nurse, who had suckled and cared for her in the first years of her life.

It was in this lecture that Jung described how this 25-year-old woman came to him after seeing two other analysts unsuccessfully, having dreamed in both cases of being at a frontier train station gazing into an impenetrable dark forest—the dreams mentioned earlier in this chapter. Jung interpreted the forest as her unconscious, into which her therapists were not equipped to guide her. Jung asked his patient if she had had a similar dream when she started treatment with him; she "gave an embarrassed smile" and related the following dream:

> *I was at a frontier station. A customs official was examining the passengers one by one. I had nothing but my handbag, and when it came to my turn I answered with good conscience that I had nothing to declare. But he said, pointing to my handbag: "What have you got in there?" And to my boundless astonishment he pulled a large mattress, and then a second one, out of my bag."* She was so frightened that she woke up.[51]

If this had been Freud's clinic in Vienna and Jung had been his erstwhile mentor who saw sex organs in everything, the sexual meaning of an authority figure pulling things out of her handbag (not to mention the railway setting) would have been clear enough. The fact that it was a "customs official" doing the pulling might have also pointed toward its being a sexual wish aimed at Jung himself, perhaps also a wish to be delivered of a child by him. What was Jung, the famous anthropologist of the soul, but a kind of "customs official"? Likely it *was* clear to Jung, but perhaps he was just being delicate in interpreting it to his patient (he reported) as a dream of a disguised bourgeois wish for a conventional marriage (the mattresses being "marriage beds"; it may indeed have been *Jung* she wished to marry). Maggy strongly resisted this interpretation. Although she was seeing a very nice respectable man that she loved—probably Adam Reichstein (the lawyer son of her landlady Gustawa Reichstein[52]), whom she later did marry—she fiercely did not want to wed ... that is, unless Jung himself compelled her to. Would he compel her to? (She wanted to be forced.) Not possible, he insisted.[53]

We can read between the lines here that it is nothing other than Maggy's transference love for her doctor that accounts for her protest at his suggestion that she really wanted to marry her boyfriend. Jung's description of the verbal outpouring from Maggy that ensued is almost Lovecraftian in its hyperbolic allusiveness to his patient's primeval sexual wantonness, reinforcing the impression that she was trying to seduce her doctor. It certainly seems to have had the desired effect at arousing his interest:

> Behind these resistances, it then turned out, there was hidden a most singular fantasy of a quite unimaginable erotic adventure that surpassed anything I had ever come across in my experience. I felt my head reeling, I thought of nymphomaniac possession, of weird perversions, of completely depraved erotic fantasies that rambled meaninglessly on and on, of latent schizophrenia, where at least the nearest comparative material could be found.[54]

According to Jung, what followed was several weeks of therapeutic impasse—maybe even embarrassed silence. Maggy said nothing of interest, perhaps ashamed of her divulgence of her wild sex fantasies, and Jung could make no headway ... until one night, Jung himself had the vivid dream mentioned earlier, about Maggy sitting high atop a castle tower far above his head, so that he had to bend his head all the way back to see her up there, "golden in the light of the evening sun."[55] He awoke with the lines from Schenkenbach in his head, about the Virgin Mary. Again, if it had been Freud, he would have had no trouble admitting this bending his head all the way back and the tall tower were phallic, sexual symbols.

Thanks to remarks Jung made a decade later to his protégé, the English analyst Peter Baynes, we know that his feelings toward Maggy indeed went beyond Platonic admiration for her ideas and her interesting mandalas. Jung admitted deep attachment to his Dutch patient and even described her to Baynes as "the ideal anima-woman."[56] "Anima-woman" is Jung-speak for a kind of intellectual and erotic muse.[57] There is no evidence, either in the material de Moura has made available or in Jung's writings, that Jung transgressed ethical bounds with Maggy, as several biographers have suspected him to have done with other female patients.[58] But—and this indeed is the main thrust of his 1937 lecture—Jung did argue that if he was to help this patient break out of her too-rationalistic shell, he himself needed to walk the dangerous path of giving her more than the stony and impenetrable silence that was Freud's preferred method and that has been the standard of psychoanalytic practice since then. Thus, instead of concealing his dream from Maggy, he divulged it to her, "with the result that the superficial symptomatology, her argumentativeness, her insistence on always being right, and her touchiness vanished."[59]

Here Jung's description of the effect of his intervention—this time by telling his own dream—is almost a clone of the response he says his offering her the scarab provoked: softening her extreme "masculine" rationalism. [60] In fact, since this lecture was written over a decade before his works on synchronicity, the cloning would have gone in reverse: This 1937 narrative of therapeutic epiphany, unpublished and languishing in his desk drawer, may be the source or template for the scarab story.[61] It is because of the similarity between the two accounts that I surmise the scarab incident likely occurred around the same time, early in her therapy when she was still relatively closed off to the irrational and Jung felt frustrated with her treatment—thus probably in 1920.

Jung relates that his divulgence of his feelings toward his patient triggered an unfolding series of baffling—and sometimes, though he did not say so outright in his paper, erotic—physical symptoms in Maggy: "They first took the form of an indefinable excitation in the perineal region, and she dreamt that a white elephant was coming out of her genitals. She was so impressed by this that she tried to carve the elephant out of ivory...." The symptoms migrated then to her uterus, requiring a referral to a gynecologist ("an inflamed swelling ... about the size of a pea, which refused to heal ... and merely shifted from place to place"), then to her bladder ("She had to leave the room two or three times during the consulting hour. No local infection could be found."), after which it went to her intestines ("causing gurgling noises and sounds of splashing that could be heard even outside the room" as well as "explosive evacuations of the bowels"). Then, after these symptoms abated, Maggy developed a fantasy "that the top of her skull was growing soft ... and that a bird with a long sharp beak was coming down to pierce through the fontanelle as far as the diaphragm."[62]

And here's where it gets really interesting. Coincidentally—or the later Jung might have said, synchronistically—it was only Jung's encounter, right at this time, with the book *The Serpent Power* by Sir John Woodroffe, writing under the pen name of "Arthur Avalon," that enabled him to explicate Maggy's symptoms for her. This volume, published in 1918 by the Theosophical Publishing House, introduced the West to Kundalini yoga and included descriptions of the chakra system that closely matched the symptoms Maggy was producing. The base chakra, Jung learned in Woodroffe's book, is symbolized by an elephant, corresponding to her dream. The second, sexual chakra is symbolized by a Leviathan-like water monster, "symbol for the devouring and birth-giving womb." And so on.[63]

Jung was puzzled and amazed at this correspondence. He acknowledges the unlikelihood that Maggy had somehow, as a toddler in the Orient, imbibed a whole sophisticated Tantric symbology—an intimate understanding of the body's chakra system, as well as knowledge of the sexual serpent Kundalini that rested at its base—from that illiterate Malaysian *ayah* of hers. Maggy could not remember her young childhood or even a word of Malay. Even Jung, who timidly draws out a few parallels between the chakra system and Western philosophy, admits his perplexity and does not glibly chalk it up to the collective unconscious. We must of course give Jung the benefit of the doubt here, that Maggy herself was not reading *The Serpent Power* concurrently, which would have invalidated his lecture (a lecture that Maggy's younger sister Mischa attended, in fact).[64] But given what we already know about Maggy's dream-precognition, it seems perfectly possible that her bodily symptoms, along with their associated dreams and fantasies like the elephant coming out her genitals, precognitively (or presentimentally) anticipated the doctor's learned explication, based in this case on *his* imminent or concurrent reading. It would be a case of "feeling her future" not just with her dreams but with her whole body, in what looks very much like a hysterical seduction, a kind of erotic performance.[65] Jung notes that Maggy found her bizarre symptomatology not unpleasurable but exciting.

That precognition could be somatized this way—as a Kundalini serpent's dance of tantalizing, strange symptoms wending their way up

Maggy's chakras, tied to the rewards of her doctor's learned explication, which was in turn based on a (to him) exciting new book about Eastern religion—is a natural extension of J. W. Dunne's insights about the relationship between precognitive dreams and imminent learning experiences. It also is a natural extension, I think, of the findings in presentiment research. Like Daryl Bem's study participants tending to accurately pick a curtain on a computer monitor that would reveal an erotic photo, or like Dean Radin's subjects displaying heightened arousal before seeing emotionally stimulating pictures, Maggy seems to have been "presponding" to future stimuli in Jung's consulting room with her body as well as her dreams. Her inflammations and excitations and "gurgling noises" may have been, in effect, the real-life equivalent of Tyrone Slothrop's premonitory erections in *Gravity's Rainbow*.

Richard Noll's critical take on the collective unconscious assumes a fascinating new dimension when we consider the possible role of precognition as the mysterious X factor in our engagement with symbols materially encoded in culture—for instance, in popular spiritual books. The precognitive episodes in Maggy's treatment suggest the possibility that at least some of what Noll quite reasonably assumed was cryptomnesia may really have been *pro*mnesia—the production of mythological motifs in dreams and fantasies as a precognitive orientation toward exciting learning experiences ahead in Jung's clinic. In other words, it may not have been necessary for a patient to have read about some mythological motif before producing it in a dream or fantasy if Jung was going to fascinatingly supply the meaning during the next session. As I suggested previously, the precognitive unconscious cannot *know* the meaning of what it is producing; the meaning only emerges when a dream or fantasy or behavior is interpreted in light of subsequent events.[66] Jung would naturally have interpreted such productions by his patients as evidence that his favorite mythological motifs had a universal and transpersonal significance.

Another experience several years later in Maggy's therapy, in which she again precognized something *Jung* was reading and was going to tell her about, further supports such a possibility. In a letter probably sent in 1930, Maggy, whose surname was now Reichstein, reminded Jung of dreams anticipating the birth of her two children a few years earlier. Those dreams by themselves are not necessarily compelling as evidence of precognition, as married women of childbearing age may be liable to have such dreams and are also liable to become pregnant. But in the same letter, she also reminded her former doctor of another dream that bore the same coincidental, if not exactly "synchronistic," relationship to her next visit with him that the scarab dream did. This one had a much more explicitly erotic overtone, reflecting the powerful transference feelings Maggy clearly had still felt toward him while she was being treated. It also turned out to be about a book on Jung's bookshelf.

In the letter (which de Moura reproduces in his article), Maggy recalled that she had dreamed she was resting in bed, when Jung's spirit visited her "from the afterlife," bending down and kissing her. His kiss held "something very vital," which, she wrote, would bring "an improvement of my condition."[67] Maggy wrote that she brought this dream to her next session, and Jung told her that before she had arrived, he had been with another patient but had felt the inexplicable urge to cut that session short, and then did so. He said that after his patient left, he pulled down a book at random from his bookshelf and opened it to a story about a sick man who had a vision of his dead wife, along with another person who had conducted her soul to him from the afterlife. The resemblance of this story to Maggy's dream was obvious.

At that point, Maggy recalled in her letter, Jung dozed briefly— they had been seated next to each other. He then awoke to tell her a second story from the same book, which he had forgotten about. In that story, a clergyman was visited by a sick woman but felt powerless to help her. The same evening, the clergyman dozed while thinking about the woman, and the next day he received a letter from her thanking him for visiting her in spirit form during the evening—a visit which "gave her a sense of extreme well-being."[68] This story also closely resembled Maggy's dream.

De Moura suggests that the book Jung had consulted in this instance may have been none other than *Phantasms of the Living*—Jung had two copies on his shelf, the original and a German translation—but notes that neither story (as Maggy recalls them) matches exactly any of the stories in that book.[69] It is possible that it was a different book, or there may be a "telephone game" effect here—Maggy's letter was asking for clarification on a memory several years removed, of a story told by another person. It could even be that Jung changed or embellished the story when telling it to her; at this great distance, there is no telling. But whether Jung recounted the stories accurately or not does not matter. The point is that Maggy seems to have dreamed in advance of another moment in her treatment. As in the scarab incident, it was her dream that prompted Jung's divulgence—making it another time loop.

And once again, as with her "Kundalini" symptoms and dreams, this one centered on one of her doctor's imminent reading experiences—or really, his excited sharing of it. The erotic nature of the dream hints yet again at a fascinating precognitive dimension of the transference relationship that few clinicians have even begun to explore.[70]

We do not know what context or issue Maggy Reichstein was dealing with at that point in her life, but clearly this episode made enough of an impact on her that she reminded her former doctor of it in a letter years later. The fact that what Jung bore her in the dream was "very vital" may be another dream pre-presentation of this event's significance for her. What was "vital" in it may have been simply the amazing-unsettling-rewarding emotional mélange that time loops always provoke in us bears of little brain.[71]

According to de Moura, Maggy remained in treatment with Jung through the mid-1920s but continued to take inspiration from him and remained in his circle long after her treatment was over. She debated with him, corresponded with him, painted mandalas (she was regarded as a gifted artist and became known in his inner circle as the "Mandala Lady"), translated his works into Dutch, and influenced him in other ways until the end of his life (he died in 1961). Even though she remained anonymous in his writings, Jung privately credited her with awakening him to Eastern philosophy and religion. "I learned a lot from you," he wrote in one 1929 letter.[72] Maggy died in 1975, at 81.

The Hermeneutic Moment

However evocative it may have been for generations of Jung's readers, the theory of synchronicity, like Freud's wish-fulfillment theory of dreams, ultimately obfuscates the precognitive dimension of the individual unconscious and fails to adequately explain the time-looping effects precognition gives rise to in our lives and relationships. Those temporal tautologies are among the difficulties that have always kept people from taking the entire topic seriously and shunted investigators onto other, less hard-to-think and less taboo paths. Synchronicity, like the unconscious itself, is a kind of "halfway house" concept. It offers people a convenient idiom in which to talk about an extremely common, paranormal-seeming dimension of human life, "impossible coincidences," without glibly dismissing their significance, yet at the cost of reframing them as something beyond or outside rational understanding altogether, safely sequestered from scientific inquiry. We can now do better.

Dunnean precognition, as an orientation toward meaningful experiences and encounters ahead, is both more powerful as an explanation and more human. If the material world (including myths and symbols materially encoded in texts) comes to seem acquainted with our thoughts, it is neither because we are simply deluded about the probabilities of coincidence (as psychologists never tire of insisting) nor because we live suspended in an amnion of cosmic meaning that imprints its ageless archetypal patterns on our lives. Rather, it is because our brain is somehow predigesting, pre-metabolizing our future engagement with that world, via some natural and probably universal mechanism we have yet to fully understand. Synchronicity is simply what it looks like when people orient toward future meaningful encounters with no inkling that this is what they are doing.

It is no accident that both Freud and Jung were fascinated with ancient artifacts—Freud displayed scarabs and other artifacts in his Vienna office, for example—and both liked to use archaeological metaphors of unearthing and discovery to describe their past-oriented hermeneutic enterprise. Ruins and artifacts seem like they belong to domain of history and memory—hence these two, highly history-conscious thinkers both embraced a picture of health that reconnected us to what is dead and buried. Curative moments in the clinic, for both men, meant awakening to influences belonging to our personal or collective past.

I suggest we should flip those artifacts and ruins, see them instead as things *awaiting discovery*, latent in the landscape of our future. The most baffling "contents" of the personal unconscious may be things we will consciously think and feel in our future, and the "contents" of the collective unconscious may simply be the world of culture, ideas latent in our world, including books we ourselves will read as well as those that our doctors (as well as teachers and gurus) will excitingly explain to us. Those hermeneutic moments in analysts' consulting rooms, where unconscious contents were brought to light, may have actually been the *cause* of the dreams and symptoms that preceded them. How many more cases like Maggy's—or Freud's "Herr P."—are hiding unrecognized in the psychoanalytic literature, simply because this causally perverse possibility never occurred to anyone? In other words, were Maggy and Mr. Foresight especially precognitive patients, or were they just unusually bad at hiding their precognition in a therapeutic context that resolutely oriented their doctors toward the past in their search for meaning?

Could it even be that the clinical setting effectively turns a patient into a medium or fortune teller—one who is compelled, by a medical reframing of his or her precognition as pathology, to pay the "client" (the doctor), rather than the reverse?[73]

It would be hard to answer these questions, given how inextricably entangled precognition is with hindsight. Discussion in a therapist's office invariably deals with past events, since those are the only ones we consciously know about. Thus dreams about the next day's epiphanies might still *seem* to be about past events that were dredged up and discussed during a rewarding session.[74] The rare cases where precognition is discernible in historical case studies are those that contain some kind of tracer—some intrusive material fact about the hermeneutic moment that clearly distinguishes it as the dream's or symptom's source—such as the scarab arriving at Jung's office window, or Freud showing Dr. Forsyth's calling card to Herr P. Most case descriptions lack this kind of detail. The way the discussion unfolded in the consulting room, including the (surprised, shocked, resistant) reactions of the patient, have gone unrecorded even in Freud's more detailed case studies.

But the question I am raising really goes beyond just the prevalence of precognitive episodes here and there in psychotherapy, or of the transference relationship as "psi-conditioned" (as Jule Eisenbud termed it).[75] What if it is somehow our misunderstood, unacknowledged, looping relationship to our future that makes us ill—or at least, that contributes to our suffering—and not our failure to connect appropriately to our past? Could some neuroses be time loops misrecognized and denied, the way we haunt ourselves from our futures and struggle to reframe it as being about our past history?

The next two chapters will examine this question through the lives of two famously precognitive and neurotic writers. Both show strikingly how creativity may travel together with trauma and suffering along the resonating string that connects us to the Not Yet.

Fate, Free Will, and *Futility* —
Morgan Robertson's Tiresias Complex

Who can tell us of the power which events possess ...
Are their workings in the past or in the future; and
are the more powerful of them those that are no lon-
ger, or those that are not yet? Is it to-day or to-morrow
that moulds us? Do we not all spend the greater part
of our lives under the shadow of an event that has not
yet come to pass?

— Maurice Maeterlinck, "The Pre-Destined"
(1914)

The monkey wrench precognition appears to throw into the problem of free will is an important part of the force field inhibiting
serious consideration of it by many people in our culture. It may have
been a fear of the inevitability of things prophesied that made the whole
subject so anathema to Freud, for example. In a society that places priority on success and the individual's responsibility for its attainment, it
is both taken for granted and a point of fierce conviction that we choose
and that our choices are not completely made for us by the inexorable
clockwork of matter—the Newtonian inertia that brought the *Titanic*

and the Iceberg, mere inert objects, together. Scientists may pay lip service to determinism—Freud himself did—but the inevitability of material processes due to causes "pushing" from the past somehow feels less restrictive than a block universe in which our fate is already set. The radical predestination implied by time loops may rob "great men" of their ability to claim credit for their successes. When Freud received a medallion that showed that a youthful "fantasy" had really been prophetic, in the same stroke as signaling that he was well on his way to getting his wish of being a (dead) bust admired by the living, it was a doubly awful realization, a kind of *doom*—another Anglo-Saxon word for fate (also judgment).

There's a flip side to doom where precognition and time loops are concerned, though. A successful medical pioneer like Freud might naturally reject those possibilities outright and then, when confronted with evidence of their reality, feel like he'd seen a revenant; but someone gripped by feelings of failure, guilt, and shame may be more liable to embrace precognition and actively seek evidence of its workings. The point is not merely to secure some greater measure of control over one's destiny—the presumed simplistic wish skeptics typically impute to ESP believers—but mainly to secure a sense of *absolution*. The block universe implied by precognitive experiences carries with it the sense that our fate is out of our hands … and thus, "I am not to blame." It is a way to wipe away whatever guilt a person feels in life.

This was a keen insight made by psychiatrist Jule Eisenbud, who noted in his clinical work that "paranormal foreknowledge" in his patients was often tied closely to guilty or shameful feelings. He observed a pattern of deeply ambivalent patients expressing uncanny precognitive-seeming ability as a gambit to elicit the guilt-absolving sense of "it was fated and I could do nothing." A prime example among his patients was a married but secretly homosexual clergyman with a habit of producing precognitive dreams as part of a defense against his sexual orientation, of which he was deeply ashamed: "Securing a glimpse of what was to be and then seeing this actually come to pass seemed to reassure him that whatever happened was inevitable, and that in the final judgment, with which he was perennially preoccupied, he would therefore be absolved from culpability."[1] (In the 1940s, another psychoanalyst, Jan Ehrenwald, noted a very similar case of dream precognition, also in a male patient fighting against his own homosexual impulses.[2])

It is through this same lens of guilt, specifically the Oedipal guilt so beloved of Freudian analysts, that Eisenbud interpreted the life and work of the most famously precognitive of writers, Morgan Robertson—the man who, some believe, foretold the sinking of the *Titanic* 14 years before it occurred. [3] When *Futility* is placed within the larger context of the writer's biography, the case for this 1898 novel being prophetic is considerably strengthened. Robertson's whole life was dominated by the themes of providence, immutable fate, and the impossibility of capitalizing on our psychic abilities because of the maddening visibility of prophecy only in hindsight. Robertson seems to have been a man tragically ruled, and ruined, by time loops.

Futility tells the story of Lieutenant John Rowland, a once-promising naval officer who has fallen into disgrace because of his drinking and is now working as a common sailor on the new, massive, "indestructible" ocean liner, *Titan*. *Titan* is making her third round-trip voyage across the Atlantic, from New York to Liverpool, when Rowland happens to encounter an old flame, Myra Gaunt, among the passengers. Myra's rejection of him years earlier is what led to his drowning his sorrows in whisky and his ultimate downfall. (Coincidence of this sort was rampant in Robertson's fiction.) Myra is traveling with her husband (she is now Myra Selfridge) and young daughter, also named Myra, and seeing her awakens in Rowland all his old anguish and self-pity and sends him straight back to the bottle.

The *Titan*, moving at an unsafe 25 knots through thick fog, is unable to avoid a collision with a smaller ship, which it cuts in two, killing all the smaller vessel's passengers. The captain attempts to buy Rowland's silence on the matter but Rowland refuses, and so the Captain has him drugged in hopes it will change Rowland's mind. As the drug takes effect, Rowland soliloquizes to the boatswain on the cruelty of fate in a Godless universe:

> "The survival of the fittest," he rambled, as he stared into the fog; "cause and effect. It explains the Universe—and me." He lifted his hand and spoke loudly, as though to some unseen familiar of the deep. "What will be the last effect? Where in the scheme of ultimate balance—under the law of the correlation of energy, will my wasted wealth of love be gathered, and weighed, and credited? What will balance it, and where will I be? ..."[4]

He is answered almost immediately when an iceberg looms out of the fog ahead and slices into the *Titan*'s starboard side, causing it to fall over on its side and drown most of the passengers. Chance finds Rowland alone on the ice itself, along with little Myra, who had wandered from her mother in the minutes before the collision. What ensues is an increasingly improbable series of events, including Rowland's battle with a polar bear living on the ice, after which he burns pieces of the wrecked ship for fuel and cooks the bear for food, and delivers further soliloquies on chance and necessity, causality and the superstition of belief in a merciful God. (Remember, no one ever claimed *Futility* was great literature, just that it was prophetic.)

Months later, having lost an arm as a result of his wounds from the polar bear but gained guardianship of little Myra and given up drinking as a result, he chances to encounter big Myra in New York. She was one of only 11 others on the *Titan* who survived in one of the lifeboats. Big Myra takes back little Myra from Rowland and accuses the hapless seaman of kidnapping and torturing her daughter. But he is exonerated the next day at his trial, when he tells the true story of how he had survived and protected the girl. Big Myra's father in law, as chance would have it, was the corrupt businessman at fault for providing too few lifeboats to save the ship's roughly 3,000 other passengers. The ending of the novel is bitter, befitting its title: Rowland's period of guardianship of the little girl has straightened his ways, made him go sober, but he loses the girl, and he does not alas win back her now-widowed mother.

When the novel was reissued in 1912 with a new title, *The Wreck of the Titan*, Robertson—presumably at the request of the publisher—adjusted some of the statistics of his *Titan* to bring them even closer to the *Titanic*, and also tacked on a few lines to the end in which big Myra invites Rowland to come visit, making the ending just a bit more hopeful, bittersweet instead of just bitter. But many of Robertson's works have the same dark theme, and center on the same core issue: what Rowland calls "chance and necessity," the inexorability of cruel and unknowable (yet also, paradoxically, expected) fate. The iceberg that sinks the *Titan* is just one example of the type of calamity that most of Robertson's protagonists are, in one way or another, unable to avoid ... except in a few very interesting cases, as we'll see, through a clairvoyant or precognitive sixth sense.

A Tragic Prophet

John Rowland, like most of Robertson's protagonists, was autobiographical. Despite being a prolific and moderately popular writer, Robertson struggled with the shame of a powerful alcohol addiction, and probably as a result of the latter always lived on the brink of poverty. He was gripped by a deep and at times crippling ambivalence about chance and fate, but unlike Rowland he felt there was some higher law of coincidence or providence, and consequently he was deeply interested in (and wrote several stories about) the mysterious prophetic possibilities of the subconscious mind. The theme of inability to avert a foreseen disaster or to redeem oneself in its aftermath was central to much of his fiction, not only *Futility*.

Not much is known of the writer's early life except for some bare-bones details. Born in Oswego, NY, educated in public schools, he ran away at age 16 to become a sailor. He worked on ships for nine years before settling down in New York City and studying the jeweler's trade. Failing eyesight in his mid-thirties forced him to seek a third career, however, which is when he tried his hand at writing. Since he knew the life of the sea, it was an obvious subject, and he found he had a knack for spinning a good yarn. He later also turned his imaginative abilities toward invention, as we will see shortly, but it seems to have been only writing that brought him any success or recognition. Even that proved fleeting, unfortunately.

Many writers tie their writing ability to some kind of occult influence. Robertson belongs to a much larger pattern in the world of letters that Jeffrey Kripal has charted in his book *Mutants and Mystics*—science-fiction and comic book writers inspired in their work by paranormal and "psychic" experiences.[5] Robertson reported the distinct sensation when he was setting words to page that he was channeling, in the words of one friend, "some discarnate soul, some spirit entity with literary ability, denied physical expression, [which] had commandeered his body and brain."[6] When poet Ella Wheeler Wilcox wrote to Robertson in the aftermath of the *Titanic* tragedy to ask him about it, Robertson replied:

> As to the motif of my story, I merely tried to write
> a good story with no idea of being a prophet. But,
> as in other stories of mine, and in the work of other
> and better writers, coming discoveries and events have

been anticipated. I do not doubt that it is because all creative workers get into a hypnoid, telepathic and percipient condition, in which, while apparently awake, they are half asleep, and tap, not only the better informed minds of others but the subliminal realm of unknown facts. Some, as you know, believe that in this realm there is no such thing as Time, and the fact that a long dream can occur in an instant of time gives color to it, and partly explains prophecy.[7]

Robertson explored this "subliminal realm of unknown facts" throughout his fiction. Although Rowland in *Futility* does not display psychic powers, a recurring character in Robertson's stories, an old sailor named Finnegan (a stand-out exception to the tragic tone of most of his protagonists), possesses an uncanny but totally unconscious foresight that always saves the day. The fact that this foresight—or plain dumb luck—manifests only when Finnegan is completely drunk provokes wonder, amusement, and speculation on the part of his shipmates.

In one of these stories, "The Subconscious Finnegan," published in 1905, the thoroughly inebriated Finnegan is put at the wheel of a battleship as an experiment by his superiors, to see if the monotony of the task may hypnotize him sufficiently that a well-timed "suggestion" may cure him of his drinking problem. After cruising rapidly through a fog for a few hours, the officer in charge discovers to his horror that Finnegan has turned the ship a few degrees off its intended heading. Just as the quartermaster steps in to correct the mistake, an ocean liner looms out of the fog ahead. Only the fact that they were off course enables them to avoid hitting the luxury liner, with its "thousand electric bulbs," slipping past it to the "shouts of startled men and the screams of women and children." The ship's surgeon then tries to interpret what happened:

> There is no doubt in my mind ... that Finnegan put himself in to the subjective state, and that his subconscious self took charge of him—that is, his subconscious mind had clairvoyant knowledge of the position of that steamship, out of sight in the fog...[8]

As with Finnegan, Robertson's own prophetic gift was a fickle and ambiguous one, and he seems to have thought that drink was a necessary tool to get in touch with his muse. He felt unable to write when his muse was not available, which probably drove him to drink more to get it back, in a kind of vicious cycle. Robertson regarded himself, and was regarded by his many friends, as a kind of tragic psychic, constantly frustrated that his prophetic gift could not somehow redeem him. Several friends (writing in a 1915 volume called *Morgan Robertson the Man*) referenced Robertson's psychic interests and ability, although oddly enough, none of them mentioned his most uncanny prophecy about the *Titanic*, nowadays his only claim to fame. (Eisenbud assumes this lacuna is probably because such mention would have seemed in bad taste, just three years following the disaster.) Somehow fate always ensured that Robertson's gift of seeing the future brought him misery in the end. Although Robertson saw alcohol as an escape from these punishments, his addiction was clearly just as much responsible for them.

Very sadly, alcohol addiction left Robertson, in his early fifties, a destitute and forgotten failure in his own eyes. He died three years after the *Titanic* disaster, in 1915, at age 54, in an Atlantic City, New Jersey, hotel room—where, according to a *New York Times* account, he had been staying for some time following a nervous breakdown. He was found, oddly enough, *standing up*, leaning against a bureau. It is likely that Robertson was actually staying in the hotel in an attempt to detox from alcohol. The examining physician attributed his death to heart failure, but a bottle of a sedative called paraldehyde was on the bureau next to him, which the *Times* reported he had been taking to help induce sleep. In fact, this medication was widely prescribed at the time to treat alcohol addiction. It would have been probably his third attempt seeking medical help for his drinking.[9] Unfortunately, people who tried this cure for their alcohol addiction readily became addicted to paraldehyde, and sometimes they ended up taking it in such excess as to cause organ damage. It is thus possible that paraldehyde addiction directly contributed to Robertson's death.

Unavoidable disasters lurking in the fog of the future were a big theme for Robertson. In a short autobiographical piece published anonymously in *The Saturday Evening Post* a year before his death, "Gathering No Moss," the writer describes a remarkable interlude in his life that probably occurred sometime shortly after the turn of the century—one that, like his stories, centers thematically on the idea of foresight but the ultimate futility of avoiding obstacles ahead. Feeling creatively dried up, he said, he visited "a noted professor of psychology [who] had done some wonderful things by hypnotic suggestion"[10]—although it is likely that the problem for which Robertson sought help on this occasion, too, was his alcohol addiction. The professor, who knew Robertson's work, diagnosed him, he wrote, with "brain fag"—"I had overtaxed my brain in trying to invent too many stories"—and turned his attention to the topic of great inventions, with the idea of turning his creativity in a new direction.

> The suggestion manifested itself in an unexpected way—it always does. I had to write another story to get a needed hundred and fifty dollars, and I went down the coast many miles to consult a naval officer, a friend, about a new feature that had been added to a battleship. While there I was taken on board a submarine boat which happened to be at anchor in that particular bay. It was then I got the idea of my first invention—the periscope.[11]

A periscope, of course, is a technical solution designed to do precisely what Finnegan's sixth sense did: "see" what lies ahead, out of sight, in hopes of averting disaster. In keeping with his beliefs about fate and providence, Robertson saw his visit to the naval base as fortuitous:

> Now, I believe that nothing but hypnotic suggestion could have made me go down there to see an officer and then find the very thing needed to turn my thoughts to a new channel of invention. If I had gone at any other time the submarine boat would not have been there. Those things are not coincidences. Though no one has definitely located it, I firmly believe there is a law behind them. You cannot make me believe that when one man is thinking of another, and just at that moment sees him coming round a corner, it is a coincidence. It occurs too often.[12]

With the Navy's blessing, Robertson spent the next few years learning physics and optics sufficiently to create a design and model of the new device in order to win a patent for it—hopefully then to rescue him and his then-new wife from their always-dire financial straits. But fate crushed his hopes for a better future when his patent was denied.

A French writer had already substantially described such a device in a magazine article, and while the man had not actually made a design for it, it was enough to make the idea public property.

Robertson describes returning to his typewriter after this heartbreak as the saddest moment of his life. So, here in real life, just like in many of his stories, Robertson attributed his actions to a kind of providence, but unlike the case of happy-go-lucky Finnegan, that providence fails to redeem him and indeed only brings him deeper misery in the end.

The foregoing details are virtually always omitted when Robertson's *Futility* is held up as an example of literary prophecy (only to be debunked in many cases), but it arguably adds much weight to the "yes, it was prophetic" column of the balance sheet. Robertson's (now-) most famous novel was not some random textual dolphin caught by accident in the tuna trawling of hindsight. It happens to be just the most notable instance in the life of a writer who already thought he was guided by a subliminal sixth sense, caught in a world ruled by coincidence, and was even noted by others for his preternatural—but simultaneously "useless"—ability to discern the future in his writings.

The Sublimest Object

The *Titanic* disaster was remarkably similar to 9/11 in that it was a "media event," one that unfolded slowly over the day of April 15, 1912, as news trickled in; it was not a single devastating headline as we may now imagine. The first abbreviated telegraph reports indicated only that the ship had struck an iceberg, not that it had been lost, and some of the first news stories inaccurately reported that the ship was safely being towed to Halifax, Nova Scotia. Only gradually did the public learn the true magnitude of the disaster and loss of life. Thus, as with 9/11, the public engaged with the news as an unfolding story, producing a sequence of greater and greater shocks. It would have brought families together in conversation and brought coworkers together over the 1912 equivalent of the water cooler. People would have taken a kind of ambivalent pleasure in the news—eagerly read the story and talked about it, feeling a complex mix of curiosity and fascination and excitement and horror. In other words, they would have "enjoyed" the disaster in precisely the same way cable news audiences "enjoyed" 9/11.

The *Titanic* trauma has stuck in the craw of our culture for over a century because of these conflicting and unresolved emotions. The endless historical studies, TV documentaries, novels, movies, robotic undersea investigations, and so on could be thought of as the same kind of repetition compulsion underlying commemoration of other historical traumas like the Civil War or the Holocaust. For Slavoj Žižek, in his 1989 book *The Sublime Object of Ideology*, the wreckage of the *Titanic*, which had finally been discovered by Robert Ballard just four years earlier, was the quintessential "sublime object" of our era, reminding viewers of their awful enjoyment-in-destruction. Readers of *Time* and other magazines featuring the story gazed on the shadowy photos of the ship's ruins looming out of the gloom with the precise mixture of emotions captured in the term *jouissance*, a spooked fascination or even a kind of vertigo. "By looking at the [*Titanic*] wreck," wrote Žižek, "we gain an insight into the forbidden domain, into a space that should be left unseen: visible fragments are a kind of coagulated remnant of the liquid flux of *jouissance*, a kind of petrified forest of enjoyment."[13]

Subjecting the *Titanic* disaster, and Robertson's curious prophecy about it, to a kind of Lacanian re-reading, Žižek argued that the sinking of the ocean liner needed to be properly viewed in hindsight as something inevitable, and that its inevitability (rather than its unexpectedness) was partly the source of its traumatic impact. He has a point: Far from being unthinkable, the disaster had in some sense (and the sheer number of prophecies, even published fiction, show it) been *overthought* in advance.[14] Some disaster or comeuppance befalling the blithe elite, as well as a disaster involving an ocean liner with too-few lifeboats, was easy to imagine, if not exactly anticipate with the specificity that Robertson did.

As a Marxist, Žižek might have gone one step further and highlighted the role played by guilt in the *Titanic* story: The trauma was not simply that everyone had been expecting some spectacular disaster to befall the rich; the trauma was that they had actually been *wishing* for such a disaster and then were somewhat horrified to find their wishes fulfilled. When they saw the bold *New York Times* headline, "TITANIC SINKS FOUR HOURS AFTER HITTING ICEBERG," many readers may have felt a vague guilt for dimly-held class resentments aimed at the cosmopolitan elite they often read about in the same paper's society pages. Those names now dominated the headlines as either having perished in or (if they were women) survived the disaster. Readers may even have felt on some very dim unconscious nonrational level that their wishes/desires had actually *caused* the iceberg to sink the ship. That was another of Freud's brilliant and enduring insights: The unconscious (which appropriately he likened to the submerged, dangerous majority of an iceberg) is completely illogical; it lacks a rational sense of time, causality, and responsibility. We feel guilty when outcomes we have only dimly hoped or wished for come to pass.[15]

The "rewards" for Morgan Robertson on that big news day in April 1912 would have been even greater than for most. Beyond just surviving the disaster (in the same sense that all Americans that day had "survived"), there was also reward precisely in the fact that he had seemingly foretold it in a novel—not to mention what that foretelling implied about the immutability of fate. That *New York Times* headline came at a point in his life when he was feeling like a forgotten failure, with deepening shame at the wreck drink had made of his life and prospects. Whether or not Robertson knew of the block universe idea formulated by Minkowski in 1908, the *Titanic's* sinking would have been a stunning but welcome confirmation of precisely what his drugged protagonist Rowland had railed against just before the *Titan's* fatal collision: the inevitability of things and the *futility* of attempting to avert cruel necessity. The *Titanic's* "measurement" of the iceberg yielded confirmation that the universe was itself a big cold solid iceberg-like mass. Glimpsing this truth, as Eisenbud suggested, would have provided a much-craved sense of absolution. Remember that while the iceberg destroys the fictional *Titan* and most of its passengers, the iceberg is what *saves* the author's stand-in, Rowland (along with little Myra).

It is important to underscore that the *Titanic* disaster would have had this absolving meaning for Robertson precisely because he had already described it in his own novel—our old friend the time loop. We might thus see Rowland's grim soliloquy on the inevitability of fate as the *future train of thought* that would dominate Robertson's mind 14 years later, when real-life events turned his novel into a prophecy, the same way the "Irma" dream in 1895 may have pre-presented thoughts Freud would have 28 years later, upon a similar realization.

Because they overlook Robertson's obsession with immutable fate and the foreknowledge it somehow makes possible, and because they fail to take into account the likely state of Robertson's mind as he entered his sixth decade, nearly all the efforts to calculate the odds of the details in Robertson's story coinciding with those of the real *Titanic* disaster greatly miss the point—and not just because the problem is ill-formed, as Martin Gardner contended. Robertson's entire life and work seems to have been one long premonition of a disaster looming in the fog of his future, unavoidable because of the inexorable laws of cruel necessity, *but also rewarding to him precisely because of that inevitability*. It expressed perfectly the logic of *jouissance*, as a kind of catastrophe that brings us a reward along with it. Zeroing in on specifics of passenger capacity, tonnage, etc. is to miss this meaningful forest for the statistical trees. When the *Titanic* sank, it was the ultimate sign from the universe that there was nothing poor Morgan Robertson could have done different.

Thus, rather than read the title *Futility* in a somber, grave, tragic voice, we might imagine that Robertson inwardly would have pronounced that word with a sense of grim triumph, a kind of "I told you so."

Robertson the Woman?

With prophecy, we are in a Freudian as well as an Einsteinian universe, and thus the psychological or psychodynamic dimensions to Robertson's prophetic life may go even deeper than shame at an addiction. The world of Robertson's fiction is mostly a sweaty fantasy of manly seamen pressed into service, constantly bloodying each other in brutal fistfights. In his autobiographical moments, the writer was unrelenting in his assertion of his masculinity and his derision for effeminacy. But as Eisenbud notes, "if you scratch an intense masculinity, you can never tell what will come out."[16] Eisenbud suspected that the writer may have abused alcohol to escape from or cope with the same (at the time) unspeakable sexual orientation that Eisenbud's precognitive clergyman patient also struggled with. He interpreted Robertson's hyper-masculine pose as an overcompensation and a defense, suggesting that it may have been precisely this forbidden desire that drove Robertson to *choose* a life of the sea for a decade as a young man, yet spend the rest of his life writing of that career as though it were a kind of grim fate he could not avoid. Eisenbud hastens to remind us that, in that much more repressed time, the writer himself may not consciously have been aware of such an orientation; he may have experienced it merely as a general pain, frustration, and unhappiness.

Eisenbud also diagnosed Robertson, even more confidently, with an overwhelming Oedipus complex. There is little or nothing in the way of convincing sexuality or sexual feeling (either hetero- or homo-) in Robertson's stories. Many of his protagonists pine for young girls met as children who, after many years at sea and through some impossible coincidence, turn up as sole survivors of shipwrecks or otherwise amazingly reenter the protagonist's life.[17] Some of his love interests are mother figures; in one case, a sailor pines for his mother who he knows is awaiting his return.[18] One could add to the generational confusions also blatant castration symbolism, such as lost arms. As everyone steeped in Freud or the *Star Wars* trilogy knows, losing an arm is a classic castration symbol. (Significantly, it is upon the cold, Minkowskian iceberg itself that poor Rowland's arm is fatally maimed—it saves him, but it exacts an awful price.) Robertson's life story, as he told it himself, was that of the typical neurotic: a story of being thwarted, *cut off*, unable to capitalize or benefit from his efforts and his gifts.[19] We know little about his father, but one senses a great and thunderous "no" rolling through the writer's life.

There was also the theme of blindness. Remember that Robertson's eyesight, which began failing him in his early thirties, had forced him to abandon his second chosen career as a jeweler, and blindness was a theme in some of his stories. Blindness is another classic castration symbol, according to Freud, and the template for the "blind prophet" goes back to the ancients, including the mythological backstory of Freud's favorite tragedy *Oedipus the King*. That story is in some sense just as relevant to the tragic life of Robertson as it is to that of Freud, but in a very different way.

Oedipus's self-blinding when he realizes his own guilt links him to the blind seer Tiresias, who announces the king's guilt at the end of the tragedy. Audiences would have known the mythological backstory of the seer and his blindness, just as they knew that of Oedipus. In his younger days, Tiresias had come upon two entwined snakes in the forest and touched them with his staff; upon doing so, he was transformed into a woman. After living as a woman for seven years, Tiresias encountered the snakes again, touched them, and was turned back into a man. Summoned to Mount Olympus to report on his experience, he revealed to Hera, in front of her husband Zeus, that (based on his extensive experience) women get much more enjoyment from sex than men do. Hera blinded him in punishment for revealing this secret, and Zeus gave him prophetic foresight in recompense. Tiresias thus reveals an ancient symbolic association between these two ideas, prophecy and sexual/gender liminality or boundary-crossing.[20]

The symbolism of the Sphinx, the guardian whose riddle Oedipus had to answer to become King (and thus to marry his mother), is also relevant here. Sphinxes are symbolic guardians of time,[21] and not accidentally, *sphinx* is closely related to the word *sphincter*: a guardian (literally a "strangler") designed to mainly admit the passage of things in one direction but sometimes capable of admitting other things traveling in reverse. As I hinted earlier, suggesting that the normal order of causality can be transgressed arouses similar hostile reactions from skeptical guardians of Enlightenment science that the prospect of a phallus—the ultimate "causal arrow"—moving the wrong way through a sphincter arouses in gatekeepers of patriarchal "Christian" morals. In a sense, Oedipus and Tiresias were permutations of the same basic possibility—transgression of some kind of sexual boundary, punished by symbolic castration but also (at least in Tiresias's case) compensated with foresight. Transgressive enjoyment, which "impossibly" connects the future to the past, is thus what turns precognition into a psychoanalytic problem. As with Tiresias, the point of Oedipus's story is not merely that he "traveled the wrong way through time" by marrying his mother and killing his father; it is that he committed these crimes *and enjoyed them*, and only belatedly discovered what it was that he had been enjoying. His guilt was not over his actions but over his enjoyment. Our ignorance as to our enjoyment (that is, our blindness to it) allows both the past and future to affect our lives in uncanny and seemingly "impossible" ways like the kinds of coincidences and twists of fate that seem to have characterized Robertson's life.

Robertson may have had more in common with Tiresias than just the nexus of prophecy and literal and figurative blindness. Consider Robertson's strange story called "The Sleep Walker," which appeared in *Harper's Magazine* in 1903. In this tale, a man named Tom Beverton comes to dread the nightly attacks of his wife, first with a bucket of water, then with a curved, scimitar-like carving knife. Under the influence of a boring sea novel, she falls asleep and begins talking in the coarse, swearing tone of a buccaneer. Even after his wife puts the knife up on a high shelf, out of the reach of her sleepwalking self, it continues to exert a hypnotic power over her, repeatedly calling forth what seems like some buried male, violent personality. Meanwhile Beverton himself falls into a somnambulistic state and assumes the persona of a victimized woman. After Beverton throws the knife in a snowy field, his wife finds it in her trance and stabs him in the shoulder.

After Beverton recovers, a psychologist specializing in hypnotism (a character perhaps based on the doctor Robertson had visited for his real-life difficulties) tries to convince Beverton that he and his wife are acting out the telepathically received story of the famous Caribbean pirate Captain Henry Morgan and his captive sex slave Isobel, but with the sexes reversed. They were somehow picking up the thoughts of "some strong, projective personality—some man or woman thoroughly enthused and interested in the history of the seventeenth-century pirates."[22] Beverton listens to the doctor's explanation but believes the truth goes deeper: Reincarnation is the real answer. They had actually *been* these figures in their past lives and at night were playing out their old relationship.

Eisenbud noted that "The Sleep Walker" is a pretty weird gender-bender for such a resolutely masculine writer. What he didn't catch is that Robertson may in this story have been expressing a strange truth about how he secretly understood his own fickle creative gifts. In the volume, *Morgan Robertson the Man*, one of Robertson's friends, an artist named J. O'Neill, recalled that the writer believed that he had telepathically acquired the writing gift, the muse, of a *young woman* he had known years earlier but who had been unable to make anything of her talent due to a lack of "stickativeness." In other words, Robertson believed his fickle and inconstant "astral helper" or "psychic partner"[23] (in the words of another friend, Henry W. Francis) was specifically that of a female. He was effectively appropriating that muse telepathically, or allowing himself to be its vessel, because it was of no use to the woman anyway and he could profit better from it.

In his unconscious, was Robertson, who became a writer in the first place because of his failing eyesight, following the "archetype" of the sex-swapping prophet Tiresias? In our increasingly transgender era, should we speak of a Tiresias complex as counterpart to the Oedipus complex, and might it have some close connection to prophetic aptitude or expression? As we will see in the following chapter, the notoriously precognitive writer Philip K. Dick similarly felt that his sibylline creative muse was female, specifically his dead twin, Jane.

Whether or not alcoholism, the obvious "iceberg" the writer could not escape, drowned some more private and secret suffering related to sexual desire or even gender identity, Robertson clearly wanted fate to absolve him for some compulsion that he feared was a choice, and perhaps also give him the ability to free himself from that compulsion—an impossible, contradictory, ambivalent wish. His precognitive habit seems to have answered both needs. Eisenbud makes a very key observation in this regard, one that goes well beyond Robertson in its implications: "With such an ambivalent attitude toward fate," he writes, "all one would need, it might seem, would be heads and tails on the same throw. But any good precognitive event provides just this, since ... the metaphysical significance of such an occurrence is sufficiently in question to satisfy both schools."[24] There was surely no better "precognitive event" than reading a *New York Times* headline about a sea disaster you had written a novel about 14 years earlier.

The psychoanalytic rule of thumb is that nothing is ever an accident.[25] The disasters and misfortunes that repeat themselves over and over in the lives of neurotics like Robertson look for all the world as though some higher power or cosmic theater director is testing them or just being cruel, but these situations are actually elicited by the neurotic in deviously subtle ways. For Freudians, the thematic consistency of the neurotic's failures is always assumed to represent unresolved past situations confusedly haunting the neurotic's present reality, governed by the repetition-compulsion beyond the pleasure principle. Instead of seeing things as they are, the neurotic sees replays of situations from early life and reacts accordingly, with predictably disappointing outcomes—the idiomatic "carrying baggage."

The alternative possibility that a case like Robertson's suggests is that some of our baggage comes from our future. Robertson seems all his life to have been confusedly *pre*sponding to a future upheaval, even a kind of near miss or close call (since, having written about it beforehand, the *Titanic* disaster was in some sense "his" disaster), but treating it again and again as a *present* reality, a disaster that had already occurred or was in the process of occurring. By the time the real thing happened, he himself was already sunk, "washed up," and could not even successfully capitalize on what might have been the perfect advertisement for his precognitive gift.

What if something like this is true of many neurotics? What portion of ordinary human floundering and failure might really be attributable to misrecognized precognition, a kind of maladaptive *prematurity* of feeling and thought? We now turn to another deeply neurotic writer whose life even more clearly illustrates the painful temporal out-of-synch-ness of the strongly precognitive soul.

13

"PS: What Scares Me Most, Claudia, Is That I Can Often Recall *the Future*" — The Memetic Prophecies of Philip K. Dick

Ubik talks to us from the future, from the end state to which everything is moving; thus Ubik is not here— which is to say now—but will be, and what we get is information about and from Ubik, as we receive TV or radio signals from transmitters located in other spaces in this time continuum.

— Philip K. Dick, *Letters* (1974)

Science-fiction writers routinely forecast developments in technology and society—it's their job. Jules Verne, H. G. Wells, and Arthur C. Clarke famously predicted countless technological innovations, although it is hard to discern which of their predictions may have represented anything more than the ability to infer future milestones from then-current trends. Besides predicting the *Titanic* disaster, Morgan Robertson predicted the development of something like radar and even a Japanese sneak attack on America, although it is not clear that his precognitive faculty was involved.[1] Philip K. Dick's visions of American consumer culture and the scrambled, fragmented reality it creates have been prescient in the same way. The cyberpunk writers he influenced are credited with having foretold our hyper-mediated, information-saturated lives, but it was Dick himself who saw how maddening and stupid a tech-saturated world (with its targeted advertising, robo-calls, and digital assistants that spy on us) might become. Year after year, life in America feels more and more like a Dick novel. And while he was not known as a "hard science" SF writer, he was no slouch in that respect either. Over a decade before John Wheeler coined the phrase "it from bit," for instance, Dick was already writing about the universe as composed of information.[2]

But this kind of social and scientific forecasting is not what Phil-Dickologists mean by calling the writer precognitive.[3] Rather, it is that he had a funny habit of predicting what we would now call *memes*—singular, often fleeting ideas and obsessions in popular culture, the kinds of things that made the cover of *Time* and *Newsweek* and *Psychology Today* as ideas or issues of the moment. It became increasingly apparent to Dick over the course of his career that he seemed to write about such cultural obsessions just before they occurred, and it was this that fueled his own evolving self-myth, that he was a "precog" right out of one of his own stories.[4] Dick's private life too was a tapestry of "synchronicity," reflecting in some cases his precognition of significant events and upheavals. Even if none of his literary prophecies are as memorable as predicting an ocean liner disaster down to the name of the ship, as Robertson did, it is possible to document in Dick's life and works numerous even more striking coincidences, in part because he left such a voluminous archive of letters and journals enabling us to cross-correlate events in his life with his dreams as well as with his fiction. Such a project is also abetted by a fast-growing number of biographies and reminiscences by his many friends, wives, girlfriends, and others who knew this deeply troubled writer well and can confirm, disconfirm, or otherwise add illumination to the sometimes bizarre time loops that punctuated his personal, creative, and spiritual life.

Dick's 1969 masterpiece *Ubik* is one of several examples cited by biographer Anthony Peake. If any one of his novels embodies all the qualities (uncertain and shifting realities, etc.) that are thought of as "PhilDickian," it would be this narrative about dead—or nearly dead—people stored in a state of hibernation or "half life" and an aerosol spray product (the Ubik of the title) that somehow reverses or retards time because of the "counter-clockwise spin" it imparts. Dick submitted the manuscript to his publisher in 1966, but he subsequently encountered the idea of time as a kind of spiral energy whose polarity or spin could be reversed in a translated 1967 article by a Russian physicist and parapsychologist named Nicolai Kozyrev. Dick was so struck by Kozyrev's ideas of time as a "torsion field" that he thought it had influenced his own writing of Ubik three years earlier. Peake, who compiled many of Dick's alleged precognitive experiences in his book *A Life of Philip K. Dick: The Man Who Remembered the Future*, sums up Dick's reasoning about how an exciting reading experience could constitute the seed of *prior* creative inspiration:

> PKD concludes that the source from which he based his own plots was from information drawn out of time (in this case his own future). This information was subliminally understood and acted as the stimulus for plot devices. In other words, he perceives something, an article for example, when he is 49 years old, and this idea immediately appears in his 46-year-old mind. The idea is so powerful that the 46-year-old PKD writes a story based upon its premise, or premises. [5]

By itself, Dick's hunch that he had precognized the article on Kozyrev, or the similarity of their ideas, does not prove that precognition was at work here. But the spray-can Ubik happens to be strangely similar to other memes in our culture that were also just around the corner when Dick wrote his story. For example, in the same self-consciously techno-babble passage that explains Ubik as reversing time through its counterclockwise spin, the fictitious aerosol product is also linked to the negation of an ordinarily protective aspect of the Earth's atmosphere.[6] A few years after he published his novel, scientists linked chlorofluorocarbons from aerosol spray cans to the degradation of Earth's protective ozone layer, and by the late 1970s spray cans had become a kind of "anti-icon" of the environmental movement. But again, this was not yet a glimmer at the time Dick was writing his story about an "ubiquitous" time-retarding spray-can product. William Sarill, a friend of Dick's, has also pointed out that Ubik (the product) bears an odd resemblance to the original hype around the dietary supplement *ubiquinol*, now better known as coenzyme Q-10.[7] Although originally identified in a medical journal in 1957, it wasn't until the 1970s that ubiquinol became the subject of research in Japan focused on its heart health benefits. It was then touted as having beneficial "age-reversing" properties when it burst on the alternative health and nutritional supplement scene in early 1980s, right around the time of Dick's death. *Ubik* thus seems almost like a Dunnean-Freudian dream-image, condensing multiple cultural ideas that were just ahead in Dick's (and America's) future when the story flowed from the writer's amphetamine-fueled brain in 1966. Was he somehow channeling his own future encounters with multiple pop-science memes in this one novel?[8]

More striking than *Ubik*, consider a draft for a novel Dick wrote and submitted to his literary agency in October 1962, called "The First in Our Family"—about a small manufacturing firm that decides to branch out from making spinet pianos to building androids. Written in the first years of the Civil War Centennial celebrations but set two decades later, in the year 1982, the idea of Dick's fictional entrepreneurs is that people might pay money to watch reenactments of the Civil War fought by robots. To interest investors, they produce two prototypes, one a simulacrum of Abraham Lincoln and another of his Secretary of War, Edwin M. Stanton. Both prove all-too-human; the Lincoln simulacrum fails to adapt to modern society because the real Lincoln (according to the story) himself suffered "schizophrenia."[9]

Various publishers rejected Dick's manuscript, and thus it went unpublished and unread until the end of the decade, when it appeared in serial form under the title "A. Lincoln, Simulacrum" in *Amazing Science Fiction* (November 1969 and January 1970; it was later published in paperback form as *We Can Build You*). Consequently, there is no way it could have influenced the nearly simultaneous creation of one of the Disneyland theme park's most iconic exhibits, their "animatronic" Abraham Lincoln. Publicly debuted in 1964 at the New York World's Fair, Disney's Lincoln robot became a permanent, well-known fixture at Disneyland in Anaheim California. When he read a newspaper article that Disney was about to display a robotic Abraham Lincoln, Dick was certain he had precognized that singular merger of high technology and American nostalgia. He says he clipped the story as proof of his precognitive abilities, and then went to visit the exhibit after it opened, "to look at the goddamn thing."[10]

The skeptical counterargument that will be made here is that the Civil War was on everyone's mind in 1961-2, when Dick wrote his story, and thus it is perhaps not too coincidental that both Disney Corporation and a science fiction writer would come up with the idea of a robot simulacrum of this particular historical figure around the same time. More speculatively, one might suggest that Disney may have published somewhere their intentions to build an Abe Lincoln robot—which they did in fact conceive as early as 1962—and that Dick may have seen but forgotten it—analogous to Martin Gardner's suggestion that Morgan Robertson might perhaps have seen such an article about the White Star Line's intention to build a huge new ship called the *Titanic* in 1898. But there is no evidence of such a publication.

The coincidence, and strangeness, is actually deeper and more personal, however. Dick lived and wrote in the Bay Area, in Point Reyes, throughout the 1960s, when he wrote "The First in Our Family" and when the Disney exhibit went on display. However, in 1972, he moved south to Orange County, which encompasses Anaheim and Disneyland. In an interview in 1977, Dick recalled his astonishment at finding that a woman who lived in his apartment building[11] turned out to work at Disneyland and actually had the job of applying makeup to the animatronic Lincoln every night after the park closed:

> You talk about synchronicity that governs the universe—coincidence which is meaningful ... I rented an apartment in a building where one of the ladies living in the building worked at Disneyland. I said to her, "What do you do there?" She says, "I reapply the makeup to the Lincoln every night, so the next morning when the park is open, it looks real." ...
>
> Can you imagine how I felt, finding I lived in a building with a woman who added a touch of verisimilitude to the damn thing? "Well, let me ask you a question," I said. "You see this thing after the park is closed. How real does that thing seem to you to be?" And she says, "Well, I'll tell you exactly how real it seems to me to be." Now it's important to remember that every part of all the rides are continually scanned by closed circuit television ... So anyway, she says, "One time I was painting the Lincoln thing and one of the monitors was still on. The guy on the screen saw me and reached over and pressed the controls. And the thing stood up."
>
> "And what did you do, miss," I asked.
>
> "I peed my pants."
>
> "I take it ... that you found a high degree of verisimilitude in this simulacrum."
>
> "Sure scared the shit out of me."[12]

The coincidence or "synchronicity" is more striking when certain details in "A. Lincoln Simulacrum" are considered. It is not one of the author's most polished works. Frustrated at writing in a category of genre fiction that was so marginalized, he had in the early 1960s been attempting to write more mainstream works that less foregrounded the sci-fi elements—but this early attempt at such a hybrid is not cohesive. Although it delves a little into the fascinating idea of androids and their humanity—themes he would develop much more fully a few years later in *Do Androids Dream of Electric Sheep*—it gets sidetracked midway through to focus on the entrepreneur narrator's self-destructive infatuation with "Pris," the mentally ill daughter of his business partner, whom they have hired to design their Lincoln robot.[13] Early in the novel, the narrator imagines Pris alone with the simulacrum, working all hours to give realism to their creation, *and specifically applying paint or makeup to its face*:

> Pris, I decided, was probably at home these days, putting the final life-like colors into the sunken cheeks of the Abe Lincoln shell which would house all those parts. That in itself was a full-time job. The beard, the big hands, skinny legs, and sad eyes. A field for her creativity, her artistic soul, to run and howl rampant. She would not show up until she had done a top-notch job. ...[14]

And a few pages later:

> The Lincoln container, when Pris and Maury brought it into the office, flabbergasted me. Even in its inert stage, lacking its working parts, it was so life-like as to seem ready at any moment to rise into its day's activity. ...
> To Pris I said, "I have to hand it to you."
> Standing with her hands in her coat pockets, she somberly supervised. Her eyes seemed dark, deeper set; her skin was quite noticeably pale—she had on no make-up, and I guessed that she had been up all hours every night, finishing her task.[15]

In the interview, Dick made no allusions to details like this in his novel—only to the larger fact of his having seemingly precognized "the Lincoln." But if there was a precognitive inspiration for Dick's story, it may not have been merely a news story about Disney's Lincoln, or even his visit to the park to see it in person. It may have been precisely his astonishing encounter in his apartment building at least a decade later, with a woman responsible for making a fake Lincoln seem real, after hours. If so, it would be yet another causal loop: Dick's shock at the coincidental encounter with the woman who applied makeup to Disney's Lincoln was due to his having written a decade or more earlier about precisely such a person. Much like Morgan Robertson's *Futility* or Norman Mailer's *Barbary Shore*, Dick's novel seems like a literary-presentimental butterfly trapped in amber; its literary merits or lack thereof are less interesting than its "prophetic" qualities.[16]

There are so many examples of this kind of coincidence in Dick's life and published (and unpublished) writing that exploring the writer's mystical and prophetic side has become almost a cottage industry. Peake lists numerous other examples in his biography, some of which, such as Dick's claimed precognitive awareness of his infant son's life-threatening hernia in 1974, are well-known parts of Dick lore but may have more mundane explanations—at least, cryptomnesia cannot be ruled out.[17] Others can be explained as the writer consciously or un-consciously fulfilling his own myth after the fact. But in some cases, the priority of Dick's writing to the putatively precognized meme or event is clear from publication dates, adding up to a compelling case that this author was either more precognitive than most people or else simply more aware of and interested in a faculty that we all share but are gener-ally oblivious to.[18]

In fact, Dick and his precognitive experiences fit very well into the pattern elucidated by Jule Eisenbud. Like Morgan Robertson, Dick was a deeply ambivalent, tortured writer gripped by an addiction, lifelong guilt, and unresolved Oedipal feelings. Precognition seems to have answered much the same need for absolution in Dick's case that it did for Robertson, even if the roots of Dick's guilt were different and even though Dick seems to have been much better aware of his own complexes.

Like Freud himself, Dick had survived the loss of a sibling in infan-cy—a twin sister named Jane. He was nowhere near old enough to form a memory of Jane or her death, but his mother repeatedly told the story, and how she could not produce enough milk for both babies, who had been born six weeks premature. Dick had a lifelong obsession with his twin. Dominating his psyche was his guilt at having survived where she did not, and his anger toward his mother whose insufficiencies, he thought, starved her but whose narrative implicitly blamed Phil for "getting all the milk." "[I]f there can be said to be a tragic theme running through my life," he told one biographer, "it's the death of my twin sister and the re-enactment of this over and over again ... *My psychological problems are traceable to the loss of my sister.*"[19] Again, in the psychoanalytic framework, trauma resides not in an event as such—which may not even be remembered—but in the thoughts formed about it afterward. The story of his origins, surviving Jane's death, became the total framework for Dick's self-understanding.

Another recent biographer, Kyle Arnold, traces Dick's visionary imagination and his obsession with unreality to this trauma:

> Because of his mother's repeated retellings of the story, Jane was an intensely present absence in Dick's childhood, bridging the real and the imagined. Thoughts of Jane were thoughts of someone who had never been fully real for Dick. Like science fiction, they were thoughts of what might have been, what should have been, and what was not. They were intimations of possibilities, of stifled alternative universes. Jane was a window onto other worlds. Yet, for the most part, Dick could only gaze through the window, unable to pass through it. His creativity was catalyzed by longing. He compulsively reenacted his origin story throughout his life, repeatedly running afoul of authorities, chasing his deadly muse-twin in destructive relationships with women, and seeking salvation through a kind of desperate spirituality. As he writes in his journals, "the ultimate problem confronting me all my life has been the senseless injury to and neglect of my sister."[20]

A Freudian would see Oedipus as the subtext in all this, and Dick would have agreed. He even admitted to his third wife, Anne, that in his teens he had had a dream in which he slept with his mother—"I won my Oedipal situation."[21] His adult romantic life was a roller-coaster of obsessive and needy relationships to increasingly younger women, the "dark-haired girls" who seemed to represent fantastic versions of his lost sister and who (in his accounts) always somehow turned very quickly into his cold and unloving mother.[22] Dick's fifth wife, Tessa, was 18 when they met in 1972, 26 years his junior. When these relationships failed, it was always somehow his partners' fault, their baggage, their craziness. Like one of the two patients who first pointed Freud toward formulating the Oedipal theory, Dick also suffered a debilitating agoraphobia. In Freud's patient's case, fear of being in public represented a fear of his own murderous impulses toward his father.[23] Dick's agoraphobia too may have been a fear of his own hostility—he had a pattern of behaving badly or embarrassingly in public (even violently on a few occasions). And as we will see, a typically Oedipal un-stuck-ness in time was essentially the template for his spiritual experiences in his last decade.

The question of Dick's mental state has always cast a shadow over his reliability as a narrator of events in his life. There is no question that he sometimes exaggerated, sometimes lied, and wildly shifted his interpretations of events in his letters and conversations. As Arnold puts it, "It is as if he were saying 'I will be whomever you need me to be to take me seriously.'"[24] At times, his perception of reality was seriously distorted by paranoia almost certainly brought on by decades of amphetamine use and abuse. An ephedrine prescription at age six for asthma led to lifelong medical and nonmedical use of various stimulants. (Contrary to common belief, he was not a frequent user of hallucinogens.) Some of his most storied experiences, such as the notorious break-in of his house in 1971, occurred in the worst depths of his speed addiction and his wildly inconsistent accounts of the event cannot be taken at face value.[25]

The pressure cooker of Dick's life appears to have approached a peak in 1973, when he rushed ambivalently into marriage with his young girlfriend Tessa because he had gotten her pregnant. He was then faced with the added stress of an infant son and a marriage that became increasingly strained and untenable (as they all did). It was in this context that Dick's famous "2-3-74" mystical experience occurred. Triggered initially (he said) by light glinting off a Christian fish-symbol pendant around the neck of a girl delivering painkiller to his home after oral surgery,[26] this experience is central to the Dick legend. What layers of mythmaking have overlooked is how stressful this period in his life was. Poverty and lack of recognition are one thing when you are a young brilliant artist, but when a man finds himself in the middle of his fifth decade with little to show for it but a string of failed marriages, estranged children, loneliness, continued poverty and substance problems, and increasing serious health issues like high blood pressure, things begin to feel desperate. ("Desperate" is precisely how one of the many college girls he attempted to date in 1972 described him.[27])

Dick's own Jung-inflected mythologizing framed "2-3-74" as a "metanoia," a transcendence that results in a greater integration of the personality and thus healing. Biographer Arnold argues persuasively that it was nothing of the sort. His "intoxicating taste of radical wholeness and connectedness to the world" gradually slipped from his grasp, leaving him with the same sufferings and problems as well as a brand-new emptiness, a brand-new abandonment to add to his list. Over the following eight years until his death, Dick wrote thousands of pages of analysis to try and understand what had happened to him, and it does not lessen the value or genius of this text, the *Exegesis*, to say that it was the product of a nervous breakdown. "The *Exegesis* is the embodiment of Dick's psychospiritual nostalgia," Arnold writes.[28] It may be that many of the world's greatest spiritual texts have been produced in such a state of crisis.

Fortunately for later students of precognition, this period in Dick's life also produced some striking precognitive experiences that the writer recorded in fascinating and compelling detail thanks to a new pen pal—and muse—that entered his life just a month after his "2-3-74" visions and dreams began.

"Dear Claudia"

In early April, 1974, Dick received a short letter from a young woman named Claudia Bush who was planning to write about *Ubik* for her master's degree at Ohio State University; she wrote him humbly asking for a bibliography of his works.[29] Dick wrote her back from the hospital, saying that they were about to replace his insides with plastic radio parts, and promised to write further. Over the following years, they carried on an intense correspondence, in which Dick chronicled his evolving interpretations of his fading mystical experience and in other ways opened up about his life and feelings with considerably more openness and authenticity than he seems to have shown any other mail correspondent during this period.

It is easy to read into his affectionate, avuncular-yet-flirtatious tone a kind of crush or transference. Claudia clearly represented another Oedipal fantasy: a young, obviously intelligent, suitably admiring girl who had none of the baggage and issues that his real-life relationship with wife Tessa was already (inevitably) assuming. For Claudia's part, she felt special to be the object of so much attention by a writer she so admired; she describes that their letter-writing was, for her, "an extremely intense personal experience."[30] Claudia went on to get a doctorate in Educational Testing and Measurement, and later, as Dr. Claudia Krenz, she attempted to make scanned hypertext of all of Dick's letters available on the internet but was prevented from doing so by copyright laws. On her website,[31] Krenz downplays her own importance in this early "virtual" relationship (which began, she notes, the same year the word "internet" was coined), and she has not made her side of the correspondence available. But it is clear from the tone of Dick's letters to her that she became something of a muse during that most intense and dark period of his life—even though they never met in person.

Many but not all of Dick's lengthy "Dear Claudia" letters—Krenz says she received three a day, on a few occasions—have been published as part of his collected letters; and a few also appear in his published *Exegesis*.[32] Especially when read in isolation from his other correspondence during this period, these letters provide particularly valuable insight into Dick's thought processes, and because he wrote her so regularly about his dreams, they give us especially valuable and unique insight into Dick's precognitive habit. At the bottom of a typed letter to Claudia dated May 9, 1974, in which he speculated he had multiple personality disorder, Dick penned a handwritten postscript: "PS: What scares me most, Claudia, is that I can often recall <u>the future</u>."[33]

Although many of Dick's claims and speculations about himself may not hold up under scrutiny, his claim of sometimes recalling the future, for instance in his dreams, is actually somewhat verifiable. Dick's "Dear Claudia" letters are as valuable as any other dream corpus I know of for the study of dream precognition in vivo. In them, we have a dense, and in a few cases, daily record of Dick's unfolding dream life, enabling us to construct an anatomy of dream precognition as an orienting function unfolding over a span of time. In a way that J. W. Dunne would have immediately recognized, Dick's dreams oriented him toward a series of imminent, exciting learning experiences—specifically, interesting information latent often in his own sprawling, disorganized library, which in turn provided valuable strands to be woven into his most enduring spiritual and fiction writings over the coming years. These dreams also oriented and reoriented him toward that important "virtual" human connection to Claudia during a period when his marriage was in turmoil and the mystical presence that had given his life new meaning at the beginning of 1974 seemed to gradually abandon him.

On July 5, 1974, Dick wrote to his pen pal to describe the culmination of a series of dreams spanning the previous three months. All of them seemed to be pointing him toward a specific large blue hardback book whose title terminated with the word "Grove" preceded by a longer word starting with B, and that had been published in 1966 or 1968. "I had the keen intuition that when I at last found it I would have in my hands a mystic or occult or religious book of wisdom which would be a doorway to the absolute reality behind the whole universe."[34] Bibliophiles who pay attention to their dreams will recognize this immediately (discovering a rare or overlooked book of great value) as a common dream theme. In one dream, the book was burned around the edges, suggesting an ancient manuscript. Although Dick thought he may need to go to a library or bookstore to find this volume, his dreams ultimately hinted he would find the book in his personal library, and thus he describes spending a day scouring his house in search of a big blue book with a title terminating in "Grove."

Amazingly, he found what he was looking for, and the denouement of this weeks-long quest is as funny as anything in his novels:

> As soon as I took down the volume I knew it to be the right one. I had seen it again and again, with ever increasing clarity, until it could not be mistaken.
> The book is called THE SHADOW OF BLOOMING GROVE, hardback and blue, running just under 700 huge long pages of tiny type. It was published in 1968. It is the dullest book in the world … It is a biography of Warren G. Harding.[35]

This too is a common experience for anyone who has engaged with their dreams in any consistent and serious way. Like a trickster, dreams often dangle a promise of sublimity, only to pull banal switcheroos that would be depressing if they weren't so funny. It is Dick's willingness to confront this *bathetic* pole in his own dream life—for instance, dreams promising a book of high wisdom, only to lead him to a dull 700-page biography of Warren Harding that a book club had sent him years earlier—that makes Dick such a valuable chronicler of precognitive phenomena. He is able to find comedy in his own errors and misunderstandings, and thus readily shares them with his young admirer and, via her, with us. [36]

We do not have Krenz's side of this literary conversation, unfortunately, but a week after reporting his discovery of the Harding biography, Dick wrote several long letters to her in quick succession (two on July 13th alone) in which he mentions her great amusement at his story. He goes on to describe subsequent vivid dreams over the intervening week, including a dream of a woman Cyclops sitting amid the conspirators who killed the Kennedy brothers and Dr. King; when he takes a second look at the dream woman, she is a pretty, two-eyed sibyl (prophetess). The narrative that unfolds from this is particularly interesting from the standpoint of Dunne's observations on precognition's relation to reading experiences.

The Cyclops-sibyl dream, he wrote, led him to look up "sibyl" in his encyclopedia. He does not notice that there is likely a precognitive element in this, if we take *Cyclops* as a dream-pun on *encyclopedia*—and that the reference work yielded a description of the Cumaean Sibyl. He quoted to Claudia a description of how the sibyl offered to sell her prophetic writings to the Roman king Tarquin the Proud; when he refused her high price, she began burning her books, until at last he paid the full price for the only three left undestroyed. This recalled to Dick the earlier dream of a burned manuscript in the lead-up to finding the book about Harding. The passage also mentioned that a description of the Cumaean Sibyl appears in Virgil's *Aeneid*. After Dick mailed this letter, he wrote Claudia a second letter as a "footnote," describing how he had gone ahead and looked up the *Aeneid* in another source he had at hand, Will Durant's *Caesar and Christ*, where he learned that Virgil's poem also contained a description of the Cyclops and, most strikingly, where he found the following sentence: "Then the Sibyl takes him through mystic passages of the Blissful Groves where those who led good lives bask in green valleys and endless joys."[37]

Dick delves in subsequent letters into the possible Jungian meaning of all this, the significance of ancient Rome in his mystical experiences, and the sibyl as representing his "anima," the inner source of his own prophetic capacity. Recall here Morgan Robertson's belief that his own muse was likewise a feminine spirit of some sort. We can observe Dick here beginning to weave these dream images into his evolving self-mythology and what became a major metaphysical strand in his *Exegesis*, as well as the novel *VALIS* that was based on his experiences.

In his search for a meaning behind all these coincidences—an answer to the question "why me?"—Dick understandably gropes in many different directions for an explanation and attaches great, mostly Jungian significance to the symbols. Yet he does not go down the path of thinking he is simply accessing archetypes in the collective unconscious. Rather, he is drawn to the conclusion that somehow the ancient world is still present, only camouflaged—or indeed, that we are still in it. It all seems to confirm a dream remembered from his youth that was much like the "B___ Grove" dreams, in which he had searched for a story in *Astounding Stories* called "The Empire Never Ended." That story, he had felt certain, contained all the mysteries of existence. As a result of some of his visions and experiences in 1974, Dick came to believe he was possibly a reincarnated Christian from ancient Rome.[38]

We are rewarded best by bracketing the various interpretations, the *Exegesis* per se, and looking at Dick's project as a making of something, a creation of meaningful narratives to be read by other people, a reaching out. The term "cry for help" may sound a bit extreme, but it is not. It was during this black period of his life, most specifically in February 1976, when Tessa left him and took their son, that he attempted suicide via drug overdose, slitting his wrists, and carbon monoxide poisoning in his garage, all at the same time. Fortunately, all three plans failed. Setting aside the metaphysics and cosmology, what was Dick trying to say in his writing during this period—to Claudia, to Tessa, to his readers, and to posterity? And what whispered message was he straining to hear from his own precognitive unconscious? Arguably, he wanted to hear the same thing Morgan Robertson managed to hear, loud and clear, when news of the *Titanic's* fatal collision with an iceberg splashed across the front page of *The New York Times* on April 15, 1912.

Both in his *Exegesis* and in his private correspondence with friends like Claudia, Dick flickered between two basic stances on his experience: the secret persistence of the ancient world underneath the veneer of mid-1970s Orange County, and the idea that he was haunting himself from his own future. These are not incompatible ideas in the sense that they both point to our old friend Mister Block Universe, where the past still exists and the future already exists—and by implication, *nothing is subject to alteration*. Kyle Arnold attributes Dick's living in a science-fictional world of endlessly shifting possibilities and uncertainty to his origin story and the death of Jane. But if his origin story propelled him to perpetually fabulate new possibilities for himself and for humanity, it was counteracted by his frequent precognitive experiences, which could have provided him with a needed sense of *im*possibility, a sense that there was *no* contingency, that history *couldn't* just as easily have turned out differently, but that events are inscribed like an indelible record groove in the fabric of time and space. This, I believe, is the real latent meaning, the "unconscious" so to speak, of Phil Dick, the latent meaning that is obscured by the incessantly "shifting realities" for which he is so famous.

In the deterministic block universe that Dick so often indexed in his *Exegesis*, it is not his fault that he got all the milk and that helpless little Jane perished, that he became addicted to speed and ruined five marriages, or that he was stuck in literature's "trash stratum" while so many of his less brilliant, less talented, less original peers prospered. The constant slipping and sliding reality and uncertainty that so characterizes Dick's fictional and interpersonal universe was not the reality he wanted; it was the one he wanted to escape. He wanted the unfreedom and thus absolution brought by radical determinism. In the block universe, none of the unfolding train wreck of Phil Dick's life was his fault, and in the eternal record groove of history, like Nietzsche's *eternal recurrence*, those tragedies and disasters would keep being replayed and repeated, no matter what. In other words, his escalating precognitive experiences across the 1970s, as well as his growing sense (or true awareness) during this time that his works in the previous decade had been precognitive, may have secured from the universe exactly what Morgan Robertson's prophecies did—a sense that "it is out of my hands."

It is necessary to add: This need of his, this bias, doesn't lessen the possible truth or accuracy of his intuition about reality.

"Shy and Gentle Creatures"

Dick's precognitive experiences may have also secured a sense of his own survival. Interestingly, some of his dreams in the aftermath of his "2-3-74" experience pointed distinctly toward things he would read or be exposed to in 1977 or later—creating a kind of bridge across the darkest year of his life, 1975 and early 1976, when the spirit had abandoned him and during which he made the aforementioned suicide attempt.

In a letter to Claudia on December 9, 1974, Dick records a dream about being the "other world" associated with his "2-3-74" visions and being introduced to a race of "lovely creatures which man hadn't yet destroyed, very shy and gentle creatures"[39] and being shown a piece of futuristic technology. "At one point in the dream I was reaching to take a plate on which was a piece of cake, but a small child, in a position of authority, told me firmly, 'No, that belongs to Mrs. Fields.'" After awakening, Dick recalls wondering who Mrs. Fields was, and then "remembering" that she was a woman who had been abducted by a UFO with her husband one night in the early 1960s on a remote road and shown a star chart corresponding to Zeta Reticuli. Dick is wrong here: The woman's surname was Hill (Betty Hill), not Fields. Mrs. Fields in fact was the name of a popular, widely advertised brand of cookies and brownies—a company that was not founded until a little over two years *after* this dream, in 1977. That his dream cake belongs to Mrs. Fields is certainly an interesting coincidence (skeptics will certainly call it that) if it is not a precognitive and typically "PhilDickian" conflation of the sublime and the "trash stratum" of consumer culture. But his misassociation of this cake with UFOs becomes odder, given another detail: "In my dream, the cake was all grooved, as if worked over by a fork..." He felt that the cake was really a kind of relief map, possibly of Florida.

The same year Mrs. Fields began advertising her line of popular sweets, Steven Spielberg's film *Close Encounters* featured a famous scene in which the main character, Roy Neary (Richard Dreyfus), trying to capture an obsessive dream vision implanted by a UFO encounter on a lonely rural road (like Betty Hill's experience with her husband Barney), piles mashed potatoes on his dinner plate and works them over with a fork to create grooves, and then does the same with a pile of mud in his living room—creating a grooved sculpture of what he will later learn represents Devil's Tower in Wyoming. It is literally a kind of map in relief. (Neary then desperately attempts to reach this location despite authorities' attempts to turn back civilians.) The film culminates with a spectacular UFO landing, where Neary is introduced to a race of beautiful, childlike, graceful creatures and is lastly taken away in their spaceship, not unlike what Dick encountered earlier in his dream.[40]

Was Dick's reading, moviegoing, and TV viewing (i.e., ads for cookies and brownies) in 1977 refluxing a little over two years into his past to appear in a dream he would excitedly share with his pen muse during his most intensely visionary-slash-psychotic period? There is no proof of anything here, yet this single dream from late 1974 seems like a constellation of ideas and images Dick would almost certainly have encountered and been excited by in 1977, specifically during a time of his life when, according to Tessa, he had become actively interested in the UFO phenomenon.[41] I have suggested elsewhere that in 1974 Dick also seems to have uncannily precognized a 1975 book by ufologist Jacques Vallee describing UFOs as a "control system," which Dick probably read specifically during that bout of ufological interest in 1977.[42] This precognitive encounter with *Vallee* may have given Dick the name for his famous extraterrestrial control system, *VALIS*, which became the title of his autobiographical novel about his mystical experiences.[43]

Like Freud's Irma dream, Dick's December 9, 1974, dream gives every sense of representing interests and concerns from another, fairly specific point in his life—in this case, a happier point, over two years later. According to the fractal dream-logic we have seen before, the dream may have even represented its own precognitive nature. The piece of technology he had been shown by the "shy and gentle creatures" was something in or from the future that he was meant to bring back to the past.[44] Precognitive dreams often contain some "time gimmick" representing time travel, clocks, rearview mirrors, or the act of looking back retrospectively (see the Postscript for an example of my own). Was Dick's renewed interest in life in the late 1970s, including UFO topics, imbued with a relief at having survived a particularly dark period, and was this what rippled back in his "brain line" as prophetic *jouissance* to form a dream in late 1974?

Dick continued to correspond with Claudia Bush, although less frequently, for the rest of his life. It was in another letter to her dated February 25, 1975, a couple months after the "shy and gentle creatures" dream, that Dick reported possibly the most striking of his prophetic visions, although again he had no way of knowing it was prophetic. He describes trying to summon back the spirit that had left him, when he saw the following: "hypnagogic images of underwater cities, very nice, and then a stark single horrifying scene, inert but not a still: a man lay dead, on his face, in a living room between the coffee table and the couch."[45] This inert figure was, Dick said, clothed in the skin of a fawn, like some ancient Greek or Roman sacrifice. Apart from the detail of the fawn skin, "in a living room between the coffee table and the couch" precisely describes how his own unconscious body was found after the first of the strokes in 1982 that ultimately killed him, at age 53.[46]

*Phil*logocentrism—Dick and the Future of Prophecy

Because most of us mortals cannot accept or even imagine that we are ever seeing or feeling the future, we contort all our anomalous experiences to fit some version of commonsense linear causality. Dick, almost alone among writers, at least in his most lucid and insightful moments, saw through culture's linear-causal mystifications, the no-saying of our cultural fathers. Just as he partly thought that ancient Rome was still alive behind the cheap-stage-set veneer of 20th century Orange County, another part of him just as compellingly thought he was haunting himself from the future. Again, he *needed* to believe in the Minkowski block universe, to forgive himself for Jane's death and the rest.

Jeffrey Kripal, in his study *Mutants and Mystics*, suggests that the connection between psychical phenomena and imaginative writing and art is a particularly close one[47]—although which came first, a career in imaginative literature or the tendency to have science-fictional experiences, may be impossible to specify. I argue that all creative people are "psychic"—that some ability to hear and record the faint resonating string of one's prophetic *jouissance* as it extends through the glass block is what creativity *is*. Writers being avid readers, they are constantly drawing from ideas latent in their libraries and other media. Those in more realistic genres (e.g., Norman Mailer) may less commonly notice their time-looping relation to culture because their reading experiences may not ordinarily be exotic enough to serve as tracers.

Resonances between future upheavals and present situations manifested in dreams and creative flow states may even be responsible for the very shape of culture, a constant cycling between precognition and confirmation. Kripal has argued that science fiction and comic books should be thought of as just our culture's mode of expressing the same real, baffling, and socially distrusted dimension of human experience that in past ages produced the great spiritual classics of the world's religions.[48] He notes that the history of religions is really "a long series of science fiction movies."[49] It is no accident that the science fiction genre has been marginalized and rejected by most cultural gatekeepers for most of its history. As Dick's alter-ego Horselover Fat remarks in *VA-LIS*, symbols of divinity initially appear in our world in the easily overlooked "trash stratum." Science fiction *is* that trash stratum, and yet its power to shape society, in the long run, may be overwhelming. Indeed, Phil Dick may occupy a unique, special place at the juncture between the linear-causal classical worldview and the precognition-accepting landscape of the future. I think to understand his special role, we cannot shy away from considering the "accident" of his name. Remember, in psychoanalysis, there are no accidents.

In the brain's associative search system, puns—not only verbal but also visual, aural, tactile, etc.—are probably the most characteristic form of coincidence, forming the nuclei not only of our memories but also of *attractor* phenomena in the symptom space of precognition. (In dynamical systems theory, an attractor is a set of values toward which a chaotic system tends to evolve; attractors are also central to the retro-causal "syntropy" theory of Ulisse di Corpo and Antonella Vannini as future states exerting a backward pull on living systems in the present.[50]) Dreams are practically built from verbal as well sensory puns—they are the real "bricks" of our dreams, and you might even call them the stem cells of synchronicity. But the individual unconscious is not the Jungian world of noble and poetic archetypes; it is a cringingly personal, Freudian world of low, schoolyard humor and wordplay. In such a world, there's an awful lot in a name, especially one as suggestive as Dick's. The associative networks in the brains of readers, and himself, will have made a special place for him because his name happens to be that of the Phallus.[51] I can't help but feel that this is an important part of the Dick story, one that delicacy prevents most biographers and critics from touching.

In Lacanian psychoanalysis, the Phallus does not simply denote the male member; rather it is an emblem of the possibility of castration, of *being itself* under the sign of erasure, *da* as contrasted with *fort*. It is the spool that young Ernst repetitively tossed from his crib to experience the *jouissance* of his own presence. The constantly flickering Phallus is also a symbol of the impossible trauma of sexual difference (i.e., what does it mean, what did I do wrong [or right], that I am *only* a _____ [boy/girl]?). It also "stands for" (pun maybe intended) the father's name as traditional anchor in the Symbolic order. Consequently, it is a virtual/absent emblem of the Real, the black hole around which that order revolves, producing in its vicinity the same time distortions that black holes in space can generate.

For Phil, his dead twin Jane, a "dead Dick," was an all-too-real embodiment of all the traumas, concrete and abstract, that are contained in this one symbol indicated by his surname. And his given name would have been a constant reminder of Jane's emptiness, the fact that he got his *fill* of their mother's milk, leaving Jane to starve. All these facts, these stupidly real puns, may have been like nails in his flesh, constant reminders of his origin myth, and his guilt. As a living and dying pun, Dick was a martyr to his own name.

Again, life in America, and on Earth, becomes more PhilDickian by the year; and every year there is some new biography, some new account of Dick's mysticism or his madness or just his quirks, and Hollywood continues to mine his books and stories for film—and more recently, TV—ideas. Could it be that history and culture converge more and more on Dick's writings, increasing their prophecy quotient, precisely because of the associative attracting power of that name? In other words, while it may be Dick's authentic precognitive abilities that contributed to his fame, it may be his name that made him so prophetic, in a kind of four-D feedback loop.

Only time will tell what spiritual use might be made of the Dick myth by future generations, or what influence his writings and life may yet have on the religious landscape of America. The literary critic Harold Bloom argued that the "American religion" is essentially Gnostic, having much in common with the numerous heresies Rome sought to extinguish in the first few centuries AD.[52] It is a worship of the innermost spiritual self, the uncreated spark seeking to free itself from the bleak material world in which an evil or stupid demiurge had long ago imprisoned it. Dick came to believe it was his life's mission to "restore Gnostic gnosis to the world in a trashy form,"[53] and indeed, readers of his fiction and especially his *Exegesis* may for the first time find their own hitherto implicit sci-fi Gnosticism articulated more clearly and directly than they have ever seen.[54] Despite or because of its painful origins, the *Exegesis* is probably one of the greatest, and certainly one of the weirdest, spiritual works of the 20th century. For one thing, as a spiritual text it uniquely satisfies our postmodern love of banality—Dick's life fully embodied what might be called the *banality of the spiritual*. He was a visionary and a mystic, but also an ordinary, lonely, suffering guy in a cheap apartment with a crappy rug, trying unsuccessfully to date his college student neighbors. And in the end, he was slain not by the dark Gnostic forces of the Black Iron Prison or the conspiracies he so believed in and feared, but by high blood pressure.

Musings about sparking a new religion may have been at the back of Dick's mind when he was writing his *Exegesis*. Various writers have drawn comparisons between Dick's mystical revelations and the Gnostic visions of L. Ron Hubbard.[55] Arnold points out that Dick would have been all too aware (and envious) of Hubbard's weird success at turning science fiction into a religion with devoted followers. Dick's mother had been a reader of Hubbard's *Dianetics*, and living in California Dick would have encountered Church of Scientology members frequently. Fortunately, Dick lacked the money sense and guile to do much in the way of deliberate religion-founding. And his unreliability as a narrator notwithstanding, he was basically an honest chronicler of his experiences—he mainly wanted to understand them, not convince people of any single metaphysical picture that could provide the focus for a new belief system. Nothing in Dick's writings suggests the easy answers that followers of new religious sects are often looking for.

But it is not hard to imagine some future society, maybe in a thousand years, after a nuclear holocaust perhaps, where the Bible has acquired a further testament, the *Exegesis*, and the iconography of Christ on the Cross has been replaced by some stylized representation of the 53-year-old Phil Dick sprawled unconscious on the crappy rug, next to his coffee table. In that future religion, God will be VALIS (or Ubik), a face and a voice—perhaps our own—speaking to us from our own future.

14

The Arrival of Meaning and the Creation of the Past

With trembling hands, I made a tiny breach in the
upper left hand corner ... widening the hole a little,
I inserted the candle and peered in ... at first
I could see nothing, the hot air escaping from the
chamber causing the candle to flicker. Presently, details
of the room emerged slowly from the mist, strange
animals, statues and gold—everywhere the glint of
gold. For the moment—an eternity it must have seemed
to the others standing by—I was struck dumb with
amazement, and when Lord Carnarvon, unable to
stand in suspense any longer, inquired anxiously
"Can you see anything?", it was all I could do to get out
the words "Yes, wonderful things".

— Howard Carter, diary entry (November 26, 1922)

In the 2016 film *Arrival* by director Denis Villeneuve, based on "Story of Your Life" by Ted Chiang, linguist Louise Banks (Amy Adams) is part of a scientific team summoned to Montana to help decipher the language of visiting extraterrestrials, known as "heptapods," so that their intentions can be clarified. She starts to have frequent visions of a dying girl that she cannot place—she fears she may be going crazy from the strain of her assignment. The audience naturally assumes that these are flashbacks, memories of a child she lost in her past.

As Louise begins to realize that her increased understanding of how the aliens communicate is helping liberate her cognitively from linear time, she begins having visions that aid in her work, including reading from the definitive book on the aliens' written language that she herself is destined to write and publish in her future. From the book's dedication, she realizes that the girl in her visions is a daughter she is going to have and who will eventually die of a rare disease. And at a key moment, when the world is on the brink of war with the visitors, she is able to contact a Chinese General on his private cell phone and talk him out of his belligerence after she "premembers" his phone number, which he will show her at a celebration months or years in the future—an event celebrating international unification in the aftermath of humanity's first contact with extraterrestrial beings, made possible thanks largely to her intervention.

It is a story about time loops, in other words. And what "arrives" at the climax and at various turning points—excitingly in some cases and sadly in others—is the *meaning* of Louise's baffling experiences.

The heptapods, with their circular language, feel at home in the block universe of Minkowski spacetime, where past, present, and future coexist. In Chiang's short story, the scientists attempting to crack the code of their language get an important clue from Fermat's principle of least time (Chapter 6), which suggests a kind of teleological interpretation of light's behavior—it needs to know where it is going right from the start, in order to take the fastest possible route to get there. Chiang resolves the perennial questions about precognition and free will by suggesting that knowledge of future outcomes causes a psychological shift in the experiencer: an "urgency, a sense of obligation"[1] to fulfill what has been foreseen. "Fatalism" would be one word for it but inflected more positively—perhaps not unlike how Morgan Robertson and Phil Dick may have seen it: as absolution rather than restriction.

In the film, one of the heptapods sacrifices its life to save that of Louise and her team members from a bomb planted by some soldiers, even though it clearly knows its fate well in advance. Their race even knows that in 3,000 years, humanity will offer them some needed assistance, and thus their visit is just the beginning of a long relationship of mutual aid in the block universe. At the end of the film, Louise *chooses* to have her daughter, even knowing that the girl will die. It is a sublime, albeit melancholy, vision, one that not all people are capable of withstanding. Louise's physicist husband, the father of their daughter, divorces her because he cannot accept her choice and her foreknowledge of its outcome.

Precognition is seldom as clear as it is depicted in *Arrival* or "Story of Your Life," for all the reasons we have explored throughout this book. Information refluxing from the future will always be largely oblique and unrecognizable, misunderstood, and more often forgotten completely until events transpire to make sense of or confirm it. But of all films that have been made about precognition, *Arrival* probably is closest to "getting it right," and Louise Banks' experience can serve as a useful template for understanding the unconscious and its looping relation to time, meaning, and causality.[2] Until unfolding events make sense of our anomalous experiences, any meaning we give them will be premature and will inevitably falsify them.

As I argued, the main difference between precognition and what we usually think of as memory is that information from the Not Yet must lack meaning until precognized events come to pass. Unlike the past, the future does not speak a language we can recognize. Rich sensory experiences (such as where you were and what you were doing when you learned something new) provide the context for much of what we know from past experience, enabling us to place that information in our personal chronology and even providing rich associations that help recall facts and events—for instance the famous power of smells and places to evoke a recollection. Information from our future will by definition lack any context that could give it meaning or, in most cases, even allow us to recognize it as meaningful. Like finding letters in our mailbox with no return address, we might toss aside our strange dreams, visions, and weirdly non-sequitur passing thoughts as junk mail. If we do not discard them, we may make up inaccurate stories about where they came from (those source-monitoring errors).

Additionally, precisely because precognitive information lacks sense when we receive it, and because the psyche abhors a vacuum of meaning, we may have already imposed some suitable (but false) framing on such experiences by the time confirmation arrives—further abetting the unseeing of their precognitive nature. If you already assume that a dream symbolically represents recent preoccupations, or unresolved wishes from childhood, or archetypes relevant to your individuation—or more likely, just assume dreams are the deranged product of the sleeping brain—why bother looking for any additional meaning in the dream, even when events unfold that oddly resemble its contents?

The depth psychologies examined earlier, Freud's psychoanalysis and Jung's analytical psychology, were bold in their recognition that something about us transcends our ordinary understanding—that there is much more in heaven and earth than is dreamt of in our philosophy. But if those traditions celebrated humanity's mysterious richness, they also redirected our inquiry toward their founders' favored past-oriented psychology or transpersonal metaphysics.[3] By insisting on a prescribed set of hermeneutic coordinates for our dreams and symptoms (the Oedipal situation; archetypes of the collective unconscious), Freud's and Jung's frameworks prematurely satisfied their own and their followers' hunger for meaning and thereby falsified our true relation to time. Wishing into existence a dream life (and universe) already pre-saturated with meaning, we will never have the opportunity to discover, or even imagine, that we could sometimes be in the astonishing presence of wishes and thoughts we ourselves will consciously have at some later point down the road.

Not waiting for meaning's arrival—not waiting for the sugar to melt[4]—can come back to haunt us. With three decades of hindsight, the dream of Irma's injection showed the 67-year-old Freud, obliquely and in a fashion he probably couldn't accept, his belated, better-informed perspective on the turning point that led to him becoming the "answerer of riddles" celebrated by his colleagues. From that late vantage point, I suggested, he tried to wish away a nagging realization that *he might have been wrong about dreams*—at least, wrong in his rejection of their prophetic possibility. It was in the same stroke a reproach to himself for ignoring his friend Fliess's warning about his smoking that, had he heeded it, might have averted what turned into 16 years of pain and drastically compromised quality of life. Again, at the time he had the dream, it was not a "warning" he could have heeded; but as an ordinary irrational mortal, he might naturally have blamed himself anyway for *not* treating it as a warning. It is our confused belief in free will and an open-ended universe subject to our shaping that naturally leads to such (possibly quite erroneous) retrospection. How entangled our neuroses and regrets are with our cosmology is a rich topic awaiting some future quantum psychoanalysis.[5]

The Unconscious of Matter

Both the hermeneutic moment in the psychoanalytic clinic and the act of measurement in a physics lab create a state of knowing by giving meaning to what until then lacked it, in a way that has decisive effects for the object of knowledge—who, in the former case, is also a subject.[6] According to most mainstream descriptions of what happens in the double-slit experiment, the photon in its unmeasured state is a lot like an ambivalent neurotic, taking both paths simultaneously through two available slits because it cannot make up its mind or commit to taking one slit or the other. This ambivalence, literally a kind of self-interference, shapes the observed behavior of matter on a fundamental level. When the wavefunction "collapses" to something definite, it is like making that photon's unconscious conscious. "Where *it* (the unconscious) was, there will *I* (the conscious ego) be," in Freud's famous phrase. *Where the wave was, there the particle will be.* The world of self-interfering wavefunctions is essentially the unconscious of matter.

Richard Feynman's "path-integral" (or "sum over histories") approach to quantum problems is especially Freudian. Instead of viewing light as consisting of waves, he visualized a photon as a little ball taking *every possible* path through space to get to its destination; most "wild" paths destructively interfere, but those in the vicinity of the most efficient path reinforce each other, producing the ray-like behavior we observe. This is how he explained Fermat's principle of least time, in his lectures published as *QED*: The path taken by the light ray is the last man standing, so to speak, after all other possible vectors cancel each other out.[7] In other words, it is just like the existing-yet-not-existing, agonistic virtual realm of the unconscious, where every possible motive and dark desire battles for supremacy without us ever being the wiser. Off-stage, perpetually unseen, is a bloody battlefield strewn with matter's slain possibilities and intentions. (As James Gleick put it in his biography of Feynman: "The seemingly irrelevant paths are always lurking in the background, making their contributions, ready to make their presence felt in such phenomena as mirages and diffraction gratings"[8]—nature's parapraxes and dreams, one might say.)

Physicists have been more careful than psychoanalysts not to reify or hypostatize their metaphors—Feynman, for instance, did not assume that his signature path integrals were necessarily anything more than a mathematical predictive trick. (Thus, it is sometimes said that quantum physics really has no theory; the Copenhagen Interpretation is really an injunction *not* to interpret but just "shut up and calculate."[9]) But it is hard not to make assumptions about reality based on our metaphors, even mathematical ones. This is known in the social sciences and linguistics as the Sapir-Whorf hypothesis, another crucial touchstone for the scientists in "Story of Your Life": The words and symbols we use affect how we think. We may not be able to unlock greater precognitive ability simply by learning a different kind of language, one with a nonlinear grammar. But it could be that it is our language of cause and effect that keeps us from seeing that those uncollapsed wavefunctions and "buried" unconsciouses don't *already* exist as something off-stage or invisible. We need some new metaphors, and, again, a new "backwards" way of thinking, to see how factors relevant to the present may be spread out in time, in both directions.

Over three centuries ago, Enlightenment physics and the natural philosophy and psychology that flowed from it walled off that whole half of time, entombing the Not Yet behind a thick stone barrier. Causes pushed from the past, and effects were theoretically predictable just from that pushing. The world subsequently forgot all about teleology, the quaint old idea that where we are going might exert some kind of complementary influence, pulling or nudging us in certain directions. Then a century ago, physicists realized there was something about matter's behavior—a lot, in fact—that those pushing causes couldn't tell them. Since then, a resignation to uncertainty has served as a Band-Aid, and made careers for brilliant mathematicians like Feynman, who refined quantum physics into the most powerful predictive theory ever created. Much of the technology we now take for granted depends on the startling accuracy of equations that predict matter's statistically "random" behavior. But mysteries have remained. Basic problems remain insoluble (like reconciling quantum physics with Einstein's theory of gravity, for instance). And with new technology that can zero in on ever smaller scales, the weirdness just gets weirder.

A few bold explorers have realized that that whole half of time the Enlightenment walled off may hold part of the answer, and they have begun to pierce it with their drills. What is gleaming in their torchlight already is, as Howard Carter whispered when he peered for the first time into King Tut's tomb, "wonderful." With all due respect to a brilliant teacher, Feynman's world of particles taking every possible path is an effortful, indeed "exhausting" picture of reality.[10] The retrocausal alternative offered by Yakir Aharonov, John Cramer, Huw Price, and others seems much more elegant, not to mention less wasteful of God's effort. The path of light is the fastest possible simply because the destination has exerted its own backward influence—*pulling the light ray taut*, you might say. What looked like the "capricious" randomness of identical particles is really an *inflection* of particles' behavior by their differing future histories.[11] The future may be an equal participant in determining the present moment.

Again, it is not that measurement simply reveals something about already-existing reality that was hitherto unknown (the old-fashioned realist view) *or* that it causes some magical transition from waviness to definitiveness, helping the universe make up its mind, or even bringing it wholly into being. Rather, the measurement is partly responsible for shaping the particle's *previous* history. A particle's behavior is unpredictable, "uncertain," before it is measured because the experimenter's measurement will turn out to have been the missing piece of the puzzle of the particle's behavior in the first place. Not only is it teleological; it makes the behavior of matter on a fundamental level *tautological*—time-looping.

If the retrocausal interpretation does prevail, quantum physics may one day come to be characterized as a set of rules governing what can be known, when, and with what degree of certainty within a physical world that is *already* shaped by our present interpretations—a kind of hermeneutic engagement with the material past that is perpetually constructive of that past. The "entanglements of matter and meaning"[12] described by Karen Barad in her work may turn out to be the contours of space, time, and knowledge that constitute natural firewalls against paradox. In other words, forget "nonlocality"; what entanglement and its secret alter-ego uncertainty really reflect is *the limits around the ability of intentional precognitive creatures to make meaning from noise prematurely.* "Free will" may simply be what it feels like when fated beings make decisions under uncertainty, bounded by those firewalls.

As Barad underscores, we cannot *change* an already-existing past—create a different timeline from the one we know. (How would we even know we had done so?) But there is so much we still don't know or correctly understand about the past in the block universe we do inhabit that we can discover anew, at every moment, how our present choices were already included in and even actually shaped that past.

The hermeneutic moment that seems to give rise to preceding dreams and symptoms in clinical contexts—at least in some very suggestive cases like Maggy Quarles van Ufford's precognitive seduction of Jung or Herr P.'s "foresight/Forsyte" obsession—exactly mirrors what is being shown in physics laboratories, and thus suggests an interesting reframing of clinical causation to parallel the retrocausation paradigm in physics. When anomalies point toward new paradigms, those anomalies often become universal and expected features within the new worldview. Are the rare precognitive events caught inadvertently in the amber of clinical writing perhaps revealing a universal principle and not the exception? Again, could it be that neuroses, the secret saboteurs of happiness, might often be premonitory formations, back-acting echoes (or "prechoes") of future realizations and epiphanies both traumatic and rewarding?

The idea that the cure is the retroactive cause of the symptom and the interpretation the cause of the dream is not that far from what Jacques Lacan proposed already in the early 1950s. Lacan had departed from Freud's resolutely past-centered way of picturing the psychoanalytic project, emphasizing instead the performative dimension of human life—the ongoing making of meaning in speech and cultural interaction. The individual unconscious for Lacan was not some buried stratum whose contents sometimes pressed up, breaking the surface, like the ruins of Rome. It was part of an unfolding continuum resembling a Möbius strip, a geometrical object with a single surface. When you travel along it, you pass or overtake yourself before returning to your original starting point. Symptoms and dreams confronted in psychoanalysis reflect the traverse of this Möbius in time, and human life takes on a looping, self-overtaking character as a result. (In the 1960s, Lacan also became interested in the geometry of knots and objects like Klein bottles having a single surface, as models for what transpires in analysis.) And Lacan's version of the "collective unconscious" was similarly both flat and looping: It was simply *language*, the Symbolic order, which precedes us and within which we struggle more or less successfully to find our place and our voice.

With his flat ontology, Lacan saw that the apparent senselessness of a neurotic symptom or a bizarre dream is a real function of the fact that no meaning exists "in" it yet; its sense must emerge in lived acts of communication and interpretation. "What we see in the return of the repressed," he wrote, "is the effaced signal of something which only takes on its value in the future, through its symbolic realization, its integration into the history of the subject."[13] Once again, *meaning must arrive*—and that arrival will be seen to have had a decisive impact on what went before.

Slavoj Žižek built a whole philosophy on the Möbius-like temporal self-overtaking suggested by Lacan's work, tying it to Hegelian and Marxian dialectical thinking as well as the European idealist tradition more generally (e.g., Schelling). In his early work, Žižek liked to invoke the typical science-fiction trope of a time traveler visiting himself in the past to illustrate how some baffling symptom is actually caused by its cure. He later defined an *event* (in either individual or collective history) as an occurrence that creates its own causes, in hindsight.[14] He has even applied this idea to the question of free will versus the determinism implied by contemporary neuroscience, such as Libet's discoveries about the lag of conscious will behind the initiation of motor actions. For Žižek, freedom consists not, as V. S. Ramachandran argued, in a kind of belated veto power ("free won't"), but more subtly in the ability to choose the causal arrows that led to our actions—a kind of hermeneutic engagement with our own past.[15] Even if our actions are dictated unconsciously, our freedom consists in the way we define them after the fact.

However, careful to avoid rocking the prevailing materialist boat and courting dreaded "New Age obscurantism," Žižek has always held that this is only a retroactive reordering of the *symbolic* universe, the way we reframe things retrospectively.[16] What looks like prophecy is really just a kind of revision of memory. One way to describe much of Žižek's work, in fact, would be as an *analytic of hindsight bias*.

I am arguing that we should go farther and not fear the obscure: Symptoms might really, literally, be time-loop formations built around our ambivalent "enjoyment" of salient epiphanies and traumas ahead. Those loops tie meaningless behavior in the present with meaningful future experiences, but in a way that indeed can only be accurately discerned in hindsight. The "twist" in the Möbius reflects that we traverse this loop doubly, both as cause and as meaning, giving rise to wyrd's "symbolic" (but maybe in fact just oblique) character.

It would mean that we can no longer assume that past experiences are safely tucked away in the folds of memory, untouched and unchanged by our reflection on them in the present. In the flux of our lives, we continually are updating our knowledge, but that updating exerts (or really, exert*ed*) an effect *already* in creating the conditions that led to it. In this book I have presented evidence that people sometimes precognize not only their future thoughts but their future remembrance of past thoughts. Although we cannot create a different past, which would foreclose our own being-there in the present—the self-destructive fantasy-slash-anxiety expressed in time-travel stories—our active engagement with history and memory can disclose anew at every moment how our present realizations about our past were already included weirdly *in* that past, in ways that were not quite recognizable or comprehensible *until this very moment.* We are always at the center of a radiating (and converging) web of causes and effects, a shifting vantage point constantly disclosing and uncovering new information not only about how our history shaped our conditions of being in the present but how our *realizations about* that shaping shaped our history in turn. This is what I mean by a precognitive hermeneutics: *ongoing excavation of the retrocausal links between present and past.*

Zapped in a Parking Lot

I have drawn on psychoanalytic writings and applied these ideas to the psychoanalytic situation (and a couple of highly neurotic writers) not because I think the main relevance of this is in psychotherapy—I am not a therapist or even (currently) a patient. Apart from the light psychoanalytic theory sheds on the self-ignorance that facilitates precognition, it is because the clinic serves as a useful "toy model" for precognitive social causation more generally. It helps us think about what Rice University religion historian Jeffrey Kripal calls the "sociology of the impossible."[17] Because here's the thing: It would not only be our own past we are creating through our hermeneutic efforts. We would be shaping each other's pasts, too.

As I was nearing completion on this book, Jeff Kripal invited me to read a draft of a book manuscript he had co-written with Elizabeth Krohn, the lightning-struck precog mentioned in Chapter 1. I had already been aware of Elizabeth from other writings Jeff had shared, but in reading the full story—including her side of the story—I couldn't help but be "struck" by how vividly this case seemed to illustrate the way people's actions in the present may actually shape not only their own histories but also the histories of other people they meaningfully interact or collaborate with.

Jeff's own backstory is relevant. He had transitioned mid-career from a focus on Hindu mysticism to studying the history of the human potential movement and then, more recently, the paranormal as a marginalized dimension of modern religion. As he has described in a few books, the crucial turning point toward this latter trajectory was a chance encounter with a piece of trash in a Sugar Land, Texas movie theater parking lot one hot summer day in 2006.[18] He had just seen *X-Men 3: The Last Stand* and was feeling, he said, "perplexed" at the similarities between this superhero mythology and the "evolutionary mystical system" of one of the pioneers of the human potential movement, Michael Murphy, co-founder of the Esalen retreat in Big Sur, California.

As he approached his van, Jeff spotted a "golden and shining" *X* on the pavement next to it. He initially thought it was a cross, but it turned out to be an X-shaped piece of cheap costume jewelry. Like the overdetermined symbols in Freudian dream interpretation, this *X* connected to much more than just the *X-Men* mythology. It also replicated one of the most storied moments in modern science-fiction folklore, Phil Dick's "zapping" by the fish pendant worn by the girl delivering painkiller to his house in early 1974. It was also a lot like the beetle tapping at Carl Jung's office window on that day in 1920, a perfectly timed material sign pointing toward some kind of breakthrough. For Jeff, the *X* in the parking lot catalyzed an awareness of the new direction he needed to take in his career: taking seriously, as religion, the really far-out (yet, as he would come to find, astonishingly common) stories of people who experience events that transcend everyday understanding, making them the motor of their creativity and spirituality thereafter.

The *X-Men* comics Jeff had loved in his youth were tales of misfit, superpower-endowed "mutants" who find acceptance and guidance in understanding and applying their new talents under the mentorship of their schoolmaster, Professor X. Jeff saw Esalen, where he had spent much time over the previous eight years hosting symposia and researching the history of the institute/retreat,[19] as a kind of real-world "X School." Esalen was founded in 1962, a year before Stan Lee and Jack Kirby envisioned their Westchester, New York, school in the *X-Men* comic. (If you aren't familiar with *X-Men*, or Esalen, think Hogwarts in the *Harry Potter* series—same idea. Or if, like me, you were more of a *Dune* kid, think the training academies of the Bene Gesserit sisterhood, alluded to throughout Frank Herbert's series.)

In his monumental study that resulted from the gleaming *X*, *Mutants and Mystics*, Jeff identified several "mythemes" found throughout the lives and works of Dick and many other science fiction and comic book writers. One is *mutation*: People are transformed by their experience, and elevated—perhaps toward the next stage in their own development, or toward the next stage in human evolution—and they sometimes develop new powers as a result. Another is *radiation*: Light and energy are common experiences—just as happens in comic books, people are literally zapped (or communicated with) via light. And there is *alienation*: These individuals may experience contact with nonhuman entities or intelligences, as well as find *themselves* suddenly marginalized and denigrated, "othered" or alienated. Jeff developed these ideas further in *The Super Natural*, a collaboration with the writer Whitley Strieber, whose famously strange experiences beginning with an "abduction" (by whom or what he still cannot say) in 1985 set off a series of amazing, troubling, and baffling experiences, and a series of controversial books, beginning with his 1987 bestseller *Communion*. [20]

In October, 2015, Jeff was invited to comment on a near-death-experience case at an event at Houston Medical Center. The individual concerned was a 55-year-old mother of three, Elizabeth Krohn. Back in 1988, at age 28, Elizabeth had been struck by lightning in the parking lot of her synagogue while on her way to a service that would honor the memory of her grandfather, who had died one year before. She said that after the flash of lightning, she continued to walk into the synagogue only to realize that no one was noticing her, and that she was floating a few inches off the ground. She looked outside and saw her own inert body on the wet pavement and the smoldering soles of her brand-new (and expensive) black and white pumps. She then had an experience of the afterlife in a kind of extraterrestrial garden that lasted, she thought, about two weeks, although in Earth time it was only a few minutes. Someone called for a doctor, and this being a big city synagogue, there was no shortage of those to attend her.

Physically, Elizabeth was mostly unhurt except for burns on her feet—she did not even require a hospital stay—but after her "reentry" into her body she was never the same. She describes that she went from thinking like her shoes, in shiny, crisp, black-and-white terms, to seeing shades of gray. She went from never remembering her dreams to having and recording startlingly specific, accurate dreams about imminent events, including dreams of disasters (or news reports thereof). This metamorphosis meant a new trajectory in her life, which included dealing with her new superpower. Although exciting and intriguing on one level, it also depressed her—it was in some ways a curse because she could do nothing with her premonitions except excitedly/nervously check the news afterward to find out if what she'd seen had come to pass.

Elizabeth struggled confusedly with her new life and new experiences, tentatively trying out giving psychic readings in another city so that her increasingly "New Age" identity wouldn't jeopardize her husband's career. Eventually she and that husband divorced, and she married someone better suited to her new life. And eventually, fortuitously, she met Jeff, who worked in an office at Rice University just three blocks from the synagogue where she'd been zapped, and who had over the previous decade become literally the world expert in real-life zapping by super-natural energies and the "mutant" paranormal powers often acquired as a result. Elizabeth provided the most vivid, concrete, and uncannily close example yet of everything he had been studying and writing about since the X in the movie theater parking lot. She was not some author encountered via a text or a comic book; she was a real, flesh-and-blood person right in his own community.

They quickly agreed that they needed to collaborate on a book, published in 2018 as *Changed in a Flash*.[21] In the process of their collaboration, Jeff invited Elizabeth to Esalen, where she met Strieber and many big lights of the human potential movement. The experience helped her gain greater peace with and understanding of her gifts. In keeping with Elizabeth's belief in the afterlife, she now sees herself as a kind of flesh-and-blood "spirit guide" able to heal the rupture between the living and the dead. So in a very real way, Jeff played Professor X, helping a real-life "mutant" come to grips with and learn to use her powers in a rewarding and constructive way.

In other words, in Elizabeth Krohn, Jeff Kripal met an almost too-perfect example of everything he'd been studying and thinking about since his own zapping in a local movie theater parking lot. If he were a novelist, Elizabeth is the character he would create. Although in fact, a writer deeply influential on him already wrote it. During the course of their collaboration, Jeff lent Elizabeth a copy of the novel *Youth Without Youth*, by the Romanian religion scholar Mircea Eliade, about an aging suicidal intellectual struck by lightning behind a church on Easter, who then develops precognitive ability. She returned it to him saying "That's not fiction." Also in the course of their collaboration, Elizabeth and Jeff bonded over the movie *Arrival*, since it seemed so nicely to illuminate Elizabeth's own struggle toward finding meaning in her precognitive experiences.

Whether her lightning strike physically altered Elizabeth's brain circuitry in some way, jarring loose some restraining bolt on latent precog talents, or whether it just altered her perspective on life and its precariousness in a way that made her more receptive to the precognitive sublime (as I would cautiously hypothesize), she became much more aware of her responsiveness to events and experiences in her future. If what I have been proposing is correct, those occasional dreams about air disasters and other crises would be just the tip of a largely unconscious iceberg of precognitive orientation to future rewards in Elizabeth's life. The rewards of the air disaster dreams would be the repellant *jouissance* of survival. But behind them may have been the reward of meeting and reading and collaborating with Professor X, Jeffrey Kripal, which led to her making greater peace with her abilities thanks to the community of other experiencers and experts he linked her with (at Esalen for instance). Jeff and his world, and the book he helped her write, were big rewards looming in her future. All the rewards of this adventure may have echoed back along her timeline—or her "brain line" as Dunne would put it. "I knew that I already knew him," Elizabeth said of her first meeting with Jeff, "and I knew that we would write a book."[22]

And it would have been a two-way street. Encountering and collaborating with Elizabeth was a major reward for Jeff, a fruitful collaboration and friendship, not to mention professional validation (the perfect "case study") that happened to be latent in his own future and backyard, and which he may have been attuned to precisely in the creative flow state he seems to enter when he engages with these topics.

Arguably—and now I come to my main point with this story—precognition did not just cause Jeffrey Kripal and Elizabeth Krohn to collaborate; their convergence may have also shaped both of them *into the past*. Might Elizabeth's entire "career" as *a lightning-struck mystical mutant* be seen as a premonitory "symptom" (in Lacan's sense) of her ultimate tutelage by and collaboration with the real-life Professor X? Jeff certainly didn't cause the lightning strike per se, any more than Carl Jung caused a scarab to appear at his window right as his patient was telling him her dream about a scarab—his powers are not *that* great. But had he and his work not been ahead in Elizabeth's future timeline, her experiences after the strike, and even during the strike, might arguably have assumed a very different shape, or taken a different direction. Maybe she would not in that case have become a precog like something out of a Phil Dick novel or an *X-Men* comic or Eliade's *Youth Without Youth*. The trajectories of trauma are many and varied, and unfortunately many paths available to survivors in our trauma-bound culture (mental illness and drug addiction being all-too-common ones) are nowhere near as inspiring or indeed enchanting as the one offered by Jeff in his writings on the paranormal. In other words, thanks to Elizabeth's precognitive sensitivity, Jeff and his framings of the "super natural" may well have had a hand in shaping her experiences long before zapping and mutation were even glimmers in *his* eye.

And again, the shaping would have been a two-way affair. Like Asimov's thiotimoline molecule, that overdetermined X in the movie theater parking lot in 2006 seems to have had at least one carbon valence bond extending a decade into Jeff's own future, linking it not only to the glinting fish pendant in Dick's myth (which Jeff would subsequently write about[23]) but especially to Elizabeth Krohn's life-altering atmospheric-electrical mishap, also in a parking lot. How could this fact not have added to its "gleam" that day, drawing his attention, perturbing his own perception? How could that moment, and the subsequent career path that ensued, not itself be "precognitive" of his ultimate meeting and collaboration with Elizabeth? It was almost as if the work he did after that X and in the decade leading up to their meeting was destined—although fated may be a better word—precisely to supply a radical, and importantly, intellectually legitimate framing on *her* experience. Their fates may have been "entangled," in other words, by their future collaboration.

Through the Wall of Time

Skeptics will dismiss this (and everything I have suggested in this book) with little more than an eye roll, as simply an attempt to redefine hindsight bias for credulous, paranormal purposes. Žižek would call it "New Age obscurantism." That is fine, that is their choice. But I maintain that if we accept even some of the evidence for precognition that I have cited—and that anecdotes, real human stories, supply in spades—then we can no longer bracket time loops as isolated incidents, some trivial or exceptional annex to human experience (as even many parapsychologists still cautiously and defensively suggest about psi, with its big p-values but "small effects"). And we also can no longer assume that these experiences exert no major influence on human affairs and the shape of social life.

The potential implications of time loops for philosophy and history are obvious from just a moment's thought, as they are for the social sciences. The sociologist Max Weber famously stated that "man is an animal suspended in webs of significance that he himself has spun"[24]; the anthropologist Clifford Geertz later added, "and I take culture to be those webs."[25] I think it is likely that precognition could play an important role in both the spinning of and getting stuck in those cultural webs.[26] I am not aware of any sustained efforts to explore these domains yet, although there is increased willingness in some quarters to talk about "consciousness" (and quantum theories thereof), as well as an increased willingness to discuss some parapsychological phenomena on their own terms.[27] A handful of researchers in or on the peripheries of scientific psychology (including not only parapsychology but also neuroscience and clinical psychology) are making inroads in discussing and publishing on precognition and other psi phenomena in more mainstream forums.[28] The study of religion, on the other hand, is at the vanguard of admitting more open discussion of these and many other paranormal phenomena (thanks in part to Kripal's work).[29]

Some cautious but fascinating beginnings have also been made toward studying precognition and time loops in literature and the arts. Malcolm Guite's 2017 book *Mariner*, to cite one recent example, is a moving examination of Samuel Taylor Coleridge and the ways his masterpiece poem *Rime of the Ancient Mariner* uncannily precognized (although Guite doesn't use that term) the poet's tortured life *after* he wrote the poem.[30] In the efforts of Guite, of Kripal on sci-fi and comic book authors,[31] or of Anthony Peake on Phil Dick,[32] we may be seeing a dim adumbration, like a gravestone rubbing, of a future precognitive cultural studies, a *psychic deconstruction*. Unlike traditional literary criticism, which often looks for unacknowledged prior influences on a writer's ideas, this would attend to possible subsequent influences.[33] It would also be highly biographical, necessarily placing literary or artistic creation within the overall context of the creator's life experiences even after the work was created.

In short, the effects of time loops could be—*and would have always been*—pervasive across many or most aspects of human social and cultural existence. We are only now evolving the eyes to see it. It could require radical revision of the guiding theories and paradigms in many fields that study humans and the meanings they make—"The textbooks," as they breathlessly say in movies, "will need to be rewritten." (Textbooks are lucrative, I hear, so why should professors object?) Among the many new questions culture historians and critics will need to ask is: Could especially prolific and influential writers, artists, and other shapers of culture—the Phil Dicks, the Freuds and Jungs, the Jeff Kripals, and so on—be literally shaping the past, almost like inadvertent alchemists of history, via *their readers'* precognitive gift-slash-curse of precognition?

Like today's quantum physicists parsing the effects of measurement in their retrocausation experiments, future investigators of meaning's retrograde effects will no longer be able to ignore their own possible past as well as ongoing entanglements with their objects of study. They will be forced to attend closely to how each one of their own articles and books (and textbooks) in the present may have acted back on the past to co-create what they are studying and writing about. How coherent and how deep the effects of present writing and scholarship are on *prior* literary or cultural history is at this point anyone's guess, but if there are still cultural historians in the 22nd century, they may well be kept busy mapping the subtle effects on knowledge and human experience of a "geist"—literally a *zeit-geist*—that moves through history in temporal retrograde. Through it all, skeptics will, somewhat justifiably, become apoplectic at the difficulties of separating truth from wish-fulfillment in this (as Kripal puts it) hyper-looping "super story."

Obviously, though, time loops have implications beyond academia and science. They are relevant to our everyday lives and relationships. For one thing, it may no longer be just a mushy New Age platitude to suggest that humans really do share an "invisible connection" with each other, as anti-materialists since Frederic Myers have always maintained; there is also a very good reason why any trace of such a physical connection vanishes when scientific spotlights are trained on the *spaces* between us. Instead of traversing the present, as some kind of invisible telepathic bridge across space, or some nonlocal Platonic collective unconscious, our "occult" interhuman connection traverses the fourth dimension, the Not Yet, as the real, physical encounters and interactions with other people and ideas awaiting us on the road ahead. I like to think of the secret psychic structure of social life as a kind of four-D lattice: Our pre-cognitive, presentimental unconscious orients us to those confluences where our individual world-lines snaking through Minkowski space-time meaningfully entwine and intersect. Bernard Beitman describes it as "connecting with coincidence."[34] It's an apt phrase, and we no longer need invoke some "acausal" synchronistic field stage-managing significant moments, or archetypal meaning-machines doing the connecting. *We* connect, *we* stage-manage, via our own amazing tesseract brains.

By paying closer, more thoughtful attention to her dreams, synchronicities, and passing thoughts, the precog ranger of tomorrow may learn to detect the bent twigs of her own passage ahead of herself in time and recognize them for what they are. She will understand how to follow them along a mostly unknown, obscure path, trusting that they orient her toward meaningful rewards (and "survival"), but she will also know that those meanings cannot be known in advance. If the traces of our future passage are like bent twigs, a "spoor" to be followed (or like cryptic notes in our own handwriting), the time loops they leave behind in our lives are in some ways even more interesting: They are like astonishing geological formations or imprints, bearing the traces of past intentional behavior by precognitive beings (ourselves) who didn't yet realize they were precognitive, and who were thus groping for meaning in other culturally available directions. Even if the past is not subject to change, we can excavate those fossils, brush them off and hold them up for scrutiny, and come to appreciate the ironic, looping paths our lives and desires and enjoyment took through the glass block. We may find that our past, even our distant past, is a kind of mirror, and see in it ourselves, winking back knowingly, across those instantaneous years.

A Ruin from the Future

*If you bring forth what is within you, what you bring
forth will save you. If you do not bring forth what is
within you, what you do not bring forth will destroy you.*

— *The Gospel According to Thomas* (1ˢᵗ or 2ⁿᵈ century)

Like many who become interested in so-called psychic phenomena,
it is dreams that have been my entry point to the topic and that,
more than anything else, have convinced me of their reality. I have been
interested in dreams since I was a teenager, and since my late 20s—
since my first Epson portable computer circa 1994 (a heavy gray tank,
by today's razor-thin laptop standards)—I have always kept a dream
journal open in whatever word processor I happened to be using at
the time. At this point I have recorded thousands of dated dreams and
dream fragments. Early exposure to Freud and then other psychoanalytic schools (Jungian, Lacanian, and so on) as well as later adventures
in Buddhist dream yoga and lucid dreaming equipped me, over time,
with a brimming toolkit to apply to my dream-work. Despite all these
tools, my recognition that dreams could be precognitive was only a very
belated one, yet exploring precognitive dreaming has surpassed, in both
its power and its fascination, any other hermeneutic approach.

With a handful of puzzling exceptions that I swept under my mental rug (including a dream seemingly anticipating the events of 9/11, which I have described elsewhere[1]), I had never noticed the phenomenon of dream precognition until I began reading the literature of parapsychology around 2010. It had simply not occurred to me to go back to my dream records *after a day or two had passed* and examine them in light of events and thoughts during that interim. I had generally spent time interpreting my dreams right when I wrote them down, and if I returned to them, it was usually weeks or months later, long after the events in my life proximate to the dream were forgotten. It was only after reading J. W. Dunne that I began following Dunne's guidance and was astonished by how frequently my dreams did correspond to some experience or train of thought over the next couple of days.

Some correspondences to subsequent experiences are oblique enough that a degree of free-associative unpacking is necessary to clarify the relationship, and thus would not hold evidential weight with anyone skeptical of Freudian methods, even if they were not doubtful of dream precognition in principle. Others are so clear, striking, and specific that they beggar belief as "just coincidence" or the law of large numbers at work. Sometimes a dream will show me the cover of a previously unknown book I'll find the next day at a used bookstore, or it will wittily represent a mishap like a sink backing up at work, or falling down a flight of icy steps, or something I wished I'd said to a friend but failed to. Mostly they relate to striking items encountered in the media—often stories on Twitter, since that is how I preferentially engage with the news. I have described several examples (out of, by now, a couple hundred Dunne dreams that I have recorded) on my blog *The Nightshirt*.[2] I am increasingly persuaded, on the basis of my own experience and its consistency with what many others have also reported, that precognition is a regular aspect of dreaming, not a rare occurrence at all.

Dunne wrote that if you notice a precognitive referent in a dream, it will typically be over the next day or two. If I notice a dream correspondence, it is generally within one or two days of the dream, although sometimes as much as a week. Another recent writer replicating Dunne's experiment, Bruce Siegel, found that his dreams often matched things that happened within such a time frame, and often even in the first few minutes on waking,[3] and that has sometimes been my experience as well. But this narrow temporal window between a dream and its "fulfillment" may to some extent reflect a kind of file-drawer effect, the fact that it requires more time and resources to compare dreams to events at a greater distance in time. Living in a day of paper records that took up space, Dunne recommended actually discarding dream records after two days, since the returns on the effort of comparing one's daily dream journal with events at greater remove diminish beyond that radius. You need to set limits, simply for practicality's sake. But the fact that it may not be worth the effort of actively looking for more distant future referents in dreams does not mean such referents don't exist. (This, in fact, was the precise confusion over which Victor Goddard corrected Captain Gladstone in their brief, bizarre conversation in Shanghai in 1946, the day before Goddard's crash on a Japanese beach.)

In my case, years of keeping detailed electronic dream records, even without any thought of checking for precognitive referents, has proven on at least one occasion to be of immense and startling value in my personal hermeneutic "paleontology." The dream appeared (in hindsight) to pertain directly to the completion of this book, and thus makes an appropriately "loopy" personal example of everything I have been arguing. Apologies in advance—there is nothing less interesting than someone else telling you their dream. Yet the dream, I believe, contained a signal that I *should* tell it, so here goes.

The dream in question had occurred in the summer of 1999, and it excited me greatly on waking—in fact it *felt* like one of the most "significant" dreams I had ever had at that point, even if I couldn't say why or how it was significant. The description of the dream's manifest content ran to nearly two single-spaced pages in my journal, but here's the short version: An old high-school teacher of mine named Thomas (playing the role of a kind of initiatory guide, or what Carl Jung would call a "psychopomp") stood before a chalkboard in a classroom on the Emory University campus, where I was then completing my PhD, and asked me to reflect on the "loss of Dick" in the context of the alchemical motif of the *androgyne*, a hermaphrodite that appears in many 17th-century alchemical books. Such books were an interest of mine at the time. This teacher then led me outside, past a stone fountain around which the nerdy blond-haired kid Martin on *The Simpsons* was running in circles, and then, beyond it, to the door of an impressive old ruined tower, circular in plan. On descending into the basement of the old building, I found myself in a dimly lit room, also a kind of classroom, where I had to step over a man lying unconscious on the floor between a coffee table and a couch in order to approach a blackboard with a long row of circular or semicircular symbols—the first one composed of three interlocking *Omegas*, the last being a kind of stylized letter *A*, formed from a swooping curl on the left, a flat top, and a descending straight line. This was somehow a very important lesson; the precise flow of meanings of these symbols, one to the next, needed to be "fussily" preserved without damaging them. I then went into a more brightly lit antechamber where I inspected a broken speaker on the wall by the door and realized with some anxiety that there may be no way to repair it. Lastly, I went back out the front door of the building, having made a kind of looping path through the basement of the old tower. As I walked back out into the light, I turned and looked again at the edifice and realized, with a kind of excited delight, that it was actually brand new, but just "made to look old." It seemed like a profound and significant realization. I wondered who the "builder" of this tower was, and realized it was, in some weird way, me.

I mulled over the possible meanings of this dream for days, thinking and writing about its images and symbolism, because it had such an exciting sense of promise. I had just read Jung for the first time, in fact (one of his books on alchemy), and I was excited by the dream's alchemical-seeming elements, such as a fountain placed outside a ruined circular tower, as well as by the time-reversing implications of the "*Omega(s)*-to-*Alpha*" progression of the rounded, vessel-like symbols. However, given my years of interest in Freud, certain elements, like the "loss of Dick," as well as the ruined tower itself, also seemed like obvious castration symbols—standard Freudian stuff. Among the many thoughts I had about this dream, I noted my intuition that the tower somehow represented the dream itself. A small, amateurish watercolor, "The Ruined Tower," still sits on a bookcase in my home—a relic of brief, Jung-inspired efforts to commemorate my dream life. It is one of only two dreams I ever painted.

Fast forward to a Sunday in July, 2017. I was sitting at my computer struggling with some difficult decisions about chapters and sections to cut from the first draft of this book so it would flow better, when a strange feeling of familiarity, and of "pieces falling into place," came over me. It took me back to that well-remembered dream, the elements of which suddenly assumed startling new, clear meaning in light of what I was just then doing.

First of all, with some chagrin, I had just cut a section about the poet Samuel Taylor Coleridge that had centered on his possible precognition of later-published details about *fountains* in his poem "Kubla

Khan." I cut it because I discovered I had been wrong on a date, and my specific argument about Coleridge as a precog now held less weight.[4] (When I had free-associated on the *Simpsons* character Martin, who was circling the fountain in my dream, I found I associated him with a single squeaky pedantic utterance: "*Highly Dubious!*"—a remark that would precisely apply to what I now thought about what I had written about Coleridge.)

I had also decided, with some difficulty, to excise the section on Philip K. Dick's dream about his own death and its significance as a kind of castration complex in his own life, centered on his name—although I later changed my mind about this cut. At the time I had the dream, in 1999, Phil Dick would have never entered my mind as an association to this dream. I knew virtually nothing about that author and had read only one of his books many years before as a teenager (*Do Androids Dream of Electric Sheep*, the basis for the movie *Blade Runner*). I certainly had no idea that the writer had been found *unconscious on the floor between a coffee table and a couch* after the first of the strokes that killed him in 1982, let alone that he himself had dreamed of that very scene seven years before (reporting it to Claudia Bush in the February 1975 letter I mentioned in Chapter 13: "a stark single horrifying scene, inert but not a still: a man lay dead, on his face, in a living room between the coffee table and the couch"[5]).

I had two associations to my teacher, Thomas—the first was an inspiring-slash-ominous quote from the Gnostic *Gospel of Thomas*, which I had just come across in another book: "If you bring forth what is within you, what you bring forth will save you. If you do not bring forth what is within you, what you do not bring forth will destroy you."[6] (Hence my sense that I should "bring forth" this dream, despite how personal, and perhaps boring, it may be to readers.) But I also somehow knew, probably from the same book, that *Thomas* means *twin*. People we are not especially close to often appear in dreams to supply some pun having to do with their name, and so this struck me at the time as possibly significant—although I did not know how. I had no reason at that point in my life to be thinking about twins, and of course did not know that Phil Dick had lost his twin sister, Jane, in infancy, let alone the significance of that fact in the writer's life.

On the day I suddenly thought back to this old dream, I was experiencing frustration about the sequence of chapters I had written. I needed to find the best way to present a lot of (I thought) interesting material about time loops in a manner that flowed linearly, one idea to the next, to make my argument, but the structure was not right yet, and I'd maddeningly wasted a lot of time shuffling chapters and sections around. In fact, I had my black notebook open in front of me on my desk, with the chapters arranged side by side, in different orders, so I could think through the problem. These pages, I suddenly saw, were very much like the blackboard in my old dream, where a sequence of circular or semicircular symbols (i.e., loops) was represented, as an illustration of getting things in the right order. Successfully completing the Great Work in alchemy, I later learned, is all about getting sequences right, but indeed, a book project is itself a "great work" that requires the same sort of care and "fussiness," and creates similar frustrations about arranging things in the proper sequence. I was now feeling anxious that more things would need to be cut in order to work. Besides cutting the fountain section and (temporarily) "losing" the part about Dick's death, I was also wrestling with the material on the gender-swapping prophet Tiresias (now in Chapter 12). Tiresias, it should be noted, was not unlike the alchemical *androgyne*, who is simultaneously male and female, showing both sexual characteristics at once. (Again, at the time, I mainly saw this in Freudian terms, as castration symbolism.)

There's more. The same day I thought back to this old dream, when I was grappling with these editorial questions as well as finally feeling like I could see the light at the end of the tunnel, I was additionally preoccupied with something very specific and unrelated: recent sore throats that I worried might reflect some serious health problem involving my larynx … that is, my "speaker." In fact, I was using my work to avoid thinking about this latest health scare, and vacillating, as hypochondriacs often do, about whether or not to make an appointment to see my ear, nose, and throat doctor the following Monday. (I eventually did see my doctor, and the sore throats turned out to be nothing serious.)

It may not be coincidental that I had at that point been actively pondering Sigmund Freud's "Irma" dream (Chapter 9)—a dream which, I was coming to see, was an "old dream" by the time in Freud's life when a dire otolaryngological condition gave it *new* meaning. I had no way of suspecting that my own dream journal would just then supply a striking example of a similarly time-looping "old dream that was really brand-new" related to the completion of the book you now hold in your hands. If any of my original, mostly unimpressive insights about the dream held water so many years later, it was the sense that the "ruined tower" at least partly represented the dream itself. I could not have known, in 1999, what the "made to look old" phrase I had written down could have possibly meant.

When I opened my dream journal from 1999 to inspect the details of this old dream, I found something else striking: The date of that dream was just two days from the current date—in other words, it had occurred 18 years earlier, almost to the day. If the dream was a human, it would have been exactly old enough to vote.[7]

My discovery of this distant dream connection to my life in the summer of 2017 was a kind of hermeneutic comeuppance, reinforcing the slight regret I already felt at all those years of interpreting my dreams through some simplistic Freudian or Jungian lens, gently contorting dreams to mean something about my past or childhood complexes or imposing some picturesque but toothless archetypal framing before forgetting them and moving on. The "great men" of 20th century depth psychology, who had so authoritatively pronounced on what dreams mean and how dreams mean, encouraged specific varieties of engagement with the dreamworld that would naturally reinforce their own favorite theories, always directing attention elsewhere than toward the simple question Dunne asked: What comes after the dream? What comes next? (It would have been far worse, of course, to have been led astray by the "great men" of scientific dream science—the Hobsons and the Cricks—who would have us turn away from seeking meaning in our dreams altogether. I cannot imagine a sadder fate than to believe, because one had never heard otherwise, that dreams are meaningless.)

Discovering this "ancient" dream connection also reinforced for me that the things seen in dreams are not about possible futures, the safe suggestion made by nearly all contemporary writers on precognition. That no longer seems to me plausible, and it makes little sense of the evidence. (It doesn't even seem appealing, for reasons I have discussed elsewhere.[8]) By the laws of chaos, the butterfly effect, *any* deviation in my actions over the course of those intervening 18 years would have scrambled the events in my life, leading to a completely different Sunday, one that would *not* have included this exact list of actions and preoccupations: wrestling with the proper sequence of interlinked chapters in a book on time loops, regretfully jettisoning a "dubious" chapter about a fountain, thinking about the death of Phil Dick and his twin sister Jane and how much "phallic" speculation to dis-include (i.e., "lose"), and getting scared about the health of my larynx—and then at the end having a stunning realization in which I looked back at an old dream with the excited realization that it only looked old but was really, in some sense, brand new. That last part, you will note, makes it into a time loop: My "turning back" to this dream in hindsight was included in the dream itself.

Oh, and there's one more thing … That stylized *A* that completed the symbol series on the chalkboard in my dream? The one with the swooping curl on the left? Look at the publisher's imprint on the spine of this book.[9]

Am I just crazy, like many said Phil Dick was, making everything connect up to form a vast paranoid pattern? Am I like Morgan Robertson. nursing some deep need for absolution in and by the block universe of Minkowski? Am I simply the victim of common fallacies in judgment, perception, and reasoning, seeing nonexistent faces in the random clouds of causality?

Other people's dreams, and synchronicities, and visions, and so on never seem as compelling as they do to the experiencer, simply because meaning is always an individual, personal thing. If you have not yet experienced a troublingly specific premonition that "came true," or a dream that corresponded too precisely to a subsequent event to accept as coincidence, then why would you bother to question the one-wayness of folk causality? The specificity and precision of an individual's mnemonic associations (and thus dream symbolism) cannot be adequately conveyed to a stranger, and this alone puts dream meaning beyond the reach not only of scientific consideration, but of public consideration more generally. And since precognition mainly enters our life through the oblique doorway of our personal associations (and often our dreams), it is very hard to really convince others, even if their minds are not closed to the possibility. "You had to be there," as the say. But the fact that you had to be there does *not* mean there's no there there.

Adding to the difficulty, psychology supplies ever more reasons why your seemingly anomalous experiences cannot be trusted—those hundreds of cognitive biases you can find listed on Wikipedia. There are good reasons to worry over and address biases in science, and important reasons to address racial, gender, and other biases that affect how fairly people are treated; and ever-vigilant self-doubt is part of wisdom. (As Richard Feynman said, "It is imperative to have uncertainty as a fundamental part of your inner nature"[10]—the best possible case for neurosis.) But bias is well on the way to becoming the new *sin* for a secular age that takes its gospel from TED talks and the popular science press. Somehow our unique and subjective point of view has become an intractable, ever-morphing stain on the soul that we can endlessly self-flagellate over, as well as use to justify policing others—or just not listening to them—when it suits us. This is why we should be very wary of "your unconscious biases"-style pop psychological science; it may sound like a tool of greater tolerance, but it can easily become a lever of intellectual conformism. For the reasons I argued at the beginning of this book, the imperfect nature of our perceptions and judgments is by itself *no disproof* of phenomena or experiences that fall outside Enlightenment science's explanatory scope, yet it is really the only thing the self-appointed skeptical guardians of that already obsolete worldview have to build their case on. Only reason can help us judge who's right.

In our collective "de-biasing," we must not disparage and denigrate the singularity of the individual viewpoint, for it is that viewpoint that ultimately lets meaning into the world. Without it, all is just noise, information but without value, the number "42" echoing in the dark. Ralph Waldo Emerson said it best in "Self-Reliance": "The eye was placed where one ray should fall, that it might testify of that particular ray."[11] It is one of the most profound sentences in one of the most profound essays ever written. And it takes on a sublime new meaning in a participatory and transactional universe, such as that described by John Cramer, where our gaze goes out to meet a distant star and shake hands with it deep in the past. I think Emerson would wholly approve of the "experimental metaphysics" being done in today's physics labs. It reveals in such a stark new way that we are not randomly thrown in the world, mere "absorbers" of whatever comes at us—we create the world, including the past, by giving meaning to what we see. And when what we "see" is a memory, for instance of a dream, we actually might—if we are lucky (and especially if we have a written record to show we aren't crazy)—even glimpse our own presence in that past, our looping intervention in our own history.

I'm here to tell you this: When you catch a glimpse, in a recorded dream, of your own turning back and visiting that dream after some time has passed, you are seeing something truly rare and sublime, the most exquisite butterfly in the precog ranger's life list. "Time gimmicks" in dreams are the tip-off. They are not some smuggled, oblique signal *by* your unconscious *to* you—they *are* you, a representation of your peering, *right now*, into that dream, your peering into your past. It can give you chills. You'll never know the pleasure, though, unless you keep a dream diary. (If you take nothing else away from this book, take away this: *Keep a dream diary.*)

Among the many things I could say about the ruined tower dream, winking at me from 18 years ago like it is just inches from my face, is that it steered me down a path that, through many twists and turns, ultimately led to my interest in parapsychology and precognition over a decade later … and thus, this book. It played some role, however small, in leading me to the place where I could look back on it with radically new eyes and see it as something brand new, despite its appearance of antiquity. Had I not looked back on the dream, I would not have had the dream in the first place; the dream *was*, quite literally, my looking back. And my completion of this book is literally the completion of a circle, a loop.

As T. S. Eliot wrote in his 1943 poem "Little Gidding"—which was influenced, incidentally, by Dunne's *An Experiment with Time*—

> We shall not cease from exploration
> And the end of our exploring
> Will be to arrive where we started
> And know the place for the first time.[12]

Introduction: Beyond Folk Causality
(or, One Damn Thing *Before* Another)

[1] Asimov, 1948, 1953, 1960.

[2] Dixon et al., 2009; Popescu, 2009. See Chapter 6 for more detail on this experiment.

[3] Bem, 2011.

[4] Ibid.

[5] Judd & Gawronski, 2011.

[6] The pioneering parapsychology researcher Dean Radin writes: "Sometimes skeptics offer constructive critiques [but] many critiques are bizarrely irrational and positively drip with emotion. … [T]here's something peculiar about psi that seems to push otherwise calm, rational scientists beyond civil discourse and into rabid, foaming-at-the-mouth frenzies" (Radin, 2018, 15).

[7] Sheehan, 2015, 86.

[8] Engber, 2017.

[9] Dossey, 2009; Feather & Schmicker, 2005; Rhine, 1961.

[10] Bergson, 1944(1907), 12.

[11] That paranormal events of all kinds must be thought of as stories (specifically human stories) is an argument made forcefully by Jeffrey Kripal (see especially Kripal, 2010, 2017).

1. The Size of the Impossible—Disasters, Prophecy, and Hindsight

[1] The 2012 film *Chasing Ice* shows a Jakobshavn calving event, the largest ever seen or filmed: a piece of ice the size of Manhattan breaking off the glacier.

[2] Brown, 1983.

[3] Rodgers, 2014.

[4] Stevenson, 1974(1960), 1974(1965).

[5] Stevenson, 1974(1960), 87.

[6] Ibid., 89.

[7] Ibid., 88. Charles Francis Potter, who reported his wife's premonition in his 1939 book *Beyond the Senses*, went on to become an outspoken Unitarian theologian and prominent humanist; he advocated against supernaturalism in religion, crusaded for the right of euthanasia, and advised Clarence Darrow on the subject of evolution in the lawyer's 1925 defense of John Thomas Scopes (https://en.wikipedia.org/wiki/Charles_Francis_Potter).

[8] Stevenson, 1974(1965), 109-110.

[9] Ibid., 108.

[10] Stevenson, 1974(1960), 90.

[11] The relevant part of Stead's novel is reprinted in Gardner, 1998.

[12] Stevenson, 1974(1960), 90-91.

[13] One of the psychics Stead consulted, "Count Harmon," told him in 1911 that mortal danger "would be from water, and from nothing else"; and in a letter dated June 21 of that year, Count Harmon warned him that travel would be dangerous in April, 1912. Another psychic, Mr. W. de Kerlor, predicted Stead would go to America, but this was accompanied by a strange vision: "I can see … the picture of a huge black ship, of which I see the back portion; where the name of the ship should be written there is a wreath of immortelles … I can only see half of the ship …", which he took to mean "limitations, difficulties and death." Later Mr. de Kerlor related a dream that he felt was about Stead: "I dreamt that I was in the midst of a catastrophe on the water; there were masses (more than a thousand) of bodies struggling in the water and I was among them. I could hear their cries for help." (Ibid.)

[14] Gardner, 1998. When Robertson's story was reprinted in 1912, with the new title *The Wreck of the Titan*, some of these statistics of the *Titan* were changed to bring them even closer (in most cases) to those of the *Titanic*. Numbers here reflect the 1898 version.

[15] Eisenbud, 1982.

[16] Gardner, 1998, 33.

[17] Hand, 2014.

[18] Gardner, 1998, 35

[19] https://en.wikipedia.org/wiki/List_of_cognitive_biases

[20] Gardner (1998) notes that in May, 1912, an American pulp variety magazine, *Popular Magazine*, ran a short story called "The White Ghost of Disaster," by a writer named Mayn Clew Garnett, about the loss of an 800-

foot ocean liner named *Admiral* and over a thousand of its passengers after hitting an iceberg, going 22.5 knots (the same speed as the *Titanic*), on a run between New York and Liverpool. Although published after the *Titanic* sank, the story had been written earlier and was already in press at the time of the disaster. Unfortunately, little is known about the author.

[21] Ibid., 3.

[22] Ibid., 4.

[23] The relationship between Kubrick's film and the Hilton brand, an early example of product placement, may have even made the property attractive to Hilton Hotels when the hotel's original developer Peter Kalikow went into bankruptcy shortly after its construction and was forced to sell it.

[24] Pearlman, 2016.

[25] Dannatt, 2001.

[26] Cotter, 2001.

[27] *Recalled Comics*, 2017.

[28] https://en.wikipedia.org/wiki/Party_Music

[29] https://en.wikipedia.org/wiki/The_Lone_Gunmen

[30] Mossbridge & Radin, 2018.

[31] See Feather & Schmicker, 2005, for some interesting examples.

[32] See for instance, Bernstein, 2005; Dossey, 2009; McEneaney, 2010.

[33] Loftus, 2010, 211.

[34] Hollywood special effects technician Andrew Paquette kept a 20-year database record of his dreams, which he says he initially started compiling to disprove his wife's belief that his dreams were precognitive. He came around to agreeing with his wife. Among numerous examples recorded in his book *Dreamer* (Paquette, 2011), he notes recording a cluster of dreams more than a decade before 9/11 that seemed to foreshadow the events of that day. None specifically involve the World Trade Center, and most are vague enough (as well as distant enough in time from 9/11) that a skeptic could easily attribute them to natural fears of terrorism striking that city. But Paquette also notes that two weeks before the attack, in late August 2001, he found himself in Legoland theme park in California with a terrible headache, trying to explain to his daughter why a big brick cityscape of Manhattan was missing the twin towers: "Maybe it was too big to build it to scale" (Ibid., 215), he suggested, but immediately told his wife he thought his disaster dreams about Manhattan were about to come true. He says the headache went away at that instant.

[35] 9/11 is just the most famous of the disasters Mandell allegedly foresaw in dreams and depicted in paintings. In 1993, Mandell painted an explosive event involving a car near an airport, noting it was possibly Heathrow; it cor-

responded exactly to an IRA mortar attack there in March 1994. His drawing of three cars side by side matched exactly a news headline photo, including the striking detail of the exact same radiator grille in the car that had launched the mortars, and identical damage to the adjacent car. He reported that a voice in his dream said to him, "This is what you're going to see in the newspapers when this event happens." In June of 1997 and then again in April of 1999, Mandell dreamed of a Concorde in France with its engines on fire; again, his depictions (and very specific details like the pilot's attempt to reach a nearby airport) matched news of the crash of Air France flight 4590 after taking off from Charles de Gaulle airport on July 25, 2000. It was the only fatal incident in the history of the Concorde. For more on Mandell, see Peake (2012) and Channel 5 (2003).

[36] White, 2017. White also manages to debunk some old myths, such as that President Lincoln dreamed of seeing his own dead body laid out on a catafalque—the story was probably made up by one of Lincoln's bodyguards. But several members of Lincoln's cabinet did independently record that on the morning before his fateful visit to Ford's Theater, Lincoln reported to them a strange and compelling dream about being on a great ship, "some singular, indescribable vessel" (Ibid., 151) rushing through the water to an indefinite shore; he had had such a dream before at various momentous turning points, and thus thought it meant some great moment was at hand for his country.

[37] Larry Dossey's *The Power of Premonitions* (Dossey, 2009) is an excellent summary of this topic.

[38] Ibid.

[39] Wiseman, 2010, 153.

[40] Ibid.

[41] On the arbitrariness of defining an "event," see Braude, 1997, and Chapter 5 of this book.

[42] Peake, 2012, 260.

[43] See Llewellyn, 2013.

[44] When they do keep such databases, as Andrew Paquette did, it often supports dream precognition (Paquette, 2011). See also Siegel, 2017.

[45] Canales, 2015.

[46] Fitzgerald, 1936.

[47] Priestley, 1989(1964), 194.

[48] See Strieber & Kripal, 2016.

[49] Gardner, 1998, 32.

[50] Priestley (1989[1964], 194) observes:

It is true, as the representatives of common sense hurry to tell us, that we like to deceive ourselves. But this cuts both ways. Certainly there is self-deceit in favor of appearing unusual, strangely sensitive, "psychic," and the rest. But there is also self-deceit, of a much safer sort, in favor of conformism, sturdy common sense, rationality, and no nonsense. And we need hardly ask ourselves which of these attitudes is the more fashionable, the easier to adopt, the one more likely to bring good dividends and a sound reputation.

[51] Price, 2014.

[52] Priestley, 1989(1964), 193.

[53] Ibid., 193.

[54] Shermer, 1997.

[55] Although Shermer and Wiseman assume a reasoned tone in their writings, reading books by some earlier leaders of the skeptical community like Gardner or magician-debunker James Randi can often be a sad and distressing experience, given the virulent hostility and undisguised condescension they routinely displayed. Gardner, in his book on the *Titanic*, casually calls psi-believers "idiotic," books on ESP "lurid" and "atrocious," and the topic of ESP "hogwash." Hannah's books he derides for being "privately printed." Randi condescendingly lists ESP alongside "unicorns" in the subtitle of his 1982 book *Flim-Flam* (Randi, 1982), as though the topics are on par with each other, and calls two serious physicists who led a major, government-funded ESP laboratory at Stanford Research Institute "the Laurel and Hardy of Psi." In a cultural climate where scientific rationalism is policed by such partisans, it is thus all too clear why ordinary people who experience something anomalous in their lives have been hesitant to share their experiences.

[56] Strieber & Kripal, 2016.

[57] Krohn & Kripal, 2018.

[58] Ibid., 75.

[59] Ibid., 77.

2. "If I Were You, I'd Stay on the Ground for a Couple of Days"—Victor Goddard, J. W. Dunne, and the Block Universe

[1] Goddard, 1982, 251.

[2] Goddard, 1975.

[3] The most well-known "time slip" was the strange encounter with Marie

Antoinette and her courtiers reported by two English ladies, Miss Annie Moberly and Miss Eleanor Jourdain, in 1901 in the Petit Trianon garden at Versailles. See MacKenzie, 1997.

[4] In his retirement, Goddard also became a thoughtful defender of and writer on the UFO phenomenon; see Goddard, 1975.

[5] Goddard, 1951.

[6] Goddard's 1951 account in *The Saturday Evening Post* uses the pseudonym "Commander Dewing" of the "HMS Crecy."

[7] Goddard, 1951, 25.

[8] Ibid., 24.

[9] One of the dramatic embellishments of the 1956 film *The Night My Number Came Up*, based on Goddard's story, was that the Naval officer also told his dream to the pilot of the plane, and the pilot thus felt gripped by an awful fate as he was attempting to keep the craft in the air.

[10] Childhood illness is a common feature in people who later experience psychic or paranormal phenomena.

[11] Dunne, 1952(1927).

[12] Dunne relates this part of the story in his posthumously published, autobiographical work *Intrusions?* (Dunne, 1955).

[13] "The improbability of my having dreamed of half-past four *at* half-past four must be multiplied by the improbability of my having been bothered by a stopped watch on the previous afternoon without retaining the faintest recollection of such a fact" (Dunne, 1952[1927], 38).

[14] Ibid., 39.

[15] Ibid., 40-41

[16] Ibid., 42.

[17] Ibid., 43.

[18] https://en.wikipedia.org/wiki/Mount_Pelée

[19] Dunne, 1952(1927), 44.

[20] Ibid., 44. Dunne doesn't add that he could have been primed to misread the number of zeros in the news article because of his dream, but because of the similarity of the digit 4 (and a string of zeros) in both numbers, his main point would still hold in either case.

[21] Ibid., 45.

[22] Inchbald, 2017. On his blog, Dunne scholar Guy Inchbald writes: "Without [Dunne's] intervention there would probably have been no Sopwith Camel in the coming war, no Bristol Fighter, no Handley Page bomber, just

whatever the state-owned Farnborough and the French could turn out."

[23] Dunne 1952(1927), 46-7.

[24] Ibid., 49.

[25] Ibid., 50.

[26] Dunne, 1955, 87

[27] Ibid., 88.

[28] Ibid., 88-9.

[29] Ibid., 89.

[30] Ibid.

[31] What happened to Hyde? Dunne writes: "That fellow was 'sublimated' quite easily. I discovered that beneath his savagery lay a nasty streak of cowardice—probably the cause of his existence. So I turned him into a bantamweight boxer fighting dogged and gory battles with any middle-weight he could find. That cured him, and he grew up to be a soldier and a pioneer of aviation" (Ibid., 91).

[32] Moore, 2016.

[33] Dunne, 1955, 71.

[34] Barušs & Mossbridge, 2017.

[35] Radin, 2006.

[36] Dossey, 2013.

[37] The history of trauma as a psychological construct, and of telepathy as an outgrowth of the Victorian sciences of trauma, is a vast topic wonderfully charted by Roger Luckhurst in his writings *The Invention of Telepathy* (Luckhurst, 2002) and *The Trauma Question* (Luckhurst, 2008). For the role trauma may play in precognition, see Chapter 10.

[38] Kripal, 2014.

[39] Dunne 1952(1927), 52.

[40] Ibid.

[41] Ibid., 67.

[42] Goddard, 1951, 118.

[43] Dobyns, 2006.

[44] See for instance Dick, 2011.

3. Postcards from Your Future Self—Scientific Evidence for Precognition

[1] Vaughan, 1973, 18. See also Shields, 2011.

[2] Vaughan, 1973, 18.

[3] Quoted in Shields, 2011, 161.

[4] Vonnegut, 1973, 64.

[5] Jason Ã. Josephson-Storm's *The Myth of Disenchantment* (Josephson-Storm, 2017) critically examines the "disenchantment" idea in European thought.

[6] See Kripal, 2010; Luckhurst, 2002.

[7] Rhine, 1967.

[8] Carington, 1940.

[9] Rhine, 1967, 128.

[10] Krippner et al., 2002(1971).

[11] Schnabel, 1997.

[12] Targ & Puthoff, 2005(1977).

[13] See Graff, 2000; May et al., 2014; McMoneagle, 2002; Schnabel, 1997; Smith, 2005.

[14] See Targ & Puthoff, 2005(1977).

[15] Smith, 2005.

[16] See Warcollier, 2001(1948).

[17] May et al., 2014.

[18] Utts, 1995.

[19] Utts, 2016, 1379. She continues: "I have asked the debunkers if there is any amount of data that could convince them, and they generally have responded by saying, 'probably not.' I ask them what original research they have read, and they mostly admit they haven't read any! Now there is a definition of pseudo-science—basing conclusions on belief, rather than data!"

[20] Dunne & Jahn, 2003.

[21] Honorton & Ferrari, 1989.

[22] See Radin, 2013, for a good description of Honorton and Ferrari's study and background on meta-analysis in general.

[23] See Radin, 2009.

[24] See Targ & Puthoff, 2005(1977).

[25] See Marwaha & May, 2016 for a discussion; see also Targ, 2004.

[26] Feinberg, 1975.

[27] Ibid., 63-64.

[28] Kaiser, 2011.

[29] May & Marwaha, 2015; Marwaha & May, 2016.

[30] May and Marwaha's "multiphasic theory" of psi (May & Marwaha, 2015) distinguishes a "physics domain" from a "neuroscience domain."

[31] Marwaha & May, 2016, 78.

[32] May & Marwaha, 2015.

[33] One of Carington's five experiments (Experiment II) was conducted somewhat differently from the other four. All ten drawings in this experiment were made in the course of a single hour by members of a Cambridge psychology class, and the participants received feedback at the end of the class by matching each other's drawings to the group of targets. Results here were similar to the first experiment—a pattern of matches to the ten-target group, rather than to the individual intended target (i.e., displaced hits). But it is not surprising, as the effect of the final matching exercise would have functioned similarly as if feedback were acquired by reading the published results: Participants would have been influenced by the set of target drawings as a whole (and each other's drawings of them), rather than receiving feedback on a trial-by-trial basis.

[34] Carington, 1946, 36.

[35] See for example Targ & Puthoff, 2005(1977); Sinclair, 2001(1930).

[36] Targ & Puthoff, 2005(1977).

[37] I am not aware that the possibility of participants in ESP experiments precognitively accessing the "answer book" in the form of the published results has ever been studied. Such studies could be conducted readily, for instance by comparing the results of two remote viewing experiments in which participants' only possible feedback is in the published articles later. In one experiment, the "answers" published would actually be different from what the experimenter had assigned them to view.

[38] See for instance the consideration of feedback as a necessary component of skill learning in ESP research in Targ & Puthoff, 2018(1972).

[39] May et al., 1996

[40] Marwaha & May, 2016.

[41] Honorton & Ferrari, 1989.

[42] McMoneagle, 2002.

[43] McMoneagle, 1993, 226.

4. The Psi Reflex—Presentiment and the Future-Influencing-Present Effect

[1] Pynchon, 1973.

[2] Slothrop's premonitory sexual response was a daring premise for an ambitious, literary novelist like Pynchon. One of the unwritten rules of literary fiction has always been: *Thou shalt not use ESP seriously as a plot device.* Writers openly breaking this rule quickly get relegated to the ghetto of SF, which until relatively recently remained what Pynchon's contemporary Philip K. Dick called a "trash stratum." The genre gods exist to serve the prevailing materialistic beliefs about causality. Pynchon, like his similarly ESP-curious contemporary Kurt Vonnegut, cunningly avoided Dick's fate by always keeping his commitment to the reality of such phenomena (which crop up in most of his works) ambiguous, and surrounding characters who display or experience them with materialists who devote considerable cognitive effort to explaining these phenomena away in rational, linear terms (like *Gravity's Rainbow*'s "Dr. Pointsman"—as in, points on a graph). Pynchon thus didn't need to commit himself to "believing in" ESP.

[3] Carpenter, 2012; Mossbridge & Radin, 2018.

[4] Radin, 1997.

[5] Spottiswoode & May, 2003.

[6] Bierman & Scholte, 2002.

[7] Mossbridge et al., 2012; Tsakiris, 2017.

[8] Mossbridge et al., 2012.

[9] Mossbridge et al., 2014.

[10] Bem, 2011.

[11] Mossbridge & Radin, 2018.

[12] Open Science Collaboration, 2015.

[13] Bem et al., 2016.

[14] Kripal, 2010.

[15] See Radin, 2013.

[16] Sheldrake, 2011.

[17] Alvarez, 2016.

[18] Sheldrake, 2003. Sheldrake sees the sense of being stared at as an aspect of the "extended mind." But is the mind extended in space, or in time? Here we confront the power of the language we use to describe phenomena in biasing or constraining how we think about their possible causes (known as the Sapir-Whorf hypothesis). What is *called* a "sense of being stared at" could

instead be a *presentiment of meeting another's gaze*. A woman has a funny feeling, looks up, and finds that a man happens to be looking at her; she may naturally assume that the man had *already been* looking at her—"staring"—but that is just an assumption (i.e., the man could have turned to look at her at the same moment).

[19] Carpenter, 2012.

[20] Ibid., 85.

[21] Carpenter, 2015a, 255.

[22] Radin, 2013.

[23] Mavromatis, 1987.

[24] Wargo, 2016b.

[25] Rick Strassman (Strassman, 2014) for instance links "prophecy" to dimethyltryptamine (DMT), a powerful hallucinogenic compound and, he argues, a neurotransmitter naturally produced in the body in small quantities.

[26] Murphy, 1992.

[27] Beidel, 2014.

[28] Geiger, 2009.

[29] Goddard, 1975.

[30] Nasht, 2005.

[31] Cochran, 1954.

[32] Atkinson, 2010.

[33] Caidin, 2007.

[34] Targ & Puthoff, 2005(1977). Bach came to the attention of the SRI parapsychologists because his bestselling inspirational book seemed to be about an out-of-body experience, something commonly reported in the lives of the most gifted psychics they had studied (Targ, 2004).

[35] Given its link to spontaneous and even frenetic, uncritical engagement, it would be interesting to systematically record improv performances and compare them to news headlines over the following day or two. Improv is a very Zen activity that rewards not thinking, just doing, and may also capitalize on the group effects known to facilitate psi.

[36] See Wargo, 2016c.

[37] Kripal, 2010.

[38] For instance, the Israeli performer Uri Geller, who impressed many of the scientists who actually worked with him that some of his abilities were genuine (Margolis, 1999, 2013), nevertheless also used trickery in stage performances, which made it easy for pseudoskeptics like James Randi to call

him a fraud (Randi, 1982). One personality trait typical of psychics as well as performers is extroversion (Carpenter, 2012).

[39] Wargo, 2015a.

[40] Marcus, 1988, 90.

[41] Murphy, 1957.

[42] Marcus, 1988, 90.

[43] It is tempting to think Pynchon may have been precognizing these developments, but his novel probably was inspired to a great extent by the insight and/or wild imagination of the French spy and sci-fi fan Jacques Bergier. Many ideas in *Gravity's Rainbow*, such as the Nazi interest in the occult and the existence of secret societies pulling the strings during the war and its aftermath, seem to have come straight from Louis Pauwels and Jacques Bergier's early-60s blockbuster *The Morning of the Magicians* (Pauwels & Bergier, 1963), as did the idea of a psychic being able to predict bomb strikes during wartime.

[44] Taylor, 2007.

[45] A future neurobiology of prophecy may pay special attention to the neurotransmitter dopamine and structures known as the *basal ganglia* that are involved in reinforcing rewarding behaviors. The brain's reward circuits govern the conditioning process, our learning from experience, by signaling the anticipation of reward or punishment from cues. It is small constant dopamine bursts in these circuits that keep attention focused on "the next thing"—on new and possibly important information. Adaptations of the reward circuit associated with addiction are the neurobiological correlate of the psychoanalytic construct of *jouissance* (Bazan & Detandt, 2013), which I argue is central to precognition (see Chapter 10).

[46] See Baruss & Mossbridge, 2017; Dossey, 2013; Radin, 2006; Sheldrake, 2003; Targ, 2004. A notable exception is Edwin May, who argues the phenomenon will have a fully materialist explanation, probably rooted in classical, not quantum, physics (see Marwaha & May, 2015).

[47] See for example Baruss & Mossbridge, 2017; Kelly et al., 2010; Sheldrake, 2012; Targ, 2004.

[48] Carpenter (2015b, 5) writes:

> As Plato thought, meanings exist beyond the person and are not simply constructed by the person or by groups of people. In psi, we engage meanings that supersede any physical connection to the self. Yet we engage them, we are affected by them, we express implicit references to them. It seems that we find them much more than make them, and we find them far beyond the normal bounds of the body and the current moment.

[49] Carpenter, 2012.

[50] My thinking on culture and meaning is strongly influenced by Geertz, 1973; and Shore, 1996.

[51] On the distinction between meaning and information, and why the emergence of a scientific information theory in the 20th century required eliminating questions of meaning, see Gleick, 2012. This topic is addressed also in Chapter 6.

[52] That paranormal phenomena of all kinds are meaningful phenomena that cannot be understood without considering the personal, anecdotal dimension is an argument made strongly by Jeffrey Kripal throughout his work. See Kripal, 2017; Strieber & Kripal, 2016.

[53] Edwin May argues that misrecognized precognition, or what is also called "psi-mediated instrumental response," unconsciously guides and thus "augments" decisions made by experimenters, and that this may give rise to illusory mind-over-matter or psychokinetic (PK) effects in parapsychology experiments using random number generators (May, 2015). This would have implications well beyond psi research: If something like precognition or presentiment is really operative, unrecognized, in laboratories, it could account for experimenter expectation effects in everything from psychology to biomedicine. Whether some form of precognitively mediated "decision augmentation" could even account for some part of the current replication crisis remains for some future team of bold researchers to investigate.

[54] Priestley, 1989(1964), 201.

[55] Ibid.

[56] Ibid.

[57] Ibid.

[58] Ibid.

[59] The future-influencing-present effect, Priestley writes, "is apt to work for intimate relationships that most people prefer not to discuss" (ibid., 200).

5. Catching Precognitive Butterflies—Chaos, Memory, and *Premory* in the Thermodynamic Universe

[1] Flieger, 1997; White, 2018.

[2] Nabokov, 2018.

[3] Boyd, 1991, 366.

[4] Nabokov, 2018.

[5] See, e.g., Price, 1996; Sheehan, 2015.

6 Gleick, 2016.

7 See White, 2018.

8 Kaku, 2009.

9 Buonomano, 2017.

10 Price, 1996.

11 Radin, 2013, 131-132.

12 Bradbury, 1952.

13 Gleick, 1987.

14 Ibid., 8.

15 Hilborn, 2004. When later asked about the origins of the butterfly metaphor, the scientist who came up with the "butterfly" title for Lorenz's session did not recall being influenced by Bradbury's story, but that would not preclude him having read the story and forgotten about it. However, even assuming a straightforward causal reason for the coincidence, it would *not* preclude Bradbury from having precognized developments in 1970s systems science—or more likely, Gleick's 1987 book. In fact, there are passages in Bradbury's story that are stunningly similar to later writings on the butterfly effect. For instance, Bradbury writes: "Crushing certain plants could add up infinitesimally. A little error here would multiply in sixty million years, all out of proportion" (quoted in Ibid., 425).

As an added note, it is likely that Michael Crichton was thinking of Bradbury's story and its (possibly illusory) connection to Lorenz's butterfly effect when he included a "chaotician" (the character Ian Malcolm) in his bestselling 1990 novel *Jurassic Park*, about a theme park of cloned dinosaurs.

16 Braude, 1997, 239.

17 Ibid., 241.

18 Ibid., 243.

19 See Dossey, 2009.

20 Kripal, 2014, 366. W. Somerset Maugham's short 1933 tale "An Appointment in Samarra" (allegedly based on an old Mesopotamian legend) is a famous example of the same ironic logic: A terrified servant borrows his master's horse to flee to another town, Samarra, after encountering Death, who gestures threateningly at him in the local Baghdad bazaar. Later, the master goes to the bazaar himself, sees Death, and asks why he made a threatening gesture to his servant. Death replies: "That was not a threatening gesture … it was only a start of surprise. I was astonished to see him in Bagdad, for I had an appointment with him tonight in Samarra" (quoted in Žižek, 1989, 58).

21 See, e.g., Dossey, 2009; Feather & Schmicker, 2005; Rhine, 1961.

[22] Rhine, 1961.

[23] See for instance Dossey, 2009; Marwaha & May, 2016; Targ, 2004.

[24] Feather & Schmicker, 2005.

[25] Braude, 1997. See also Eisenbud, 1982, who makes a similar argument.

[26] Also, appealing to possible, alterable futures ultimately forecloses *any* possibility of studying precognition scientifically. As long as you can say of a putative precognitive dream that doesn't come true that, "well, it was a possibility that didn't come to pass," then you really are beyond the pale of science. By that reasoning, any random thought could be precognition of an alternative future.

[27] Braude, 1997; Carpenter, 2012; Radin, 2006, 2009, 2013, 2018.

[28] Eisenbud, 1982.

[29] See e.g., May, 2015.

[30] The psychoanalyst and parapsychologist Jule Eisenbud, who was generally open to PK as an explanation and even favored it over retrocausation, keenly noted that if our unconscious wishes were really that powerful, none of us would have survived our childhoods (Eisenbud, 1982).

[31] In term's of Sonali Bhatt Marwaha and Edwin May's "multiphasic theory" (Marwaha & May, 2015), this would put the "physics domain" fully within the "neuroscience domain," rather than retaining them as separate and distinct. As I will describe later, the new field of quantum biology is raising many exciting possibilities in this regard.

[32] The possibility that mind or some aspect of it exists independently of the body is part of most religious traditions, and it has obvious appeal. If consciousness can fly free of the body, for instance while asleep, it raises the possibility that it might survive the death of the body too. Survival of bodily death is the ultimate hope that arguably biases everyone in one way or another, whatever their stated philosophical or scientific position, yet science may never be able to address that question. Whatever the ultimate fate of Dunne's consciousness after his death, I argue that his dream experiences were tied to his lived, embodied experience. (For a discussion of the spiritual uses readers found for Dunne's ideas, see White, 2018).

[33] Feinberg, 1975.

[34] Jon Taylor (Taylor, 2007, 2014) also makes this argument.

[35] See, e.g., Targ & Puthoff, 2005(1977); Warcollier, 2001(1948).

[36] Feinberg, 1975. Admittedly, it would be hard to prove this is universally true: How would the individual ever know if they had precognized something after their death? This is of course to leave aside speculations about obtaining precognitive information from one's spirit in the afterlife; I am also

leaving aside the question of historical prophets like Nostradamus, who are claimed to have foretold events occurring long after their deaths. Many such "prophecies" are too ambiguous to really evaluate and their provenance is too uncertain.

[37] It is precisely such tracers that could be used to test the "precognition-only" hypothesis for ESP—that is, manipulating feedback in telepathy or remote viewing experiments by adding fictitious details to a target or omitting salient details (Feinberg, 1975). Other than studies simply controlling the presence/absence or intensity of feedback (e.g., May et al., 1996), I am not aware of studies that have actively deceived participants about "what it was" they were viewing, which could be used to identify the information channel operative.

[38] Takeuchi et al., 2014.

[39] See Carington, 1946; Carpenter, 2012.

[40] Carpenter, 2012.

[41] Wargo, 2015e.

[42] Llewellyn, 2013.

[43] Dunne, 1952(1927); Kripal, 2010; See also Carpenter, 2012; Taylor, 2014.

[44] Foer, 2011; Yates, 1996(1966).

[45] Llewellyn, 2013; Wargo, 2010.

[46] Wargo, 2016c. Like time slips, some ghost encounters could involve precognizing subsequent exposure to an interesting/unsettling story about an event such as a violent death that occurred in a specific location.

[47] Buonomano, 2017.

[48] Ramachandran et al., 2016; see also Buonomano, 2017.

[49] Loftus et al., 1995.

[50] Taylor, 2007, 2014.

[51] Loftus et al., 1995.

[52] Buonomano, 2017, 172.

[53] Silberer, 1959(1909); Mavromatis, 1987.

[54] Friedman et al., 1990.

[55] Echeverria et al., 1991.

[56] Dobyns, 2006, 276. Dobyns does not favor the block-universe interpretation, however; he argues that retrocausation can be accommodated within a more open-ended view of future (and even past) history.

6. *Destination: Pong* (or, How to Build a Quantum™ Future Detector)

[1] Kaiser, 2011, 99.

[2] Levi-Strauss, 1966.

[3] Barad, 2007. For highly readable descriptions of the double slit and other basic experiments in quantum physics, see also Herbert, 1985.

[4] Barad, 2007. As Barad describes, the weirdness even goes deeper: The experimenter does not actually have to collect the "which path" information— just the *physical possibility of doing so* is enough to change the behavior of the particles being measured. It suggests a complex entanglement between the "agencies of observation" and the object being observed (the photon).

[5] See Herbert, 1985.

[6] Barad, 2007.

[7] See Rosenblum & Kuttner, 2011; Stapp, 2011.

[8] Barad, 2007.

[9] Herbert, 1985; Rosenblum & Kuttner, 2011; Stapp, 2011.

[10] Barad, 2007; Zurek, 2009.

[11] Sheehan, 2015.

[12] See Price, 1996.

[13] Cramer, 2006; Price, 1996.

[14] Quoted in Rosenblum & Kuttner, 2011, 212-213.

[15] Price, 1996, 2012; Price & Wharton, 2015, 2016; see also McRae, 2017.

[16] Price & Wharton, 2015, 2016.

[17] Price & Wharton, 2016.

[18] Dixon et al., 2009. A hundredfold amplification may sound like a lot, but it was an extremely tiny deflection of the mirror—a few hundred quadrillionths of a radian.

[19] The retrocausal implications of the Dixon et al. (2009) experiment are discussed in Merali, 2010, and Popescu, 2009.

[20] Musser, 2014.

[21] Stapp, 2011.

[22] Feynman, 1985; Gleick, 1993.

[23] Aharonov et al., 2017.

[24] Price, 1996.

[25] Aharonov & Tollaksen, 2007, 3.

[26] Merali, 2010; see also Shoup, 2015.

[27] Barad, 2007.

[28] Scully et al., 1991; Barad, 2007.

[29] Barad, 2007, 315.

[30] Barad does not privilege any particular "human" locus as a decisive part of "spacetimemattering"—she sees her project as radically post-humanist in the tradition of feminist thinkers like Donna Haraway. She could be contrasted with political scientist Alexander Wendt, who applies the popular consciousness-centric interpretation of quantum mechanics to social theory in his book *Quantum Mind and Social Science* (Wendt, 2015).

[31] Price & Wharton, 2015, 7.

[32] Price, 1996; Price & Wharton, 2015. Many have pointed out that randomness or "quantum uncertainty" cannot offer anything like free will. It's just that mainstream interpretations of quantum physics do not appear to foreclose it with the same finality that the block universe does. In the block universe, as York H. Dobyns puts it, "all of space and time must take on the immutability of the past" (Dobyns, 2006, 274).

[33] See for instance Aharonov et al, 2015; Merali, 2010.

[34] Becker, 2018.

[35] Ball, 2017; Chiribella et al., 2009; Castro-Ruiz et al., 2018; Oreshkov et al., 2012; Rubino et al., 2017.

[36] Vedral, 2018.

[37] Palus, 2017.

[38] Gleick, 2012.

[39] Barad, 2007.

[40] Lloyd, 2006.

[41] Gleick, 2012.

[42] Lloyd, 2006.

[43] Ibid.

[44] Gleick, 2012.

[45] On the interesting question of whether the user of information, the meaning-maker, needs to be conscious (or in any way human-like), see Barad, 2007.

[46] Kaiser, 2011.

[47] Remember what I said though about a healthy knowledge ecosystem de-

pending on error. While the natural excitement of hippie physicists to maybe use entanglement for faster-than-light communication proved a pipe dream, their work and their mistakes directly paved the way for some incredibly exciting technical applications that are only recently coming to fruition. One is *quantum cryptography*: Entanglement can work like a wax seal on a regular, slower-than-light message, revealing a third party's effort to read the message (Ibid.).

[48] Barad, 2007. This was demonstrated in "which-path" versions of the double-slit experiment. In 1979, two physicists at the University of Texas at Austin, William Wootters and Wojciech Zurek, found that the interference pattern on the screen was not too badly washed out even when there was near-certain (but not completely certain) information about which slit each photon had traversed.

[49] Kaiser, 2011.

[50] See Moldoveanu, 2010.

[51] Tamblyn, 2017.

[52] Lloyd et al., 2010. For an explanation of Lloyd's proposal, see Moldoveanu, 2010; Zyga, 2010, 2011.

[53] Moldoveanu, 2010.

[54] Lloyd et al., 2011, 3.

[55] Lloyd's is only one among several proposals for creating closed timelike curves; see Moldoveanu, 2010, for discussion.

[56] Zyga, 2015.

[57] Asmundsson, 2017.

[58] Moskvitch, 2018.

[59] Ball, 2017; Chiribella et al., 2009; Castro-Ruiz et al., 2018; Oreshkov et al., 2012; Rubino et al., 2017.

[60] Procopio et al., 2015.

7. A New Era of Hyperthought—From Precognitive Bacteria to Our Tesseract Brain

[1] L'Engle, 2007(1962). Mrs. Who and her strange companions Mrs. Whatsit and Mrs. Which are clearly descendants of Shakespeare's "weird sisters" from Macbeth (see Chapter 9), as well as being a clear inspiration for the Time Lords in *Doctor Who*, which debuted on the BBC the year after L'Engle's story was published.

[2] See White, 2018.

[3] Hinton, 1888, 99.

[4] Ibid., 49.

[5] See, e.g., Dunne, 1955, 70.

[6] More recently, MIT physicist Jeremy England has argued that entropy *inevitably* produces lifelike physical properties, and thus life itself in many cases—a radically counterintuitive idea (see Wolchover, 2014).

[7] Jantsch, 1980.

[8] See Davies, 2013; Walker & Davies, 2017.

[9] Bergson, 1944(1907).

[10] Koestler, 1972. Kammerer's seriality influenced Carl Jung's theory of synchronicity, which represented an attempt to supplement physical causation with meaning as the glue connecting events (see Chapter 11).

[11] Sheldrake, 2009.

[12] See Dunne & Jahn, 2017.

[13] Sheldrake, 2012. The term "promissory materialism" was originally used in this context by the philosopher of science Karl Popper.

[14] Di Corpo & Vannini, 2015.

[15] *Philosophy Bites*, 2012.

[16] Davies, 2004.

[17] McFadden & Al-Khalili, 2014.

[18] Ibid.

[19] Quantum computing theorist Seth Lloyd and others are examining how to use the natural quantum tunneling properties of viruses to design an efficient energy-transport system that could lead to more efficient and cheaper solar cells (Chandler, 2015).

[20] See also Sheehan (2015), who speculates on the possibility of living systems peering into their future by subverting the second law of thermodynamics.

[21] For example: If a move to the left sends an "I survived" message back a fraction of a second in time, for example by causing some detectable perturbation or deviation in one group of measured particles, whereas a move to the right causes no such a deviation, and if the organism is wired to automatically favor the option with the deviation, then this system—multiple precognitive circuits or time eyes linked together to guide behavior—will tend to produce "the correct answer" at a greater than statistically random frequency. The time eye could thus also be called a *right-answer detector*.

[22] Craddock et al., 2012.

[23] Volk, 2018.

[24] Hameroff, 1998.

[25] Craddock et al., 2014.

[26] Margulis, 2001.

[27] Margulis, 1999; Margulis & Sagan, 1986.

[28] Jantsch, 1980.

[29] Ramón y Cajal, 1989, 363.

[30] *NPR*, 2013.

[31] Kelly et al., 2010.

[32] Sheldrake, 2012.

[33] Grosso, 2015; Kripal, 2017.

[34] Kripal, 2017.

[35] Kastrup, 2015; Kelly et al., 2010.

[36] The philosopher Slavoj Žižek, for instance, sees the question of consciousness as the mysterious *Real* of Lacanian psychoanalytic theory, a kind of spectral presence that returns or persists precisely to the extent that reductive materialist neuroscience tries to exclude or marginalize it (Žižek, 2006b). More comfortable with the philosophical idiom of "subjectivity," Žižek has advanced an ontology that has come to be called "transcendental materialism," in which subjectivity emerges from fundamental instabilities in the material world (which he argues is really insubstantial, per mainstream quantum physics), but is not reducible to the latter (Žižek, 2013).

[37] Atmanspacher et al., 2004.

[38] Brainerd et al., 2013.

[39] Wendt, 2015.

[40] Penrose, 1994.

[41] Hameroff & Penrose, 2014.

[42] Physicist Henry Stapp (Stapp, 2011, 2015) has also focused on these cellular pores as the sites where consciousness takes charge of the brain. He does not view consciousness as a product of brain quantum processes but as a kind of "experimenter," steering the brain's activity by making observations (i.e., measurements) of the quantum behavior of calcium ions traveling through ion channels.

[43] Walker, 1970; see also Hansen, 2001; Walker, 2000.

[44] In their survey of the emerging field of quantum biology, *Life on the Edge*, Johnjoe McFadden and Jim Al-Khalili (McFadden & Al-Khalili, 2014) pro-

pose that the answer to quantum consciousness may lie with the brain's electromagnetic field. That field may couple to quantum-coherent (entangled) ions moving through ion channels and thereby synchronize them, enabling the "binding" of multiple cortical processes.

[45] Chalmers, 1995.

[46] Dent, 2017.

[47] Ibid.

[48] Adamatzky, 2017.

[49] My "time eye" should thus not be confused with the "psychic retina" proposed by Edwin May and Joseph G. Depp (May & Depp, 2015), which would be a receiver of information traveling *to* the brain from external future events.

[50] Feinberg, 1975.

[51] Taylor, 2007, 2014.

[52] This suggests some role for subcortical circuits that handle learning from rewarding experiences and the formation of habits based on them. It is another reason why conditioning processes like those described by Thomas Pynchon in *Gravity's Rainbow* may be important for understanding our ability to "post-select" on future rewards.

[53] Wargo, 2016a.

[54] McFadden & Al-Khalili, 2014.

[55] A physicist named Matthew Fisher, for instance, has discovered that phosphorus atoms bound in clusters around calcium ions (called "Posner clusters") may retain their coherence, even in the brain, for hours or days at a time; he proposes that the spin of these phosphorus atoms may serve as qubits in the brain's quantum computer (Fisher, 2015; Ouellette, 2016).

[56] Andreae & Burrone, 2018.

[57] Although I am proposing a different mechanism based on post-selection, the idea that precognition focuses on rewards is not that different from how precognition is explained in the "syntropy" theory of di Corpo and Vannini (2015). They suggest that in humans and other sentient organisms, emotion acts as a signal current from future attractors: Love is a signal of being on a harmonious, life-conducive path, whereas anxiety signals deviation from it. Thought, by the same token, reflects signals from the past, based on learning and experience. See also Taylor, 2014.

[58] For a summary of Libet's discoveries, see Libet, 2004.

[59] Ibid.

[60] Wegner, 2002.

[61] Ramachandran, 2011.

[62] Clark, 2016.

[63] Wolf, 1989, 1998. See also Penrose, 1994; Wendt, 2015. Physicist Henry Stapp (Stapp, 2015) has proposed that Libet's findings reflect consciousness collapsing the wavefunction of readiness potentials in the nervous system, thereby giving the illusion that action precedes consciousness rather than vice versa.

[64] Buonomano, 2017.

[65] See e.g., Dossey, 2013; Dunne, 1952(1927); Targ, 2004.

[66] See Baruš & Mossbridge, 2017.

[67] Deary et al., 2012.

[68] Bem, 2011.

[69] Costa de Beauregard, 1975, 92.

[70] Dean Buonomano's *Your Brain Is a Time Machine* (Buonomano, 2017) is a good summary of the topic.

8. Sometimes a Causal Arrow Isn't Just a Causal Arrow— Oedipus, Freud, and the Repression of Prophecy

[1] Douglas, 1966.

[2] George Hansen's *The Trickster and the Paranormal* (Hansen, 2001) is a comprehensive study of the liminal nature of paranormal and parapsychological topics and the taboos that surround them.

[3] Jones, 1955, 14.

[4] Rudnytsky, 1987, 6.

[5] Anzieu, 1986.

[6] Freud, 1965(1899).

[7] 1899 was also the year Freud's *Interpretation of Dreams* was published, although "A Premonitory Dream Fulfilled" was not included in that text. It has been appended to some later editions.

[8] Freud, 1974(1899), 49.

[9] Ibid., 50.

[10] Ibid.

[11] Ibid., 49. Frau B.'s acceptance of her doctor's account seems to reflect the same kind of deference to (usually male) authority that has often allowed skeptical reframings of anomalous experience to prevail without challenge. She may have either altered her own beliefs about the matter, or just kept

silent about them—there is no way to know.

[12] Ibid., 51.

[13] Dunne, 1952[1927]), 207.

[14] Freud, 1965(1899), 547-548.

[15] Ibid., 548.

[16] Freud, 1965(1901), 336. In a later edition of the book, Freud added another similar case reported by psychoanalyst Otto Rank in 1912: Rank had been approaching a bank to change some bank notes for silver coins to give as Christmas presents and, when he saw a long line in front of the bank, mentally rehearsed how he would try to be quick about his request: "Let me have gold, please." Rank immediately noted the error in his thoughts—that he meant silver, not gold—when suddenly he encountered a school friend of his brother's, named Gold; Gold's brother, in turn, was a publisher who had failed to help Rank years earlier in his career, preventing a degree of material prosperity he had hoped for. Rank explained this with a typical psychoanalytic "must have," augmented by what in modern psychological parlance would be called "priming":

> While I was absorbed in my phantasies, therefore, I must
> have unconsciously perceived the approach of Herr Gold;
> and this was represented in my unconscious (which was
> dreaming of material success) in such a form that I decided
> to ask for gold at the counter, instead of the less valu-
> able silver. On the other hand, however, the paradoxical
> fact that my unconscious is able to perceive an object
> which my eyes can recognize only later seems partly to be
> explained by what Bleuler terms 'complexive preparedness'
> (Ibid., 337-338).

[17] Luckhurst, 2008.

[18] Luckhurst, 2002.

[19] Richet wrote: "All powers considered supernatural are but human powers, muscular or psychic, but since they are removed from awareness they appear to have arisen from outside ourselves" (quoted in Wolf, 1993, 59-60).

[20] Ricoeur, 1970.

[21] Sartre, 2002, 211.

[22] Popper named this evidential loop the "Oedipus effect," and even noted how strange it was that the whole business of prophecy was left out of Freud's writings: "[I]t will be remembered that the causal chain leading to Oedipus' parricide was started by the oracle's prediction of this event. This is a char-acteristic and recurrent theme of such myths, but one which seems to have failed to attract the interest of the analysts, perhaps not accidentally" (quoted

in Borch-Jacobsen & Shamdasani, 2012, 125).

[23] Flournoy, 2007(1900).

[24] Freud, 1961(1930), 16.

[25] Siegel (2017) calls these "lead-up dreams." The Russian philosopher Pavel Florensky discussed these types of dreams at length in his *Iconostasis*, regarding them as proof that "Dream time is *turned inside out*" (Florensky, 1996[1922]).

[26] Carpenter, 2012.

[27] On why a "flatter" picture of the mind is (counterintuitively) more appealing and realistic than depth psychologies, see Chater, 2018. Chater argues that most of what has been misconstrued as mental depth really reflects the essentially improvisational nature of cognition.

[28] See Luckhurst, 2002.

[29] Jones, 1957; Luckhurst, 2002.

[30] The essay was published in his 1932 volume *New Introductory Lectures in Psycho-Analysis*, although none of the pieces were ever actually delivered as lectures.

[31] Freud, 1965(1932), 46.

[32] Ibid., 47.

[33] Ibid.

[34] This case was the most important of three to be included in a 1921 presentation to his inner circle, called "Psychoanalysis and Telepathy," but Freud accidentally left this case behind; he himself interpreted this as a parapraxis, "omitted due to resistance" (Luckhurst, 2002, 272).

[35] In fact, nowhere in the article does Freud specify the "grounds of his impediment," so his "though" is curious—what does her nickname for P. have to do with his sexual problems? Possibly a lot, as we will see.

[36] Freud, 1965(1932), 60.

[37] Ibid., 61.

[38] Ibid., 62-63.

[39] This case later intrigued the French poststructuralist philosopher Jacques Derrida, who made it the focus of his typically inscrutable, and arguably misnamed, piece, "Telepathy" (Derrida, 1988).

[40] Although Freud goes on to examine potential counterarguments to this as a genuine case of thought transference, he ultimately comes down favoring the "occult" explanation, and only laments that a physical explanation is not yet forthcoming for such phenomena. He sees his own theory of the unconscious

as perhaps paving the way to such an explanation:

> The telepathic process is supposed to consist in a mental act in one person instigating the same mental act in another person. What lies between these two mental acts may easily be a physical process into which the mental one is transformed at one end and which is transformed back once more in to the same mental one at the other end. The analogy with other transformations, such as occur in speaking and hearing by telephone, would then be unmistakable. And only think if one could get hold of this physical equivalent of the psychical act! It would seem to me that psycho-analysis, by inserting the unconscious between what is physical and what was previously called 'psychical', has paved the way for the assumption of such processes as telepathy. (Freud, 1965(1932), 68.)

[41] Carpenter, 2012; Ehrenwald, 1954; Eisenbud, 1970, 1982.

[42] Eisenbud, 1982, 56.

[43] The more one studies prophecy and the lives of precogs even outside of the psychoanalytic literature, the more one realizes that sexual and generational transgression is weirdly entwined with the whole topic. For whatever it may (or may not) be worth, J. W. Dunne, precognitive dream pioneer and the guiding light for this book, married late in life, at the age of 53; his bride, with the impressive English name Cicely Marion Violet Joan Twisleton-Wykeham-Fiennes, was 28—she was 25 years his junior, in other words. Maggy Quarles van Ufford, who "precognitively seduced" her doctor, Carl Jung, via her dreams as well as "Tantric" physical symptoms (see Chapter 11), was 19 years Jung's junior. Philip K. Dick, whose remarkable precognitive life has been examined by several writers, married a string of successively younger women—his fifth wife, Tessa, who was 18 when they met, was less than half his age (see Chapter 13).

[44] Eisenbud, 1982, 7.

[45] Ibid., 7-8.

[46] Echeverria et al., 1991; Friedman et al., 1990; Lloyd et al., 2011; see also Dobyns, 2006.

[47] "To say that this group's dreams are accurate is like shooting an arrow into a field, drawing a target around it after it has landed and saying, 'wow, what are the chances of that!'" (Wiseman, 2010, 153).

[48] Echeverria et al., 1991; Friedman et al., 1990. Physicist Nick Herbert (personal communication) suggests calling the quantum forces that protect self-consistency "Novikov Forces," in analogy to the quantum forces that prevent two electrons from occupying the same quantum state (the Pauli

Exclusion Principle).

[49] Eisenbud, 1982, 7-8.

[50] Ibid., viii.

[51] Marwaha & May, 2016.

[52] Freud, 1965(1899), 659-660.

9. Wyrd and Wishes—Metabolizing the Future in Dreams

[1] Frank Herbert keyed in on this ancient usage in his *Dune* series, where "weirding words" had a compelling force over the hearer.

[2] Freud, 1965(1899), 139-140.

[3] Ibid., 140.

[4] See discussion of the issue of Freud's feelings about responsibility and the Irma dream in Forrester, 1990.

[5] Freud, 1965(1899), 154.

[6] The Irma dream has been subject to countless reanalyses, with some psycho-analysts arguing that it really focuses on the Fliess situation and Freud's wish that his friend be blameless in the various malpractice incidents that were tarnishing his reputation and tainting Freud by association. In this respect, Slavoj Žižek (Žižek, 2006a, 32) makes the amusing observation:

> The interpretation [of the dream of Irma's injection] is surprisingly reminiscent of an old Soviet joke: 'Did Rabinovitch win a new car on the state lottery?' 'In principle, yes, he did. Only it was not a car but a bicycle, it was not new but old, and he did not win it, it was stolen from him!' Is a dream the manifestation of the dreamer's unconscious sexual desire? In principle, yes. Yet in the dream Freud chose to demonstrate his theory of dreams, his desire is neither sexual nor unconscious, and, moreover, it's not his own.

[7] Freud, 1965(1899), 154.

[8] Mavromatis, 1987, 193.

[9] Anzieu, 1986.

[10] Barad, 2007.

[11] Žižek, 2006b.

[12] Hobson & McCarley, 1977.

¹³ Crick & Mitchison, 1983.

¹⁴ Valli & Revonsuo, 2009.

¹⁵ Rock, 2004.

¹⁶ Winson, 1986.

¹⁷ Hobson, 2002.

¹⁸ Llewellyn, 2013.

¹⁹ See Wargo, 2010.

²⁰ This may have to do with how dreams not only encode memories but also preserve a rudimentary sense of chronology in our lives. Chronology can only come from a sense of experiences occurring in proximity and thus remaining associated closely with each other in our long-term-memory store. There is no fixed objective temporal yardstick in our brains (or anywhere) but only a cross-correlation of events, somewhat the way tree-rings corroborate and calibrate Carbon-14 data and vice versa. Chronology, ultimately, is an echo-chamber of self-reference, in our individual biographies as much as in the study of human and geologic (pre)history.

²¹ Wargo, 2010.

²² Other paradigms in memory research point to the same "associative halo" principle: For instance, in the Deese-Roediger-McDermott paradigm, participants are shown lists of words that share some connection to another word that is not on the list (for instance "sheet," "pillow," "bed," and "dream," but not "sleep"); when tested later, participants generally falsely remember reading the absent word ("sleep"). (See https://en.wikipedia.org/wiki/Deese–Roediger–McDermott_paradigm)

²³ McNamara, 2013.

²⁴ Hobson, 2013, 621.

²⁵ One writer and investigator of his own dreams, Bruce Siegel (Siegel, 2017), recently estimated that a quarter of his sample of 241 dreams was precognitive, most "coming true" within hours of the dream, some within minutes of awakening. My own experience with precognitive dreaming, although less systematic, has been similar—but see this book's Postscript.

²⁶ Dunne, 1952(1927), 62.

²⁷ Krippner, Ullman, and Honorton, 2002(1971).

²⁸ Graff, 1998, 2000, 2007.

²⁹ Paquette, 2016. Paquette writes that he was told the purpose of (relatively rare) dream symbolism—to facilitate the dream message making the transition to waking consciousness—by a "nonlocal character" encountered in a lucid dream. Thus, he believes dreams may access a real alternative reality

rather than being solely a representation of his own thoughts or memories. This raises an interesting problem: Any claim for what is a "symbol" standing for some latent meaning, versus a simple association, or versus a literal representation of some real alternative reality would require already knowing (or presupposing) what the rules governing the transformation of experience into the language of dreams consist of. Any claim about the meaning of a dream in relation to external reality has some degree of circularity, as it will always be predicated on accepting some particular theory of dreams and dreaming. It is a version of what in philosophy and criticism is sometimes called the *hermeneutic circle*, and it is one reason any claim about meaning is ultimately unfalsifiable. (What Freud-bashers fail to recognize is that a claim of *no meaning* in a dream is also unfalsifiable, for the same reasons.)

[30] Siegel, 2017. This has been my own experience as well—see Wargo, 2015c, 2015e.

[31] See Ehrenwald, 1954; Eisenbud, 1970, 1982.

[32] Eisenbud, 1982, 57.

[33] Ibid., 108.

[34] Siegel, 2017.

[35] Dossey, 2009.

[36] Krohn & Kripal, 2018.

[37] "Dew" is an old, probably ancient esoteric symbol for dreams and dreaming. Dreams, like dew, evaporate quickly with the morning sunrise (Wargo, 2015d). It is conceivable that Goddard was aware of this when he chose the pseudonym "Dewing" for his Navy dreamer, Gladstone.

[38] This part of the conversation, as recorded by Goddard (1951, 102), was:

> "Well," said the commander, "this will seem rather stupid to you. But I've just been reading a book by a philosopher bloke called Dunne, *An Experiment With Time*. He had discovered that some dreams, or some bits of dreams, come true. But if they are going to come true, they come true within the next two days. He builds up rather an interesting philosophy out of it all. Guess I've got a bit dream-conscious. Still, if I were you—"
>
> Inclined to argue with the commander, I said, "Dunne makes out, doesn't he, that when the subconscious mind is released from the duty of serving the conscious mind—because the conscious mind has gone off duty, too; gone to sleep—then the subconscious can dash off into space and time and have a wonderful spree making sequence pictures to taunt the sleeping conscious mind's eye,

mixing up past and future events? And isn't it his point that this is what we call dreaming?"

"Yes, that's the idea. You must have read his book."

"I have," I said, "and it didn't say that two days is the limit for coming true. What it did say was that Dunne found out, once he had begun to get dream-conscious, he had such a collection of dreams to record, and had to watch so closely for bits of them coming true, that if something didn't happen within two days he would discard his dream records more than two days old and concentrate on newer dreams."

"All the same," said the commander, "if I were you, I'd stay on the ground for a couple of days."

[39] Jones, 1957.

[40] Resnik, 1987.

[41] Schavelzon argued that probably complications and illnesses peripheral to the cancer per se killed him, at age 83, and not the cancer itself—which may in fact have been spurred by the radiation treatments and surgeries he received (Ibid.).

[42] Moss, 2009; see also Dossey, 2009.

[43] Jones, 1957.

[44] Anzieu, 1986, 155.

[45] Fichtner, 2010.

[46] See Forrester, 1990.

[47] Jones, 1957, 96.

[48] Fichtner, 2010, 1153.

[49] Jones, 1957, 95.

[50] Of course, psychoanalysis itself, which Freud had been in the process of developing when he had the dream, is all about speech and the difficulties of speaking, the impediments—resistances—to honest disclosure (Forrester, 1990).

[51] Anzieu, 1986.

[52] There is some question whether Kekulé actually told dream account to his audience at the *Benzolfeier* event or only added it to the text of his speech in the published proceedings (Wotiz & Rudofsky, 1993).

[53] Ibid.

[54] If there was any truth to Kekulé's dream story, cryptomnesia cannot be

ruled out—that is, a dream-representation of an idea in an article that the dreamer had previously seen but consciously forgotten (or as Freud might have said, "repressed").

[55] Freud, (1965[1899]), 660.

[56] Anzieu, 1986.

[57] Freud, 1961(1930), 17.

[58] Ibid., 17-18.

[59] Ibid., 18.

[60] Ibid.

10. Prophetic *Jouissance*—Trauma, Survival, and the Precognitive Sublime

[1] Guinness, 1985.

[2] Ibid., 34-35.

[3] See Gurney et al., 2007(1886); Kripal, 2010, 2014.

[4] Forrester, 1990.

[5] Ibid. See also Luckhurst, 2008.

[6] Luckhurst, 2008.

[7] Laplanche, 1993, 41.

[8] Quoted in Rudnytsky, 1987, 12.

[9] Forrester, 1990, 197.

[10] Jones, 1957.

[11] Winnicott, 1971.

[12] Freud, 1984(1920).

[13] Freud may have gotten a dose of inspiration for his concept of "death drive" from one of his students, the Russian analyst Sabina Spielrein. In her 1911 paper "Destruction as the Cause of Coming into Being" (Spielrein, 1994[1911]), which she read to the Vienna Psychoanalytic Society shortly after her admission to Freud's group, Spielrein identified the paradoxical or counterintuitive relationship in the unconscious between generation and destruction, sex and death—an equivalence for which evidence could be found not only in patients' dreams but also throughout mythology. Her linking of the diametrical forces of creation and destruction was influential on both Freud's and Carl Jung's work. Unfortunately, history has preferred to focus on Spielrein as Jung's patient-turned-lover, and her contributions to psychoanal-

ysis were mostly forgotten after her death in the holocaust (Launer, 2014).

Freud's death drive is not exactly the same thing as what Spielrein was offering: Hers was an observation that creation entailed a giving up of the ego and self—a notion that mystics would understand readily but that Freud would have considered narcissistic and regressive.

[14] Interestingly, in Thomas Pynchon's *Gravity's Rainbow*, the process speculated to be behind Tyrone Slothrop's premonitory erections was an extinction of some initial conditioned response "beyond the zero," to a "transmarginal" realm virtually identical to *jouissance* as it figures in Lacan's work, or to the substitution of negative reinforcement for positive reinforcement in drug addiction.

[15] Lacan, 1998; Daly, 2014.

[16] Twain, 2010; Charman, 2017.

[17] Twain did not write down his dream when it occurred, which might have provided objective basis for verifying it. He dictated it to his stenographer in the context of relating an 1885 meeting of the "Monday Evening Club" in Hartford, Connecticut when he told the dream to several other esteemed gentlemen (mostly clergymen) over cigars, by which point, he estimated, he had told it upwards of 80 times to different people. This gave his memory and his verbal artistry ample opportunity to sort and rearrange events into a seamless narrative of psychic connection. One of Twain's companions that evening, Reverend Dr. Nathaniel Burton, pointed out, via an example of his own, that a dream retold often enough becomes "one part fact, straight fact, fact pure and undiluted, golden fact, and twenty-four parts embroidery" (Twain, 2010, 277). Twain writes that, although he did not really doubt the dream's salient points, Burton's argument compelled him to stop telling the dream thereafter, lest it further alter in the telling.

[18] See Charman, 2017.

[19] Halperin, 2014.

[20] See Twain, 2010, 350-352.

[21] Ibid., p. 561.

[22] Charman, 2017.

[23] It may be precisely such thoughts that are pushed not only out of awareness but actually into the past, where they "recur" in advance (or "precur") as premonitions and dreams that make no sense at the time. It reminds me of the original series *Star Trek* episode "All Our Yesterdays," about a planet where political undesirables were exiled via time machine into various times in the planet's history, where their voice could have no meaning.

[24] May & Depp, 2015; see also Graff, 2000.

[25] Larry Dossey, commenting on Twain's dream about seeing his brother

dead, notes that from May's entropy gradient theory alone we might have expected the writer to dream of the boiler explosion itself and not the scene at the wake, when the nurse placed a single red rose on Henry's chest. But "for Twain, who loved his brother deeply and blamed himself for his death for the rest of his life, it was probably Henry's death itself that was the most entropic, not the boiler that blew up" (Dossey, 2009, 118).

[26] Dale E. Graff, who directed the military remote-viewing project Star Gate, makes this point in his memoir *River Dreams*: "Fire, even the threat of fire, is a bright beacon in our emotional landscape—for this reality and for psi space" (Graff, 2000, 37).

[27] Kant, 2008, 91.

[28] Freud, 2015(1918).

[29] Cathy Caruth, in her essay "Traumatic Awakenings: Freud, Lacan, and the Ethics of Memory" (in Caruth, 1996) clarifies the crucial link between Freud's "death drive" and survival.

[30] Becker, 1973, 2.

[31] Paradoxically, the logic of *jouissance* may also apply to many people's premonitions related to their own death. Most of those who perished in the World Trade Center, for instance, would have had time to be aware of what was happening, and formulate hope for rescue. Their premonitory dreams may have conveyed this intensified awareness of their own mortality in the context of a mortal crisis. Could this explain sculptor Michael Richards' obsession with being "pierced by planes" in the years and months leading up to his death on 9/11, for example? There is no way of knowing for sure, but it is very possible that he did not die in the initial impact of American Airlines Flight 11 into the North Tower. His studio was on the 92nd floor, the floor struck by the lowest wingtip of the jet. The artist may well have had time to be aware that a plane had crashed into his building, perhaps even to learn that a second plane struck the other tower. Similarly with William Stead's possible premonitions of his death aboard the *Titanic*; the uncertainty of the *Titanic* passengers' fate must have extended up until the end as some dim hope for rescue that their premonitory unconscious may have interpreted as survival.

[32] The clip is available on YouTube: https://www.youtube.com/watch?v=ZUe30aXjS20

[33] Guinness, 1985, 34.

[34] Again, the well-established fallibility of memory will of course not prevent psi-skeptics from invoking cryptomnesia to account for anomalous experiences when it suits them to do so.

[35] Ibid.

11. A Precognitive Seduction—Maggy Quarles van Ufford, Carl Jung, and the Scarab

[1] Jung, 1985(1937), 332.

[2] Forrester, 1990.

[3] Jung, 1973(1951), 109.

[4] Ibid., 110.

[5] Ibid.

[6] De Moura, 2014.

[7] Unless otherwise noted, biographical information on Madeleine Quarles van Ufford in this chapter, apart from what is stated or implied by Jung himself, comes from de Moura's article, "Learning from the Patient" (de Moura, 2014). De Moura refers to Maggy by her married surname Reichstein, but because most of the events discussed in this chapter probably preceded her marriage in 1925, I have opted to use her maiden name or, in most cases, simply "Maggy" to avoid confusion. Besides Jung's writings and de Moura's article, other sources adding minor but interesting biographical details on Maggy Reichstein née Quarles van Ufford, although without awareness that she was the famous patient who dreamed of a scarab, include Broda (2013) and Jansen (2003).

[8] Broda, 2013.

[9] De Moura, 2014.

[10] Ibid.

[11] Jung (1996, 104) describes: "She could not adapt to European conditions because her instincts refused all along the line; she would not marry, she would not be interested in ordinary things, she would not adapt to our conventions. She was against everything, and so naturally she became very neurotic."

[12] Jung, 1985(1937).

[13] Jung, 1996.

[14] According to May B. Broda (Broda, 2013), Maggy and her sisters had taken lodging at the house of Mrs. Gustawa Reichstein, a non-observant Polish Jew who ran a boarding house for young emigres (later, in the 1930s, she took in Jewish refugees) and was a friend of Jung's. Particularly difficult cases frequently stayed with her, and she is said to have assisted with their treatment. She was also a protective mother figure for her various young lodgers, tolerant of their political activism and sexual behavior.

[15] Ibid.; https://it.wikipedia.org/wiki/Ignaz_Epper

[16] De Moura, 2014.

[17] Jung, 1996, 104.

[18] Jung, 1985(1937).

[19] Noll, 1994, 1997.

[20] Jung, 1973(1952).

[21] Describing them as "exteriorizations" of course obscures the possibility that the cracks had a mundane explanation but that Jung pre-sensed these startling noises in that emotionally charged context. This seems more likely, given that the noises continued to be heard by Freud afterward. In a letter dated April 16th, 1909, Freud wrote to Jung:

> I do not deny that your comments and your experiment made a powerful impression upon me. After your departure I determined to make some observations, and here are the results. In my front room there are continual creaking noises, from where the two heavy Egyptian steles rest on the oak boards of the bookcase, so that's obvious. In the second room, where we heard the crash, such noises are very rare. At first I was inclined to ascribe some meaning to it if the noise we heard so frequently when you were here were never again heard after your departure. But since then it has happened over and over again, yet never in connection with my thoughts and never when I was considering you or your special problem. (Not now, either, I add by way of challenge). The phenomenon was soon deprived of all significance for me by something else. My credulity, or at least my readiness to believe, vanished along with the spell of your personal presence ... The furniture stands before me spiritless and dead, like nature silent and godless before the poet after the passing of the gods of Greece. (In Jung, 1965a, 361-362.)

[22] Jung, 1973(1951), 109-10.

[23] Jung, 1973(1952), 23-24.

[24] See, e.g., Hand, 2014.

[25] Falk, 1989, p. 477. In the same way and for the same reasons, the "synchronicity" of the Millenium Hilton and the rubble of the World Trade Center after 9/11 (Chapter 1) was also a product of taking a very singular point of view, a particular photo-op.

[26] Jung, 1973(1952), 19.

[27] Jung, 2015, 344.

28 Main, 2007.

29 Koestler, 1972.

30 Tart, 1981. Tart argues that by implying that there's no cause to be found, the synchronicity concept facilitates "being intellectually lazy and dodging our responsibilities" (i.e., as scientists).

31 Jung, 2015, 541.

32 Noll, 1994, 1997.

33 Not surprisingly, Freud's clinic was also an echo chamber; see Borch-Jakobsen (1996) and Borch-Jakobsen & Shamdasani (2012).

34 Beitman, 2016, 120.

35 See, e.g., Carpenter, 2012.

36 Radin, 2018; see also Radin, 2006, 2009, 2013.

37 Jung, 1973(1952), 23.

38 Despite Jung's parenthetical claim that Maggy "did not happen to know" the rebirth symbolism of scarabs, it is quite possible she did have some idea. Scarabs were popular at that point, and Maggy was a highly educated and curious woman who could have encountered discussion of scarab symbolism in any number of then-current sources, including her own doctor's *Wandlungen und Symbole der Libido*. Even if she had not encountered the idea in a book at some point, she is likely to have known the symbolism of scarabs via the decorative arts. Scarab jewelry, of the sort the dream-figure gave her, had been popular since the Egyptian Revival of the mid 19th century, its ancient meaning of rebirth or metamorphosis reasonably well understood in that context. The Parisian jewelry designer Lalique, for instance, was famous for his Art Deco, Egyptian-style scarabs, as well as for other art jewelry that depicted the surreal metamorphosis of women into insects. As a woman from a wealthy aristocratic family, Maggy would have known the language of jewelry and high fashion, whatever she knew or didn't know about ancient Egypt. (Scarabs would enjoy a second wave of popularity after 1922, with the discovery of King Tutankhamun's tomb—although I am inferring that the episode in Jung's clinic probably preceded that.)

39 Jung, 1965b, 179.

40 Jung, 2012, 253.

41 Jung, 1985(1937).

42 Noll, 1997, 151.

43 Noll, 1994, 1997.

44 Beitman, 2016, 120.

45 Ibid.

⁴⁶ Priestley, 1989(1964).

⁴⁷ Freud, 1974(1899), 50.

⁴⁸ ESP phenomena have frequently been observed to manifest especially in conditions of impeded connection. Jule Eisenbud (Eisenbud, 1982) also noted that the over-expression of precognitive abilities seemed linked to socially repressed sexual orientations and desires, literally "forbidden love," as we will see in Chapter 12.

⁴⁹ It now appears as an appendix to the volume *The Practice of Psychotherapy* (Jung, 1985[1937]), and a less detailed version of the story appears in Jung's notes to a 1932 seminar on Kundalini Yoga (Jung, 1996).

⁵⁰ Jung, 1985(1937), 330.

⁵¹ Ibid., 331 (italics in original).

⁵² Broda, 2013.

⁵³ Jung (1996, 105) describes: "At the same time she really loved a man but could not think of marrying him. And then the thought entered her head that I, or circumstances, might persuade her to marry and have a baby, but that was impossible."

⁵⁴ Jung, 1985(1937), 332.

⁵⁵ *I dreamt that I was walking along a country road at the foot of a steep hill. On the hill was a castle with a high tower. Sitting on the parapet of the topmost pinnacle was a woman, golden in the light of the evening sun. In order to see her properly, I had to bend my head so far back that I woke up with a crick in the neck.* (Ibid., 332.)

⁵⁶ According to Baynes' daughter, Baynes himself had a short extramarital affair with Maggy (who also was by that point married, with children) and called the Dutch artist a "devotee of eros" (Jansen, 2003, 225). It is when Baynes described to Jung the "extraordinary impression" Maggy had made on him that Jung described her as "the ideal anima woman. It is her vocation" (Ibid.). When Baynes was involved with Maggy, Jung inexplicably became coldly distant, and Baynes surmised that it was because of Jung's feelings for her: "I have a feeling that his coldness to me now is very largely on account of [Maggy]. He is very attached to her and feels her great value because it developed literally under his hand" (Ibid., 245).

⁵⁷ Douglas, 1993.

⁵⁸ See, e.g., Bair, 2003; Launer, 2014; McLynn, 1996; Noll, 1997. It was in the context of the scandal that erupted during Jung's intense relationship with Sabina Spielrein, a 19-year-old Russian patient he had treated at Zurich's Burghölzli mental hospital, that Freud first used the term "countertransference" in a letter to Jung. Whether or not that relationship was physically consummated has been a matter of considerable, often acrimonious debate

among Jung's followers, biographers, and critics; some of the latter, like Noll, argue that Jung actively preached the virtues of polygamy to his patients (Noll, 1994, 1997; see also Heuer, 2017). In contrast, Lance Owens (Owens, 2015) cites some evidence that the relationship with Spielrein remained sexually unrequited. (Owens argues that Jung sublimated his desires into a higher mystical gnosis, a *mysterium coniunctionis*.)

[59] Jung, 1985(1937), 333.

[60] In his "On Synchronicity" lecture, he writes, "This experience punctured the desired hole in her rationalism and broke the ice of her intellectual resistance. The treatment could now be continued with satisfactory results" (Jung, 1973[1951], 110).

[61] The similarity of the two narratives raises some question how accurate either one may really have been: On one hand, they seem like stereotyped vignettes of therapeutic breakthrough and could have been based as much on Jung's fantasies about the efficacy of his method as on reality. In addition, both narratives were written decades after the incidents they described, and he clearly didn't take notes (since de Moura remarks that Jung wrote to Maggy in 1949 asking for her recollections of the scarab incident, so he could write about it; de Moura, 2014). On the other hand, the fact that Maggy was indeed moved if not transformed by some of her experiences in Jung's consulting room is not in doubt, given her continued correspondence with Jung about events in her therapy.

[62] Jung, 1985(1937), 333-334.

[63] The meaning of these symptoms wending their way up his patient's chakras—the secret thought the bird was releasing—was, Jung asserted once again, a very conventional-bourgeois desire for a child, which Jung says his patient was compelled disappointingly to own up to:

> For as soon as the kundalini serpent reached manipura, the most primitive centre of consciousness, the patient's brain told her what kind of thought the shakti was insinuating into her: that she wanted a real child and not just a psychic experience. This seemed a great let-down to the patient. But that is the disconcerting thing about the shakti: her building material is maya, "real illusion." In other words, she spins fantasies with real things.
>
> This little bit of Tantric philosophy helped the patient to make an ordinary human life for herself, as a wife and mother ... (Ibid., 336-337.)

[64] De Moura (2014) notes that Mischa later sent Maggy her notes of the lecture, with references to the fantasies Jung didn't understand until he read Arthur Avalon's book underlined.

[65] Freud and his colleague Josef Breuer encountered and recorded many such seductions, also with appropriate clinical detachment, in their 1895 volume *Studies on Hysteria* (Breuer & Freud, 1957[1895]; see also Forrester, 1990). It would be interesting to revisit those cases with an eye to any possible precognitive symptomatology.

[66] This same mechanism might also have accounted for the tendency of Freud's patients to produce Oedipal material, as well as for the general tendency of patients to produce dreams and symptoms that match the theoretical orientation of their therapist.

[67] De Moura, 2014, 405.

[68] Ibid.

[69] Coincidentally or not, Jung does cite *Phantasms* in his *Synchronicity* monograph, just before the scarab narrative; we know that he read it and that it was an influence on his thinking, at least insofar as the authors had made an attempt to cover the same ground of meaningful coincidence.

[70] Jule Eisenbud is one exception. He chronicled numerous manifestations of "psi" behavior on the part of his patients, often intended (albeit unconsciously) to elicit his approbation, approval, or sexual interest (Eisenbud, 1970, 1982).

[71] Jung was clearly wrong when he wrote in his 1952 *Synchronicity* monograph that "nothing like [the scarab incident] ever happened to me before or since, and … the dream of the patient has remained unique in my experience" (Jung, 1973[1952], 22).

[72] De Moura, 2014, 391.

[73] See Forrester's (1990) discussion of the question of payment and contracts in relation to "free speech" in psychoanalysis.

[74] The peril of active hermeneutic engagement with symptoms or dreams is that they will turn out to be precisely that engagement that is precognized, resulting in the kind of vertiginous hall of mirrors that will, not without justification, nauseate a scientist-skeptic. A reader of my blog, *The Nightshirt*, proposed that some dreams might be precognitive of the very act of recalling or writing the dream down upon waking (or by extension telling it to a spouse over breakfast, or reflecting upon it in some way later). If thoughts sparked by the act of recording the dream are emotionally salient in some way, this could indeed be the case; falsifying that hypothesis in any given case would be extremely difficult—although again, difficulty of falsification is not in itself evidence of falsehood.

[75] Eisenbud, 1970.

12. Fate, Free Will, and *Futility*—Morgan Robertson's Tiresias Complex

[1] Eisenbud, 1982, 75.

[2] Ehrenwald, 1954.

[3] Jule Eisenbud's chapter "Is There A Merciful God in the House?" in his book *Paranormal Foreknowledge* (Eisenbud, 1982), gives essential insight into Robinson's life and works, and is a touchstone for my thinking in this chapter.

[4] Robertson, 1974(1898), 23-24.

[5] Kripal, 2011.

[6] Francis, 1915, 100.

[7] In Gardner, 1998, 2.

[8] Robertson, 1905, 88.

[9] In a short autobiographical piece called "My Skirmish with Madness" (Robertson, 1915b), he describes a few weeks he spent in Bellevue Hospital undergoing detoxification—and his ultimate return to drinking. In another autobiographical piece he wrote and published anonymously a year before his death, "Gathering No Moss," he describes a visit to a hypnotist, ostensibly to help with his writing, but likely in fact to help with his drinking.

[10] Robertson, 1915a, 29.

[11] Ibid.

[12] Ibid., 29-30.

[13] Žižek, 1989, 71. Something similar obviously can be said about the ruins of the World Trade Center, or the ruins of Auschwitz/Birkenau, or a Civil War battlefield; they all represent sites of trauma yet are also repeatedly revisited and "enjoyed" in a kind of obsessive-ritualistic way.

[14] Žižek writes, "even before it actually happened, there was already a place opened, reserved for it in fantasy space. It had such a terrific impact on the 'social imaginary' by virtue of the fact that it was expected" (Ibid., 69).

[15] There is, of course, a whole can of worms here for psychoanalytically inclined parapsychologists who take seriously the possibility of psychokinetic or PK effects—or the effects of intention. Despite their disturbing overlap with regressive ideas of the "omnipotence of thought," Eisenbud (1982) considers PK and other "active hypotheses" more realistic than true retrocausation. Again, it's a topic way beyond the scope of this book; but a good case can be made that at least some of what looks like PK is really misrecognized precognition (see, e.g., May, 2015).

[16] Eisenbud, 1982, 111.

[17] This raises the possibility, not mentioned by Eisenbud, that the forbidden, not-acted-upon desire in Robertson's life may instead have been some kind of pedophilia. Note that *Futility*, for instance, is a rescue fantasy centered on a child; at the end of the story a court absolves Rowland of guilt for abducting her.

[18] Eisenbud writes that "nowhere has [the Oedipus story] been told and retold as plainly as in Robertson's works" (Eisenbud, 1982, 104).

[19] Robertson, 1915a.

[20] See Hansen (2001) for in-depth discussion of liminality and its relation to the paranormal.

[21] When H. G. Wells' Time Traveler in *The Time Machine* visits the distant future, he finds that a great Sphinx structure has been erected on the site of his laboratory; after his machine is stolen by the Morlocks, he must penetrate that Sphinx to find it and continue his travels.

[22] Robertson, N.D., 262-263.

[23] Francis, 1915, 101.

[24] Eisenbud, 1982, 106.

[25] See Forrester, 1990.

13. "P.S. What Scares Me Most, Claudia, Is That I Can Often Recall *the Future*"—The Memetic Prophecies of Philip K. Dick

[1] Since both the invention of radar and Pearl Harbor occurred over two decades after Robertson's death, his stories possibly anticipating these developments would not fit the precognitive hypothesis advanced in this book.

[2] Davis, 1998.

[3] See Peake, 2013; Sarill, 2014; Wargo, 2015a.

[4] Dick's 1956 story "Minority Report"—which Steven Spielberg made into a movie starring Tom Cruise in 2002—still stands as one of the great sci-fi considerations of precognition and how it might be exploited as a social predictive tool. In the story, multiple psychics' impressions of the future are pooled for greater precision; today a version of this method called "associative remote viewing" is being used in attempts to beat the stock market and Las Vegas (see Broderick, 2015; Targ, 2012). Dick, like Thomas Pynchon, was prescient about prescience.

[5] Peake, 2013, 177.

[6] The relevant passage (Dick, 2012, 224) is:

> "What is Ubik?" Joe said, wanting her to stay.
>
> "A spray can of Ubik," the girl answered, "is a portable negative ionizer, with a self-contained, high-voltage, low-amp unit powered by a peak-gain helium battery of 25kv. The negative ions are given a counter-clockwise spin by a radically biased acceleration chamber, which creates a centripetal tendency to them so that they cohere rather than dissipate. A negative ion field diminishes the velocity of anti-protophasons normally present in the atmosphere; as soon as their velocity falls they cease to be anti-protophasons and, under the principle of parity, no longer can unite with protophasons radiated from persons frozen in cold-pac; that is, those in half-life. The end result is that the proportion of protophasons not canceled by anti-protophasons increases, which means—for a specific time, anyhow—an increment in the net put-forth field of protophasonic activity ... which the affected half-lifer experiences as greater vitality plus a lowering of the experience of low cold-pac temperatures. So you can see why regressed forms of Ubik failed to—"
>
> Joe said reflexively, "To say 'negative ions' is redundant. All ions are negative."

[7] Sarill, 2014.

[8] Dick's 1977 novel *A Scanner Darkly* may be another example of channeling popular science writing Dick was soon to encounter in his voracious magazine reading. The novel, based partly on his own experiences during the worst depths of his amphetamine addiction in 1970-1972, concerns a group of characters in Orange County, California who are addicted to a new synthetic drug called Substance D. One of the characters experiences complete dissociation between two sides of himself—his job as a narcotics cop and his real life as a Substance D addict, and even "informs on himself" because the drug has destroyed the connection between his two brain hemispheres. Dick was set to deliver his finished manuscript in early 1974, but wrote to his publisher asking for an extension because he had just seen an article on the new science of split-brain phenomena in *Psychology Today*; he realized his literary device was a "real thing" and that he needed to do additional research on the topic in order to sound better informed. Was he somehow precognizing the *Psychology Today* article when he wrote his novel? Again, there is no way to know for sure, but it fits a characteristic pattern in his life. (See Dick, 1991, 9; Peake, 2013.)

[9] According to his wife at the time, Anne R. Dick, in her book *The Search*

for Philip K. Dick, her husband was heavily influenced by the early 20th Century existential psychiatrist Ludwig Binswanger (Anne R. Dick, 2010). Binswanger's definition of "schizophrenia" encompassed disorders far less severe than the currently accepted definition of psychosis.

[10] Apel, 2014, 29. Although both his biographer Lawrence Sutin and his wife at the time, Anne R. Dick, assumed the story must have been written after seeing the exhibit (Sutin, 2005; Anne R. Dick, 2010), neither evidently knew that the exhibit did not go on display until two years after Dick wrote (and submitted) his manuscript. Chronology makes it impossible that Dick could have gotten the idea from Disney (Peake, 2013). It also would make little sense: Why would a writer intent on being original to the point of mind-bending base a story on something he had seen at Disneyland on a visit?

The visit to Disneyland took place late in Dick's marriage to Anne (as Anne records, it was her idea, as an apologetic gesture for an angry outburst during a fight; "I loved the rocket to the moon. Phil was fascinated by the Lincoln robot" (Anne R. Dick, 2010, 62). Anne and Phil divorced in 1965, so the visit probably took place in 1964 or 1965, at least two years after Dick had written "First in Our Family."

[11] Initially Dick lived in an apartment building in Fullerton, not far from Anaheim, then from 1973 to 1975 in a house he shared with his fifth wife Tessa; when he and Tessa split in 1975, he moved into an apartment building in Santa Ana, just south of the park. So, he could have been referring to either the apartment in Fullerton or the one in Santa Ana.

[12] Apel, 2014, 29-30.

[13] This young woman, "Pris," is herself cold and robot-like, and unable to return the narrator's affections—a deliberate contrast to the deep warmth and humanity (and ultimately, madness) of the robotic Lincoln. As Sutin (2005) notes, Pris is probably the most extreme exemplar in Dick's fiction of the "dark haired girl" type that he repeatedly became infatuated with in real life. In some ways "A. Lincoln Simulacrum" can be seen as a prequel to *Do Androids Dream of Electric Sheep*, later filmed as *Blade Runner*. In the latter story, "Pris" is one of the simulacra—now called "replicants" (and as one of the characters in the film describes her, "a basic pleasure model").

[14] Dick, 1969, 37.

[15] Ibid., 39-40.

[16] Other characters in Dick's writings similarly resembled people he would meet later. A woman he met in 1971 named Kathy so resembled a character of the same name in his novel *Flow My Tears, The Policeman Said*, published the previous year, that he said he worried she might sue him (Dick, 1991).

[17] See Arnold, 2016; Peake, 2013; Tessa B. Dick, 2010.

[18] Peake, 2013.

[19] From an interview with Gregg Rickman, quoted in Arnold, 2016, 13.

[20] Arnold, 2016, 12.

[21] Sutin, 2005, 56.

[22] Arnold (2016, 13) quotes from a 1971 journal entry, where Dick writes, "I can only be safe when sheltered by a woman … It is that I fear that I will simply die. My breath, my heart will stop. I will expire like an exposed baby. Jane, it happened to you and I am still afraid it will happen to me. They can't protect us …"

[23] Rudnytsky, 1987.

[24] Arnold, 2016, 193.

[25] Arnold (2016) makes a strong case that, just like might happen in a Phil Dick novel such as *A Scanner Darkly*, Dick really did break into his own house, perhaps in a dissociative state, and pry open his own safe, destroying specifically years of cancelled checks that could have been used against him as evidence by the IRS. He had not paid taxes in years.

[26] In her memoir, Tessa (Tessa B. Dick, 2010) claims that "2-3-74" referred to March 2, 1974, the European day-month notation, and indeed in some of his letters he refers to his experience merely as "3-74."

[27] Wilson, 2016.

[28] Arnold, 2016, 174.

[29] Krenz, 2000.

[30] Krenz, N.D. ("Philip K. Dick Words Project")

[31] Ibid.

[32] Dick, 2011.

[33] Krenz, N.D. ("Philip K. Dick, Dear Claudia Letter, May 9, 1974"); see also Dick, 1991.

[34] Dick, 1991, 157.

[35] Ibid.

[36] Krenz (N.D., "Words Project") argues that Dick's letters to her were intended for public consumption all along.

[37] Dick, 1991, 165. Unfortunately, without Krenz's side of the correspondence, we cannot tell whether Dick was in some cases precognizing her letters to him. He frequently waxes effusive at how aptly she has put something or how uncannily she seems to understand him—in one case he expresses shock at the uncanniness of a drawing of the sibyl she sent him based on his brief dream description. Was his dream image informed by her subsequent depiction, and did this account for its uncanniness, or was he just complimenting

her as part of his epistolary flirtation?

[38] Phil Dick's visionary experience of seeing the Orange County of gas shortages and the fall of Nixon as a shimmering overlay on the Roman Empire is of course strikingly similar to Freud's vision of ancient Rome flickering in the landscape of the modern city.

[39] Dick, 1991, 298.

[40] Although Spielberg's film is widely considered a masterpiece, some viewers—and later, Spielberg himself—have been put off by Neary's lack of hesitation at leaving behind his wife and children to join the extraterrestrials—a possible resonance with Dick's own familial ambivalence.

[41] Tessa B. Dick, 2010.

[42] Tessa Dick (personal communication) confirmed that Phil read some Vallee books in 1977; the book in question, *The Invisible College* (1975), would have been his most recent book at that point.

[43] Wargo, 2015a.

[44] This may be a further precognitive detail. The piece of technology the "shy and gentle creatures" showed him was, he wrote, "based on a concept buried in a basement and forgotten, [a] twin-drive opposed rotary assembly [in which] torque was passed back and forth from left to right in some way by a clutch system…" (Dick, 1991, 298). This description very closely matches descriptions and drawings of a proposed antigravity device ("the Laithwaite engine") that appeared six years later in a briefly popular 1981 book called *How to Build a Flying Saucer (and Other Proposals in Speculative Engineering)* by an inventor named T.B. Pawlicki (Pawlicki, 1981).

[45] Dick, 1992, p. 91.

[46] Dick could well have learned how he had been found, as according to Tessa he was awake and lucid in the hospital afterward (Tessa B. Dick, 2010). In that case, he would certainly have felt great relief to be alive. If we take his dream eight years earlier as a premonition, it would not have been "a premonition of his own death" (even though this is how it will typically be described), but a premonition of a disturbing mental image of his own *near-death* he would have formed in the hospital—in other words, a kind of terrifying dream about his own survival. Unfortunately, he would suffer further strokes soon thereafter, and not regain lucidity.

[47] Kripal, 2011.

[48] Ibid.

[49] Krohn & Kripal, 2018.

[50] Di Corpo & Vannini, 2015.

[51] Dick was certainly aware of this—he was not above making double enten-

dres about his name. But as a Jungian and not a Freudian, he does not seem to have been aware of how deep "Dick" went. Any dream about his own death could not help but also be a dream about castration, and vice versa. For instance, he precognizes a *thick* (Dick) book about Warren HARDing, "in the shadow of B— Groves" (meaning, in the shadow of death, as Will Durant's sentence about the sibyl leading good people through "blissful groves" in the afterlife reveals). These dreams used the "bricks" of his impending reading experiences to fashion a promise of immortality "with all the good people" as a consolation prize for the death of (a) Dick. *Dick dies but goes to Heaven*, in other words.

[52] Bloom, 1993.

[53] Dick, 2011, 421.

[54] See Davis, 1998.

[55] Arnold, 2016; Davis, 1998.

14. The Arrival of Meaning and the Creation of the Past

[1] Chiang, 2002, 132.

[2] Another film that comes close to getting precognition right is *Don't Look Now*, the 1973 supernatural thriller by Nicolas Roeg (see Wargo, 2015b). Protagonist John Baxter is a "precog" who, as a materialist skeptic, doesn't believe in his own abilities. Consequently, when he has a vision of his wife in the company of some black-clad acquaintances, he thinks she has been abducted by them, not realizing that it is a precognitive vision of his own funeral. His attempt to find his wife ends up leading him to his death at the hands of a serial killer. The only thing "mistaken" about the film, I argue, is that since precognition centers on learning experiences during our lifetime, he would not have precognized the scene of his funeral but some event leading up to his death.

[3] Otto Rank (Rank, 1968) called this resolute past-centrism "ideological." Even when it appears to involve delving into some already-existing past, any hermeneutic enterprise like interpreting a dream in the consulting room or curing a neurosis by illuminating its hidden sense is at bottom a making of meaning, not simply a finding of it. By situating traumas in the personal past of childhood (Freud) or deeper in some undead racial/species past (Jung), psychoanalysis and its offshoots were ways of directing attention away from this making, making it look like a finding—because things found always seem to have much more authority and authenticity than things newly made.

[4] Note that, although I have taken inspiration from Bergson and his writings on time and duration, he would have fundamentally disagreed with the larger

argument I am making in this book, that we can "spatialize" time as a glass block, per Minkowski and Einstein. Bergson's famous debate with Einstein was over this precise question (Canales, 2015). Yet his point about "waiting for the sugar to melt" applies whether or not the future is fixed and "already present": Meaning is not contained or enfolded, complete, in present objects and situations but must be awaited. Our present understanding of any process can only ever be partial and provisional.

[5] I would argue that such a quantum psychoanalysis already exists: Zen Buddhism. Elsewhere I have written about the block universe and its unexpected spiritual satisfactions from the standpoint of Zen (Wargo, 2017).

[6] Niels Bohr made a similar observation, noting in a 1938 lecture that "I'm sure many of you will have recognized the close analogy between the situation as regards the analysis of atomic phenomena … and characteristic features of the problem of observation in human psychology … In introspection it is clearly impossible to distinguish sharply between the phenomena themselves and their conscious perception …" (Bohr, 2010, 27).

[7] Feynman, 1985.

[8] Gleick, 1993, 250.

[9] Gleick, 2018.

[10] In an explanation of rubber bands on a BBC show called *Fun to Imagine*, Feynman joked that it was lucky for our sanity that we do not have to keep track of all those bouncing-around particles: "The world is a dynamic mess of jiggling things if you look at it right. And if you magnify it, you can hardly see anything anymore, because everything is jiggling and they're all in patterns, and they're all lots of little balls. It's lucky that we have such a large-scale view of everything, that we can see them as things, without having to worry about all these little atoms all the time." The clip is available on YouTube: https://www.youtube.com/watch?time_continue=1&v=XRxAn2DRzgI

[11] Aharonov & Tollaksen, 2007.

[12] Barad, 2007.

[13] Lacan, 1988, 159.

[14] Žižek, 2014.

[15] Žižek, 2006b.

[16] See, e.g., Žižek, 1989.

[17] Kripal, 2017.

[18] Kripal, 2011.

[19] Kripal, 2007.

[20] Strieber & Kripal, 2016.

[21] Krohn & Kripal, 2018.

[22] Elizabeth Krohn, personal communication.

[23] Jeff doesn't think he knew that story about Phil Dick prior to this experience, but is not certain (Jeffrey Kripal, personal communication).

[24] Weber, 1962.

[25] Geertz, 1973, 5.

[26] Questions of symbolic motivation were at the forefront of cognitive anthropology in the 1980s and 1990s, when I was a graduate student: How do symbols and cultural meanings become powerful and salient for individual social actors, and how does individual action in turn shape culture? (See, e.g., Shore, 1996.)

[27] Although he does not discuss precognition or related phenomena, Alexander Wendt's *Quantum Mind and Social Science* does apply quantum physics to social science and even discusses "changing the past" (Wendt, 2015). Jack Hunter (Hunter, 2018) has opened up discussion of parapsychological phenomena in anthropology with the journal *Paranthropology*.

[28] There is Daryl Bem (Bem, 2011), most obviously, but Julia Mossbridge and Imants Barušs are other examples (Barušs & Mossbridge, 2017). See also Carpenter (2012) and Kelly et al. (2010).

[29] Since *Mutants and Mystics*, Kripal has spoken of a "looping" relationship between paranormal experience, pop culture, and religion/spirituality. His most startling and radical argument in *Changed in a Flash* is that individual experiencers like Elizabeth Krohn (and those who write about them) are actually "changing the afterlife." Lifesaving biomedical technologies are bringing more people back from the brink of death, thus there are more people to share in their experiences. The growing literature on near-death experiences, which would necessarily include *Changed in a Flash*, is actually shaping what people expect, and thus what they experience, at least in the immediate term, when they die (Krohn & Kripal, 2018).

[30] Guite, 2017.

[31] Kripal, 2011.

[32] Peake, 2013.

[33] The few cases I have discussed in this book are just the tip of the iceberg. Time-reversals in the world of literary influence, or "altered states of reading," is a topic I have examined on my blog (Wargo, 2015a). In a more tongue-in-cheek vein, the French literary critic Pierre Bayard (Bayard, 2009) writes about how great authors "plagiarize" from writers who come after them. For instance, he argues that Sophocles plagiarized from Freud when writing *Oedipus the King*.

[34] Beitman, 2016.

Postscript: A Ruin from the Future

[1] Wargo, 2015c.

[2] Wargo, 2015c, 2015e, 2016b

[3] Siegel, 2017.

[4] Although see Guite, 2017.

[5] Dick, 1992, 91.

[6] Pagels, 1979, 126.

[7] On one previous occasion, I had been stunned to discover a lucid dream referring specifically to an upheaval in my life exactly a year removed in time (I wrote about that dream on my blog; see Wargo, 2016b.). But this "ruined tower" dream now took the proverbial cake. I suspect based on many temporal coincidences like this in my own and others' dream lives that there may be some way in which calendrical dates "resonate" in our biographies, possibly related to hippocampal spatial calendars that give basic structure our internal chronology, as discussed in Chapter 5.

[8] Wargo, 2017.

[9] On the Sunday in question, when I was wrestling with the rough draft, I was trying to meet a self-imposed deadline for sending it to my editor at Anomalist Books.

It was just after I discovered the correspondence of my 18-year-old dream to my current concerns, excited and a little bit awe-struck at the possibility that my old dream may have pointed to that very afternoon in my life, that my wife's friend "Anne"—the software engineer quoted in the Introduction—arrived at our apartment so I could interview her about her precognitive dreams. I did not share the discovery I had just made about my own dream, but I did have the thought, as she was talking, that I might use her stories as a kind of introduction or preface to my book. The fact that she told me three stories about death, and that the first symbol on my dream chalkboard consisted of three interlinked *Omegas*, struck me only later, as did the possible significance of the stylized *A* at the end of the series.

[10] Popova, 2015.

[11] Emerson, 1951, 32-33.

[12] Eliot, 1971(1943), 59.

Adamatzky, Andrew. (2017). "Logical Gates in Actin Monomer." *Scientific Reports* 7. https://www.nature.com/articles/s41598-017-11333-7Article number: 11755.

Aharonov, Yakir; et al. (2017). "Finally Making Sense of the Double-Slit Experiment." *PNAS* 114:6480-6485.

Aharonov, Yakir; Cohen, Eliahu; Shushi, Tomer. (2015). "Accommodating Retrocausality with Free Will." *arXiv*. arXiv:1512.06689

Aharanov, Yakir; Tollaksen, Jeff. (2007). "New Insights on Time-Symmetry in Quantum Mechanics." *arXiv*. arXiv:0706.1232v1

Alvarez, Fernando. (2016). "An Experiment on Precognition with Planarian Worms." *Journal of Scientific Exploration* 30:217-226.

Andreae, Laura C.; Burrone, Juan. (2018). "The Role of Spontaneous Neurotransmission in Synapse and Circuit Development." *Journal of Neuroscience Research* 96: 354–359.

Anzieu, Didier. (1986). *Freud's Self-Analysis*. Madison, WI: International Universities Press, Inc.

Apel, D. Scott. (2014). *Philip K. Dick—The Dream Connection*. Middletown, DE: Atomic Drop Press.

Arnold, Kyle. (2016). *The Divine Madness of Philip K. Dick*. New York: Oxford University Press.

Asimov, Isaac. (1948, March). "The Endochronic Properties of Resublimated Thiotimoline." *Astounding Science Fiction*, 120-125.

Asimov, Isaac. (1953, December). "The Micropsychiatric Applications of Thiotimoline." *Astounding Science Fiction*, 107-116.

Asimov, Isaac. (1960, October). "Thiotimoline and the Space Age." *Analog Science Fiction*, 155-162.

Asmundsson, Jon. (2017, June 14). "Quantum Computing Might Be Here Sooner than You Think." *Bloomberg Markets*. https://www.bloomberg.com/news/features/2017-06-14/the-machine-of-tomorrow-today-quantum-computing-on-the-verge

Atkinson, Nancy. (2010). "13 Things that Saved Apollo 13, Part 11: A Hollywood Movie." *Universe Today*. https://www.universetoday.com/63721/13-things-that-saved-apollo-13-part-11-a-hollywood-movie/

Atmanspacher, Harald; Filk, Thomas; Romer, Hartmann. (2004). "Quantum Zeno Features of Bi-stable Perception." *Biological Cybernetics* 90:33-40.

Bair, Deirdre. (2003). *Jung*. New York: Little, Brown.

Ball, Philip. (2017, June 28). "How Quantum Trickery Can Scramble Cause and Effect." *Nature*. https://www.nature.com/news/how-quantum-trickery-can-scramble-cause-and-effect-1.22208

Barad, Karen. (2007). *Meeting the Universe Halfway*. Durham, NC: Duke University Press.

Barušs, Imants; Mossbridge, Julia. (2017). *Transcendent Mind*. Washington, DC: American Psychological Association.

Bayard, Pierre. (2009). *Le Plagiat par anticipation*. Paris: Les Éditions de Minuit.

Bazan, Ariane; Detandt, Sandrine. (2013). "On the Physiology of *Jouissance*: Interpreting the Mesolimbic Dopaminergic Reward Functions from a Psychoanalytic Perspective." *Frontiers in Human Neuroscience* 7:709.

Becker, Adam. (2018, February 14). "Quantum Time Machine: How the Future Can Change What Happens Now." *New Scientist*. https://www.sciencedirect.com/science/article/pii/S1355219811000736

Becker, Ernest. (1973). *The Denial of Death*. New York: Free Press.

Beidel, Eric. (2014, March 27). "More than a Feeling: ONR Investigates 'Spidey Sense' for Sailors and Marines (Media Release)." Arlington, VA: Office of Naval Research.

Beitman, Bernard D. (2016). *Connecting with Coincidence*. Deerfield Beach, FL: Health Communications, Inc.

Bem, Daryl. (2011). "Feeling the Future: Experimental Evidence for Anomalous Retroactive Influences on Cognition and Affect." *Journal of Personality and Social Psychology* 100:407-425.

Bem, Daryl; Tressoldi, Patrizio E., Rabeyron, Thomas; Duggan, Michael. (2016). "Feeling the Future: A Meta-Analysis of 90 Experiments on the Anomalous Anticipation of Random Future Events [version 2; referees: 2 approved]." *F1000Research*, 4:1188.

Bergson, Henri. (1944[1907]). *Creative Evolution*. New York: Random House.

Bernstein, Jerome S. (2005). *Living in the Borderland*. London: Routledge.

Bierman, Dick J.; Scholte, H. Steven. (2002). "Anomalous Anticipatory Brain Activation Preceding Exposure of Emotional and Neutral Pictures." *Toward a Science of Consciousness, Tucson IV.*

Bloom, Harold. (1993). *The American Religion*. New York: Simon & Schuster.

Bohr, Niels. (2010). *Atomic Physics and Human Knowledge*. Mineola, NY: Dover Publications, Inc.

Borch-Jacobsen, Mikkel. (1996). "Neurotica: Freud and the Seduction Theory." *October* 76:15-43.

Borch-Jacobsen, Mikkel; Shamdasani, Sonu. (2012). *The Freud Files*. Cambridge, UK: Cambridge University Press.

Boyd, Brian. (1991). *Vladimir Nabokov—The American Years*. Princeton, NJ: Princeton University Press.

Bradbury, Ray. (1952, June 28). "The Sound of Thunder." *Collier's*, 20ff.

Brainerd, Charles J.; Wang, Zheng; Reyna, Valerie F. (2013). "Superposition of Episodic Memories: Overdistribution and Quantum Models." *Topics in Cognitive Sciences* 5:773-799.

Braude, Stephen E. (1997). *The Limits of Influence*. Lanham, MD: The University Press of America.

Breuer, Josef; Freud, Sigmund. (1957[1895]). Studies on Hysteria. New York: Basic Books.

Broda, May B. (2013). "East European Jewish Migration to Switzerland and the Formation of 'New Women'," in T. Lewinsky & S. Mayoraz (eds.), *East European Jews in Switzerland*. Berlin: Walter de Gruyter.

Broderick, Damien. (2015). *Knowing the Unknowable*. Vancleave, MS: Surinam Turtle Press.

Brown, Richard. (1983). *Voyage of the Iceberg*. New York: Beaufort Books, Inc.

Buonomano, Dean. (2017). *Your Brain Is a Time Machine*. New York: W. W. Norton & Company.

Caidin, Martin. (2007). *Ghosts of the Air*. New York: Barnes & Noble Books.

Canales, Jimena. (2015). *The Physicist and the Philosopher*. Princeton, NJ: Princeton University Press.

Carington, Whately. (1940). "Experiments on the Paranormal Cognition of Drawings." *Proceedings of the Society of Psychical Research* 46:34-151.

Carington, Whately. (1946). *Telepathy*. London: Methuen. & Co.

Carpenter, James C. (2012). *First Sight*. Lanham, MD: Rowman & Littlefield Publishers Inc.

Carpenter, James C. (2015a). "First Sight: A Way of Thinking about the Mind, and a Theory of Psi." In E.C. May & S.B. Marwaha (eds.), *Extrasensory Perception Vol. 2*. Santa Barbara, CA: Praeger.

Carpenter, James C. (2015b, December). "Scientific Revolution, Orienting Constructs, and the Challenge of Parapsychology." *EdgeScience* 24:3-6.

Caruth, Cathy. (1996). *Unclaimed Experience*. Baltimore, MD: Johns Hopkins University Press.

Castro-Ruiz, Esteban; Giacomini, Flaminia; Brukner, Časlav. (2018). "Dynamics of Quantum Causal Structures." *arXiv*. arXiv:1710.03139v2

Chalmers, David J. (1995). "Facing Up to the Problem of Consciousness." *Journal of Consciousness Studies* 2: 200-219.

Chandler, David L. (October 14, 2015). "Quantum Physics Meets Genetic Engineering: Researchers Use Engineered Viruses to Provide Quantum-Based Enhancement of Energy Transport." *MIT News*. http://news.mit.edu/2015/quantum-physics-engineered%20viruses-1014

Channel 5. (2003). "The Man Who Painted the Future." *Extraordinary People* (Season 1: Episode 1).

Charman, Robert A. (2017). "Re-evaluation of Samuel Clemens' Dream Precognition Case—Did He Foresee the Future Funeral Casket of His Younger Brother Henry?" *Journal of the Society for Psychical Research* 81:17-25.

Chater, Nick. (2018). *The Mind Is Flat*. London: Penguin.

Chiang, Ted. (2002). *Stories of Your Life and Others*. New York: Vintage.

Chiribella, Giulio; D'Ariano, Giacomo Mauro; Perinotti, Paulo; Valiron, Benoit. (2009). "Beyond Causally Ordered Quantum Computers." *arXiv*. arXiv:0912.0195v3

Clark, Andy. (2016). *Surfing Uncertainty*. New York: Oxford University Press.

Cochran, Jacqueline. (1954). *The Stars at Noon*. Boston: Little, Brown & Company.

Costa de Beauregard, Olivier. (1975). "Quantum Paradoxes and Aristotle's Twofold Information Concept." In L. Oteri (ed.), *Quantum Physics and Parapsychology*. New York: Parapsychology Foundation, Inc.

Cotter, Holland. (2001, December 3). "ART REVIEW; The Studios Were Lost, But the Artists Get Their Day." *The New York Times*. http://www.nytimes.com/2001/12/03/arts/art-review-the-studios-were-lost-but-the-artists-get-their-day.html?mcubz=0

Craddock, Travis J.A.; Friesen, Douglas; Mane, Jonathan; Hameroff, Stuart; Tuszynski, Jack A. (2014). "The Feasibility of Coherent Energy Transfer in Microtubules." *Journal of the Royal Society Interface* 11:20140677.

Craddock, Travis J.A.; Tuszynski, Jack A.; Hameroff Stuart. (2012). "Cytoskeletal Signaling: Is Memory Encoded in Microtubule Lattices by CaMKII Phosphorylation?" *PLoS Computational Biology* 8(3):e1002421.

Cramer, John G. (2006). "Reverse Causation and the Transactional Interpretation of Quantum Mechanics." In D.P. Sheehan (ed.), *Frontiers of Time*. Melville, NY: AIP Conference Proceedings.

Crick, Francis; Mitchison, Graeme. (1983, July 14). "The Function of Dream Sleep." *Nature* 304:111-114.

Daly, Glyn. (2014). "Enjoyment/*Jouissance*." In R. Butler (ed.), *The Žižek Dictionary*. Durham, UK: Acumen.

Dannatt, Adrian. (2001, September 23). "Michael Richards Obituary." *Independent*. http://www.independent.co.uk/news/obituaries/michael-richards-9260645.html

Davies, Paul C.W. (2004). "Quantum Fluctuations and Life." *arXiv*. arXiv:quant-ph/0403017v1

Davies, Paul C.W. (2013). "Directionality Principles from Cancer to Cosmology." In C.H. Lineweaver, P.C.W. Davies, & M. Ruse (eds.), *Complexity and the Arrow of Time*. Cambridge, UK: Cambridge University Press.

Davis, Erik. (1998). *Techgnosis*. New York: Three Rivers Press.

Deary, Ian; et al. (2012). "Genetic Contributions to Stability and Change in Intelligence from Childhood to Old Age." *Nature* 482:212-215.

De Moura, Vicente. (2014). "Learning from the Patient: The East, Synchronicity and Transference in the History of an Unknown Case of C. G. Jung." *Journal of Analytical Psychology* 59:391-409.

Dent, Erik W. (2017). "Of Microtubules and Memory: Implications for Microtubule Dynamics in Dendrites and Spines." *Molecular Biology of the Cell* 28:1-8.

Derrida, Jacques. (1988). "Telepathy." *Oxford Literary Review* 10:3-41.

Dick, Anne R. (2010). *The Search for Philip K. Dick*. San Francisco: Tachyon Publications.

Dick, Philip K. (1969, November). "A. Lincoln Simulacrum, Part 1." *Amazing Science Fiction* 43(4):6ff.

Dick, Philip K. (1991). *The Selected Letters of Philip K. Dick—1994*. Novato, CA: Underwood-Miller.

Dick, Philip K. (1992). *The Selected Letters of Philip K. Dick—1975-1976*. Novato, CA: Underwood-Miller.

Dick, Philip K. (2011). *The Exegesis of Philip K. Dick*. New York: Houghton Mifflin Harcourt.

Dick, Philip K. (2012). *Ubik*. New York: Houghton Mifflin Harcourt.

Dick, Tessa B. (2010). *Philip K. Dick—Remembering Firebright*. Middletown, DE: Author.

Di Corpo, Ulisse; Vannini, Antonella. (2015). *Syntropy*. Princeton, NJ: ICRL Press.

Dixon, P. Ben; Starling, David J.; Jordan, Andrew N.; Howell, John C. (2009). "Ultrasensitive Beam Deflection Measurement via Interferometric Weak Value Amplification." *Physical Review Letters* 102:173601-1-4.

Dobyns, York H. (2006). "Retrocausal Information Flow: What Are the Consequences of Knowing the Future?" In D. Sheehan (ed.), *Frontiers of Time*. Melville, NY: AIP Conference Proceedings.

Dossey, Larry. (2009). *The Power of Premonitions*. New York: Dutton.

Dossey, Larry. (2013). *One Mind*. Carlsbad, CA: Hay House.

Douglas, Claire. (1993). *Translate this Darkness*. New York: Simon & Schuster.

Douglas, Mary. (1966). *Purity and Danger*. London: Routledge.

Dunne, Brenda J.; Jahn, Robert G. (2003). "Information and Uncertainty in Remote Perception Research." *Journal of Scientific Exploration* 17:207–241.

Dunne, Brenda J.; Jahn, Robert G. (eds.). (2017). *Being & Biology*. Princeton, NJ: ICRL Press.

Dunne, J. W. (1952[1927]). *An Experiment with Time*. London: Faber and Faber.

Dunne, J. W. (1955). *Intrusions?* London: Faber and Faber.

Echeverria, Fernando; Klinkhammer, Gunnar; Thorne, Kip S. (1991). "Billiard Balls in Wormhole Spacetimes with Closed Timelike Curves: Classical Theory." *Physical Review D* 44:1077-1099.

Ehrenwald, Jan. (1954). *New Dimensions of Deep Analysis.* London: George Allen & Unwin.

Eisenbud, Jule. (1970). *PSI and Psychoanalysis.* New York: Grune & Stratton.

Eisenbud, Jule. (1982). *Paranormal Foreknowledge.* New York: Human Sciences Press.

Eliot. T. S. (1971[1943]). *Four Quartets.* Boston, MA: Houghton Mifflin Harcourt.

Emerson, Ralph Waldo. (1951). *Emerson's Essays.* New York: Harper Perennial.

Engber, Daniel. (2017). "Daryl Bem Proved ESP Is Real—Which Means Science Is Broken." *Slate.* https://slate.com/health-and-science/2017/06/daryl-bem-proved-esp-is-real-showed-science-is-broken.html

Falk, Ruma. (1989). "Judgement of Coincidence: Mine versus yours." *American Journal of Psychology* 102:477–493.

Feather, Sally Rhine; Schmicker, Michael. (2005). *The Gift.* New York: St. Martin's Press.

Feinberg, Gerald. (1975). "Precognition—A Memory of Things Future." In L. Oteri (ed.), *Quantum Physics and Parapsychology.* New York: Parapsychology Foundation, Inc.

Feynman, Richard P. (1985). *QED.* Princeton, NJ: Princeton University Press.

Fichtner, Gerhard. (2010). "Freud and the Hammerschlag Family: A Formative Relationship." *The International Journal of Psychoanalysis* 91:1137-1156.

Fisher, Matthew P.A. (2015). "Quantum Cognition: The Possibility of Processing With Nuclear Spins in the Brain." *arXiv.* arXiv:1508.05929 [q-bio.NC] https://arxiv.org/abs/1508.05929

Fitzgerald, F. Scott. (1936). "The Crack-Up." *Esquire.* http://www.esquire.com/lifestyle/a4310/the-crack-up/

Flieger, Verlyn. (1997). *A Question of Time.* Kent, OH: The Kent State University Press.

Florensky, Pavel. (1996[1922]). *Iconostasis.* Crestwood, NY: St. Vladimir's Seminary Press.

Flournoy, Theodore. (2007[1900]). *From India to the Planet Mars.* New York: Cosimo Classics.

Foer, Joshua. (2011). *Moonwalking with Einstein.* London: Penguin.

Forrester, John. (1990). *The Seductions of Psychoanalysis.* Cambridge, UK: Cambridge University Press.

Francis, Henry W. (1915). "The Psychic Mystery of His Time." In *Morgan Robertson the Man.* New York: Metropolitan Magazine.

Freud, Sigmund. (1961[1930]). *Civilization and Its Discontents.* New York: W. W. Norton & Company.

Freud, Sigmund. (1965[1899]). *The Interpretation of Dreams.* New York: Avon Books.

Freud, Sigmund. (1965[1901]). *The Psychopathology of Everyday Life.* New York: W. W. Norton & Company.

Freud, Sigmund. (1965[1932]). *New Introductory Lectures in Psycho-Analysis.* New York: W. W. Norton & Company.

Freud, Sigmund. (1974[1899]). "A Premonitory Dream Fulfilled." In Devereux, G., ed., *Psychoanalysis and the Occult.* London: Souvenir Press.

Freud, Sigmund. (1984[1920]). "Beyond the Pleasure Principle." In Strachey, J., ed., *On Metapsychology.* London: Penguin.

Freud, Sigmund. (2015[1918]). "Reflections on War and Death." *Bartleby.com.* http://www.bartleby.com/282/2.html

Friedman, John; et al. (1990). "Cauchy Problem in Spacetimes with Closed Timelike Curves." *Physical Review D* 42:1915.

Gardner, Martin, ed. (1998). *The Wreck of the Titanic Foretold?* Amherst, NY: Prometheus Books.

Geertz, Clifford. (1973). *The Interpretation of Cultures.* New York: Basic Books.

Geiger, John. (2009). *The Third Man Factor.* New York: Weinstein Books.

Gleick, James. (1987). *Chaos.* New York: Penguin Books.

Gleick, James. (1993). *Genius.* New York: Vintage.

Gleick, James. (2012). *The Information.* New York: Vintage.

Gleick, James. (2016). *Time Travel.* New York: Pantheon.

Gleick, James. (2018, May 8). "What Does Quantum Physics Actually Tell Us About the World?" *New York Times*. https://www.nytimes.com/2018/05/08/books/review/adam-becker-what-is-real.html

Goddard, Victor. (1951, May 26). "The Night My Number Came Up." *The Saturday Evening Post*, 24ff.

Goddard, Victor. (1975). *Flight Towards Reality*. London: Turnstone Books.

Goddard, Victor. (1982). *Skies to Dunkirk*. London: William Kimber.

Graff, Dale E. (1998). *Tracks in the Psychic Wilderness*. Boston, MA: Element.

Graff, Dale E. (2000). *River Dreams*. Boston, MA: Element.

Graff, Dale E. (2007). "Explorations in Precognitive Dreaming." *Journal of Scientific Exploration* 21:707-722.

Grosso, Michael. (2015). "The 'Transmission' Model of Mind and Body." In E.F. Kelly, A. Crabtree, & P. Marshall (eds.), *Beyond Physicalism*. Lanham, MD: Rowman & Littlefield.

Guinness, Alec. (1985). *Blessings in Disguise*. New York: Alfred A. Knopf.

Guite, Malcolm. (2017). *Mariner*. London: Hodder & Stoughton.

Gurney, Edmund; Myers, Frederic W. H.; Podmore, Frank. (2007[1886]). *Phantasms of the Living, Vol. 1*. Boston, MA: Elibron Classics.

Halperin, David. (2014). "Prophetic Dreams—Mark Twain, Sigmund Freud, and 'Blackhawk' Comics (Part 3)." *DavidHalperin.net*. http://www.davidhalperin.net/prophetic-dreams-mark-twain-sigmund-freud-and-blackhawk-comics-part-3/

Hameroff, Stuart. (1998). "Quantum Computation in Brain Microtubules? The Penrose-Hameroff 'Orch OR' Model of Consciousness." *Philosophical Transactions of the Royal Society of London A* 356:1869-1896.

Hameroff, Stuart; Penrose, Roger. (2014). "Consciousness in the Universe: A Review of the 'Orch OR' Theory." *Physics of Life Reviews* 11:39-78

Hand, David J. (2014). *The Improbability Principle*. New York: Scientific American/Farrar, Straus and Giroux.

Hansen, George P. (2001). *The Trickster and the Paranormal.* Bloomington, IN: XLibris.

Herbert, Nick. (1985). *Quantum Reality.* Garden City, NY: Anchor Books.

Heuer, Gottfried M. (2017). *Freud's Outstanding Colleague/Jung's 'Twin Brother.'* London: Routledge.

Hilborn, Robert C. (2004). "Sea Gulls, Butterflies, and Grasshoppers: A Brief History of the Butterfly Effect in Nonlinear Dynamics." *American Journal of Physics* 72:425-427.

Hinton, Charles H. (1888). *A New Era of Thought.* London: Swan Sonnenschein & Co. Ltd.

Hobson, Allan. (2013). "The Ancient Art of Memory." *Behavioral and Brain Sciences* 36:621.

Hobson, J. Allan. (2002). *Dreaming.* Oxford, UK: Oxford University Press.

Hobson, J. Allan; McCarley, Robert W. (1977). "The Brain as a Dream State Generator: An Activation-Synthesis Hypothesis of the Dream Process." *The American Journal of Psychiatry* 134:1335–1348.

Honorton, Charles; Ferrari, Diane C. (1989). "Future Telling": A Meta-Analysis of Forced-Choice Precognition Experiments, 1935–1987. *Journal of Parapsychology* 53:281-308.

Hunter, Jack. (2018). *Engaging the Anomalous.* Hove, UK: August Night Books.

Inchbald, Guy. (2017). "J. W. Dunne: The Forgotten Genius." *Guy Inchbald: Blocki.* http://www.steelpillow.com/blocki/dunne/Dunne.html

Jansen, Diana Baynes. (2003). *Jung's Apprentice.* Einsiedeln, Switzerland: Daimon Verlag.

Jantsch, Erich. (1980). *The Self-Organizing Universe.* New York: Pergamon Press.

Jones, Ernest. (1955). *The Life and Work of Sigmund Freud Vol. II.* New York: Basic Books.

Jones, Ernest. (1957). *The Life and Work of Sigmund Freud Vol. III.* New York: Basic Books.

Josephson-Storm, Jason Ā. (2017). *The Myth of Disenchantment.* Chicago, IL: The University of Chicago Press.

Judd, Charles M.; Gawronski, Bertram. (2011). "Editorial comment." *Journal of Personality and Social Psychology, 100:*406.

Jung, C. G. (1965a). *Letters Vol. 1.* London: Routledge & Kegan Paul.

Jung, C. G. (1965b). *Memories, Dreams, Reflections.* New York: Random House.

Jung, C. G. (1973[1951]). "On Synchronicity." In *Synchronicity.* Princeton, NJ: Princeton University Press.

Jung, C. G. (1973[1952]). "Synchronicity: An Acausal Connecting Principle." In *Synchronicity.* Princeton, NJ: Princeton University Press.

Jung, C. G. (1985[1937]). "The Realities of Practical Psychotherapy." In *The Practice of Psychotherapy.* Princeton, NJ: Princeton University Press.

Jung, C. G. (1996). *The Psychology of Kundalini Yoga.* Princeton, NJ: Princeton University Press.

Jung, C. G. (2012). *The Red Book.* New York: W. W. Norton & Company.

Jung, C. G. (2015). *Letters Vol. 2.* London: Routledge & Kegan Paul.

Kaiser, David. (2011). *How the Hippies Saved Physics.* New York: W. W. Norton & Company.

Kaku, Michio. (2009). *The Physics of the Impossible.* Garden City, New York: Anchor Books.

Kant, Immanuel. (2008). *Critique of Judgement.* Oxford, UK: Oxford University Press.

Kastrup, Bernardo. (2015). *Brief Peaks Beyond.* Philadelphia, PA: John Hunt Publishing.

Kelly, Edward F.; Kelly, Emily Williams; Crabtree, Adam; Gauld, Alan; Grosso, Michael; Greyson, Bruce. (2010). *Irreducible Mind.* Lanham, MD: Roman & Littlefield Publishers.

Koestler, Arthur. (1972). *The Roots of Coincidence.* New York: Vintage.

Krenz, Claudia. (N.D.) "Philip K. Dick, Dear Claudia Letter, May 9 1974 (marginal note)." http://www.claudiax.net/TEMPAUC/pkd-dcL050974.html

Krenz, Claudia. (N.D.) "Philip K. Dick Words Project." http://www.claudiax.net/PKDwords_index.html

Krenz, Claudia. (2000). "I was looking for UBIK at AltaVista ..." http://www.claudiax.net/phil_retro.html

Kripal, Jeffrey J. (2007). *Esalen.* Chicago, IL: The University of Chicago Press.

Kripal, Jeffrey J. (2010). *Authors of the Impossible.* Chicago, IL: The University of Chicago Press.

Kripal, Jeffrey J. (2011). *Mutants and Mystics.* Chicago, IL: The University of Chicago Press.

Kripal, Jeffrey J. (2014). *Comparing Religions.* Chichester, UK: Wiley.

Kripal, Jeffrey J. (2017). *Secret Body.* Chicago, IL: The University of Chicago Press.

Krippner, Stanley; Ullman, Montague; Honorton, Charles. (2002[1971]). "A Precognitive Dream Study with a Single Subject." In M. Ullman, S. Krippner, & A. Vaughan (eds.), *Dream Telepathy.* Charlottesville, VA: Hampton Roads.

Krohn, Elizabeth Greenfield; Kripal, Jeffrey J. (2018). *Changed in a Flash.* Berkeley, CA: North Atlantic Press.

Lacan, Jacques. (1988). *The Seminar of Jacques Lacan, Book I.* New York: W. W. Norton & Company.

Lacan, Jacques. (1998). *The Seminar of Jacques Lacan, Book XX.* New York: W. W. Norton & Company.

Laplanche, Jean. (1993). *Life & Death in Psychoanalysis.* Baltimore, MD: The Johns Hopkins University Press.

Launer, John. (2014). *Sex Versus Survival.* London: Duckworth.

L'Engle, Madeleine. (2007[1962]). *A Wrinkle in Time.* New York: Farrar, Straus and Giroux.

Levi-Strauss, Claude. (1966). *The Savage Mind.* Chicago, IL: The University of Chicago Press.

Libet, Benjamin. (2004). *Mind Time.* Cambridge, MA: Harvard University Press.

Llewellyn, Sue. (2013). "Such Stuff as Dreams Are Made On? Elaborative Encoding, the Ancient Art of Memory, and the Hippocampus." *Behavioral and Brain Sciences* 36:589-607.

Lloyd, Seth. (2006). *Programming the Universe*. New York: Vintage Books.

Lloyd, Seth; Maccone, Lorenzo; Garcia-Patron, Raul; Giovannetti, Vittorio; Shikano, Yutaka. (2010). "The Quantum Mechanics of Time Travel through Post-Selected Teleportation." *arXiv*. arXiv:1007.2615v2

Lloyd, Seth; et al. (2011). "Closed Timelike Curves via Postselection: Theory and Experimental Test of Consistency." *Physical Review Letters* 106:040403.

Loftus, Elizabeth. (2010). "Why Parapsychology Is Not Yet Ready for Prime Time." In S. Krippner & H.L. Friedman (eds.), *Debating Psychic Experience*. Santa Barbara, CA: Praeger.

Loftus, Elizabeth; Feldman, Julie; Dashiell, Richard. (1995). "The Reality of Illusory Memories." In D.L. Schacter (ed.), *Memory Distortion*. Cambridge, MA: Harvard University Press.

Luckhurst, Roger. (2002). *The Invention of Telepathy*. Oxford, UK: Oxford University Press.

Luckhurst, Roger. (2008). *The Trauma Question*. London: Routledge.

MacKenzie, Andrew. (1997). *Adventures in Time*. London: The Athlone Press, Ltd.

Main, Roderick. (2007). "Ruptured Time and the Reenchantment of Modernity." In A. Casement (ed.), *Who Owns Jung?* London: Karnac Books.

Marcus, Steven. (1988). "Norman Mailer: An Interview." In J. Michael Lennon (ed.), *Conversations with Norman Mailer*. Jackson, MS: University Press of Mississippi.

Margolis, Jonathan. (1999). *Uri Geller—Magician or Mystic?* New York: Welcome Rain Publishers.

Margolis, Jonathan. (2013). *The Secret Life of Uri Geller*. London: Watkins Publishing.

Margulis. Lynn. (1999). *Symbiotic Planet*. New York: Basic Books

Margulis, Lynn. (2001). "The Conscious Cell." *Annals of the New York Academy of Sciences* 929:55-70.

Margulis, Lynn; Sagan, Dorion. (1986). *Microcosmos*. New York: Touchstone.

Marwaha, Sonali Bhatt; May, Edwin C. (2015). "The Multiphasic Model of Precognition." In E.C. May & S.B. Marwaha (eds.), *Extrasensory Perception Vol. 2*. Santa Barbara, CA: Praeger.

Marwaha, Sonali Bhatt; May, Edwin C. (2016). "Precognition: The Only Form of Psi?" *Journal of Consciousness Studies* 23(3-4):76-100.

Mavromatis, Andreas. (1987). *Hypnagogia*. London: Thyrsos Press.

May, Edwin C. (2015). "Experimenter Psi: A View of Decision Augmentation Theory." In E.C. May & S.B. Marwaha (eds.), *Extrasensory Perception Vol. 2*. Santa Barbara, CA: Praeger.

May, Edwin C.; Depp, Joseph G. (2015). "Entropy and Precognition: The Physics Domain of the Multiphasic Model of Precognition." In E.C. May & S.B. Marwaha (eds.), *Extrasensory Perception Vol. 2*. Santa Barbara, CA: Praeger.

May, Edwin C.; Lantz, Nevin D.; Piantineda, Tom. (1996). "Feedback Considerations in Anomalous Cognition Experiments." *The Journal of Parapsychology* 60:211-226.

May, Edwin C.; Marwaha, Sonali Bhatt. (2015). "The Fundamentals of Psi." In E.C. May & S.B. Marwaha (eds.), *Extrasensory Perception Vol. 1*. Santa Barbara, CA: Praeger.

May, Edwin C.; Rubel, Victor; Auerbach, Loyd. (2014). *ESP Wars East & West*. Palo Alto, CA: Laboratories for Fundamental Research.

McEneaney, Bonnie. (2010). *Messages*. New York: Harper.

McFadden, Johnjoe; Al-Khalili, Jim. (2014). *Life on the Edge*. New York: Crown Publishers.

McLynn, Frank. (1996). *Carl Gustav Jung*. New York: St. Martin's Press.

McMoneagle, Joseph. (1993). *Mind Trek*. Charlottesville, VA: Hampton Roads.

McMoneagle, Joseph. (2002). *The Stargate Chronicles*. Charlottesville, VA: Hampton Roads.

McNamara, Patrick. (2013). "Dreams and Memory." *Psychology Today*. https://www.psychologytoday.com/us/blog/dream-catcher/201312/dreams-and-memory

McRae, Mike. (2017). "This Quantum Theory Predicts that the Future Might Be Influencing the Past." *Science Alert*. https://www.sciencealert.com/this-quantum-theory-predicts-the-future-might-influence-the-past

Merali, Zeeya. (2010, August 26). "Back from the Future." *Discover*. http://discovermagazine.com/2010/apr/01-back-from-the-future

Moldoveanu, Florin (2010, August 1). "Time Travel by Teleportation." *FQXi Community Blogs*. https://fqxi.org/community/forum/topic/650

Moore, Alan. (2016). *Jerusalem*. London: Knockabout.

Moskvitch, Katia. (2018). "The Argument against Quantum Computers." *Quanta*. https://www.quantamagazine.org/gil-kalais-argument-against-quantum-computers-20180207/

Moss, Robert. (2009). *The Secret History of Dreaming*. Novato, CA: New World Library.

Mossbridge, Julia A.; Radin, Dean. (2018). "Precognition as a Form of Prospection: A Review of the Evidence." *Psychology of Consciousness: Theory, Research, and Practice* 5(1):78-93.

Mossbridge, Julia A; Tressoldi, Patrizio; Utts, Jessica; Ives, John A.; Radin, Dean; Jonas, Wayne B. (2014). "Predicting the Unpredictable: Critical Analysis and Practical Implications of Predictive Anticipatory Activity." *Frontiers in Human Neuroscience* 8(146):1-10.

Mossbridge, Julia; Tressoldi, Patrizio; Utts, Jessica. (2012). "Predictive Physiological Anticipation Preceding Seemingly Unpredictable Stimuli: A Meta-Analysis." *Frontiers in Psychology* 3(390):1-18.

Murphy, Michael. (1992). *The Future of the Body*. New York: Tarcher/Putnam.

Murphy, Mildred. (1957, August 8). "RUSSIAN COLONEL IS INDICTED HERE AS TOP SPY IN U.S." *New York Times*, 1.

Musser, George. (2014, January 30). "The Quantum Mechanics of Fate." *Nautilus*. http://nautil.us/issue/9/time/the-quantum-mechanics-of-fate

Nabokov, Vladimir. (2018). *Insomniac Dreams*. Princeton, NJ: Princeton University Press.

Nasht, Simon. (2005). *The Last Explorer*. New York: Arcade Publishing.

Noll, Richard. (1994). *The Jung Cult*. Princeton, NJ: Princeton University Press.

Noll, Richard. (1997). *The Aryan Christ*. New York: Random House.

NPR. (2013). "Decoding 'the Most Complex Object in the Universe'." https://www.npr.org/2013/06/14/191614360/decoding-the-most-complex-object-in-the-universe

Open Science Collaboration. (2015.) "Estimating the Reproducibility of Psychological Science." *Science* 349. aac4716 http://science.sciencemag.org/content/349/6251/aac4716.full?ijkey=1xgFoCnpLswpk&keytype=ref&siteid=sci

Oreshkov, Ognyan; Costa, Fabio; Brukner, Časlav. (2012, October 2). "Quantum Correlations with No Causal Order." *Nature Communications*. https://www.nature.com/articles/ncomms2076

Ouellette, Jennifer. (2016). "A New Spin on the Quantum Brain." *Quanta*. https://www.quantamagazine.org/a-new-spin-on-the-quantum-brain-20161102/

Owens, Lance S. (2015). *Jung in Love*. Los Angeles: Gnosis Archive Books.

Pagels, Elaine. (1979). *The Gnostic Gospels*. New York: Vintage.

Palus, Shannon. (2017, May 3). "Time Crystals: A New State of Matter that Outlasts the Universe." *New Scientist*. https://www.newscientist.com/article/mg23431240-200-time-crystals-the-loopy-gizmos-that-repeat-their-tricks-forever/

Paquette, Andrew. (2011). *Dreamer*. Winchester, UK: O Books.

Paquette, Andrew. (2016). "The Rarity of Unambiguous Symbols in Dreams: A Case Study." *Journal of Scientific Exploration* 30:199-216.

Pauwels, Louis; Bergier, Jacques. (1963). *The Morning of the Magicians*. New York: Avon Books.

Pawlicki, T.B. (1981). *How To Build a Flying Saucer*. New York: Prentice Hall Press.

Peake, Anthony. (2012). *The Labyrinth of Time*. London: Arcturus.

Peake, Anthony. (2013). *A Life of Philip K. Dick*. London: Arcturus.

Pearlman, Ellen. (2016, September 7). "The Prescient Work of an Artist Killed on 9/11." *Hyperallergic.* https://hyperallergic.com/309441/the-prescient-work-of-an-artist-killed-on-911/

Penrose, Roger. (1994). *Shadows of the Mind.* New York: Oxford University Press.

Philosophy Bites. (2012). "Huw Price on Backward Causation" (podcast interview). http://philosophybites.com/2012/07/huw-price-on-backward-causation.html

Popescu, Sandu. (2009). "Viewpoint: Weak Measurements Just Got Stronger." *Physics* 2:32.

Popova, Maria. (2015). "Richard Feynman on Science vs. Religion and Why Uncertainty Is Central to Morality." *Brain Pickings.* https://www.brainpickings.org/2015/05/11/richard-feynman-science-religion/

Price, Huw. (1996). *Time's Arrow and Archimedes' Point.* Oxford, UK: Oxford University Press.

Price, Huw. (2012). "Does Time-Symmetry Imply Retrocausality? How the Quantum World Says 'Maybe'?" *Studies in History and Philosophy of Science Part B: Studies in History and Philosophy of Modern Physics* 43(2):75-83.

Price, Huw; Wharton, Ken. (2015). "A Live Alternative to Quantum Spooks." arXiv:1510.06712v2

Price, Huw; Wharton, Ken. (2016, September 14). "Taming the Quantum Spooks." *Aeon.* https://aeon.co/essays/can-retrocausality-solve-the-puzzle-of-action-at-a-distance

Price, Katy. (2014). "Testimonies of Precognition and Encounters with Psychiatry in Letters to J. B. Priestley." *Studies in History and Philosophy of Science Part C: Studies in History and Philosophy of Biological and Biomedical Sciences* 48(Part A):103-111.

Priestley, J. B. (1989[1964]). *Man & Time.* London: Bloomsbury Books.

Procopio, Lorenzo M.; et al. (2015). "Experimental Superposition of Orders of Quantum Gates." *Nature Communications*, 6:7913.

Pynchon, Thomas. (1973). *Gravity's Rainbow.* New York: Penguin.

Radin, Dean I. (1997). "Unconscious Perception of Future Emotions: An Experiment in Presentiment." *Journal of Scientific Exploration* 11:163-180.

Radin, Dean. (2006). *Entangled Minds*. New York: Paraview Pocket Books.

Radin, Dean. (2009) *The Conscious Universe*. New York: HarperCollins.

Radin, Dean. (2013). *Supernormal*. New York: Crown Publishing.

Radin, Dean. (2018). *Real Magic*. New York: Harmony Books.

Ramachandran, Vilayanur S. (2011). *The Tell-Tale Brain*. New York: W. W. Norton & Company.

Ramachandran, Vilayanur S.; Vajanaphanich, Melissa; Chunharas, Chaipat. (2016). "Calendars in the Brain: Their Perceptual Characteristics and Possible Neural Substrate." *Neurocase* 22:461-465.

Ramón y Cajal, Santiago. (1989). *Recollections of My Life*. Cambridge, MA: MIT Press.

Randi, James. (1982). *Flim-Flam*. Amherst, NY: Prometheus Books.

Rank, Otto. (1968). *Will Therapy and Truth and Reality*. New York: Alfred A. Knopf.

Recalled Comics. (2017). "The Adventures of Superman #596 Twin Towers—DC Comics, November 2001." http://www.recalledcomics.com/TheAdventuresOfSuperman596TwinTowers.php

Resnik, Salomon. (1987). *The Theatre of the Dream*. London: Tavistock Publications.

Rhine, Louisa, E. (1961). *Hidden Channels of the Mind*. New York: William Morrow & Company.

Rhine, Louisa E. (1967). *ESP in Life and Lab*. London: Collier Books.

Ricoeur, Paul. (1970). *Freud and Philosophy*. New Haven, CT: Yale University Press.

Robertson, Morgan. (N.D.). "The Sleep Walker." In *Over the Border*. New York: Metropolitan Magazine.

Robertson, Morgan. (1905). "The Subconscious Finnegan." In *Down to the Sea*. New York: Harper & Brothers.

Robertson, Morgan. (1915a). "Gathering No Moss—An Autobiography." In *Morgan Robertson the Man*. New York: Metropolitan Magazine.

Robertson, Morgan. (1915b). "My Skirmish with Madness." In *Morgan Robertson the Man*. New York: Metropolitan Magazine.

Robertson, Morgan. (1974[1898]). "The Wreck of the Titan, or, Futility." In W. H. Tantum (ed.), *The Doomed Unsinkable Ship*. Riverside, CT: 7 C's Press.

Rock, Andrea. (2004). *The Mind at Night*. New York: Basic Books.

Rodgers, Paul. (2014). "Where Did the Titanic's Iceberg Come From?" *Forbes.com*. https://www.forbes.com/sites/paulrodgers/2014/04/10/revealed-the-origin-of-the-titanics-iceberg/#71f53176b5b0

Rosenblum, Bruce; Kuttner, Fred. (2011). *Quantum Enigma*, 2nd Ed. Oxford, UK: Oxford University Press.

Rubino, Giulia; et al. (2017, March 24). "Experimental Verification of an Indefinite Causal Order." *Science Advances* e1602589.

Rudnytsky, Peter J. (1987). *Freud and Oedipus*. New York: Columbia University Press.

Sarill, William. (2014, December). "Will the Real Ubik Please Stand Up? Precognition of Scientific Information in the Fiction of Philip K. Dick." *EdgeScience* 20:5-15.

Sartre, Jean-Paul. (2002). *Jean-Paul Sartre—Basic Writings*. London: Routledge.

Schnabel, Jim. (1997). *Remote Viewers*. New York: Dell.

Scully, Marlan O.; Englert, Berthold-Georg; Walther, Herbert. (1991, May 9). Quantum-Optical Tests of Complementarity. *Nature* 351:111-116.

Sheehan, Daniel P. (2015). "Remembrance of Things Future: A Case for Retrocausation and Precognition." In E.C. May & S.B. Marwaha (eds.), *Extrasensory Perception: Support, Skepticism, and Science Vol. II*. Santa Barbara, CA: Praeger.

Sheldrake, Rupert. (2003). *The Sense of Being Stared At*. New York: Crown Publishers.

Sheldrake, Rupert. (2009). *Morphic Resonance*. Rochester, VT: Park Street Press.

Sheldrake, Rupert. (2011*). Dogs That Know When Their Owners Are Coming Home and Other Unexplained Powers of Animals*. New York: Three Rivers Press.

Sheldrake, Rupert. (2012). *Science Set Free*. New York: Crown Publishing.

Shermer, Michael. (1997). *Why People Believe Weird Things*. New York: Henry Holt & Co.

Shields, Charles J. (2011). *And So It Goes*. New York: Henry Holt.

Shore, Bradd. (1996). *Culture in Mind*. Chicago: Oxford, UK: Oxford University Press.

Shoup, Richard. (2015). "Physics Beyond Causality: Making Sense of Quantum Mechanics and Certain Experimental Anomalies." In E.C. May & S.B. Marwaha (eds.), *Extrasensory Perception: Support, Skepticism, and Science Vol. II*. Santa Barbara, CA: Praeger.

Siegel, Bruce. (2017). *Dreaming the Future*. Los Angeles, CA: MetaStory Books.

Silberer, Herbert. (1959[1909]). "Report on a Method of Eliciting and Observing Certain Symbolic Hallucination-Phenomena." In D. Rapaport (ed,), *Organization and Pathology of Thought*. New York: Columbia University Press.

Sinclair, Upton. (2001[1930]). *Mental Radio*. Charlottesville, VA: Hampton Roads.

Smith, Paul. (2005). *Reading the Enemy's Mind*. New York: Forge.

Spielrein, Sabina. (1994[1911]). "Destruction as the Cause of Coming into Being." *Journal of Analytical Psychology* 39:155-186.

Spottiswoode, S. James P.; May, Edwin C. (2003). "Skin Conductance Prestimulus Response: Analysis, Artifacts and a Pilot Study." *Journal of Scientific Exploration* 17:617-641.

Stapp, Henry P. (2011.) *The Mindful Universe*, 2nd Ed. Berlin: Springer.

Stapp, Henry P. (2015). "A Quantum-Mechanical Theory of the Mind/Brain Connection." In E.F. Kelly, A. Crabtree, & P. Marshall (eds.), *Beyond Physicalism*. Lanham, MD: Rowman & Littlefield.

Stevenson, Ian. (1974[1960]). "A Review and Analysis of Paranormal Experiences Connected with the Sinking of the Titanic." In W. H. Tantum, (ed.), *The Doomed Unsinkable Ship*. Riverside, Connecticut: 7 C's Press.

Stevenson, Ian. (1974[1965]). "Seven More Paranormal Experiences Associated with the Sinking of the Titanic." In W. H. Tantum (ed.), *The Doomed Unsinkable Ship*. Riverside, Connecticut: 7 C's Press.

Strassman, Rick. (2014). *DMT and the Soul of Prophecy*. Rochester, VT: Park Street Press.

Strieber, Whitley; Kripal, Jeffrey J. (2016). *The Super Natural*. New York: Tarcher/Penguin.

Sutin, Lawrence. (2005). *Divine Invasions*. New York: Carroll & Graf Publishers.

Takeuchi, Tomonori; Duszkiewicz, Adrian J.; Morris, Richard G.M. (2014). "The Synaptic Plasticity and Memory Hypothesis: Encoding, Storage and Persistence." *Philosophical Transactions of the Royal Society B: Biological Sciences* 369.1633:20130288.

Tamblyn, Thomas. (2017, July 12). "Scientists Teleport A Photon from Earth to Orbit for the First Time." *Huffington Post UK*. http://www.huffingtonpost.co.uk/entry/scientists-teleport-a-photon-from-earth-to-orbit-for-the-first-time_uk_5965ea7de4b09b587d636526

Targ, Russell. (2004). *Limitless Mind*. Novato, CA: New World Library.

Targ, Russell. (2012). *The Reality of ESP*. Wheaton, IL: Quest Books.

Targ, Russell; Puthoff, Harold E. (2005[1977]). *Mind-Reach*. Charlottesville, VA: Hampton Roads.

Targ, Russell; Puthoff, Harold E. (2018[1972]). "Research on Techniques to Enhance Extraordinary Human Perception." In E.C. May & S.B. Marwaha (eds.), *The Star Gate Archives, Vol. 1*. Jefferson, NC: McFarland & Company, Inc., Publishers.

Tart, Charles T. (1981). "Causality and Synchronicity: Steps Toward Clarification." *Journal of the American Society for Psychical Research* 75:121-141.

Taylor, Jon. (2007). "Memory and Precognition." *Journal of Scientific Exploration* 21:553-571.

Taylor, Jon. (2014). "The Nature of Precognition." *Journal of Parapsychology* 78:19-38.

Tsakiris, Alex. (2017). "Men Like To Be Right—Duh! Novel Experiment Demonstrates Link with Psychic Abilities." *Skeptiko*. http://skeptiko.com/men-like-to-be-right-novel-experiment-demonstrates-link-with-psychic-abilities-288/

Twain, Mark. (2010). *The Autobiography of Mark Twain Volume 1*. Berkeley, CA: The University of California Press.

Utts, Jessica M. (1995). "An Assessment of the Evidence for Psychic Functioning." *Journal of Parapsychology*, 59:289-320.

Utts, Jessica M. (2016). "Appreciating Statistics (2016 ASA Presidential Address)." *Journal of the American Statistical Association* 111:1373-1380.

Valli, Katja; Revonsuo, Antti. (2009). "The Threat Simulation Theory in Light of Recent Empirical Evidence: A Review." *The American Journal of Psychology* 122:17-38.

Vaughan, Alan. (1973). *Patterns of Prophecy*. New York: Hawthorn Books.

Vedral, Vlatko. (2018, April 7-13). "Law and … Disorder." *New Scientist* 3172:32-35

Volk, Steve. (2018). "Down the Quantum Rabbit Hole." *Discover*. http://discovermagazine.com/bonus/quantum

Vonnegut, Kurt. (1973). *Breakfast of Champions*. New York: Random House.

Walker, Evan Harris. (1970). "The Nature of Consciousness." *Mathematical Biosciences* 7:131-178.

Walker, Evan Harris. (2000). *The Physics of Consciousness*. Cambridge, MA: Perseus Books.

Walker, Sara Imari; Davies, Paul C.W. (2017). "The 'Hard Problem' of Life." In S.I. Walker, P.C.W. Davies, & G.F.R. Ellis (eds.), *From Matter to Life*. Cambridge, UK: Cambridge University Press.

Warcollier, Rene. (2001[1948]). *Mind to Mind*. Charlottesville, VA: Hampton Roads.

Wargo, Eric. (2010). "Dreams and the Art of Memory: A New Hypothesis About Dream Bizarreness." *The Nightshirt*. http://thenightshirt.com/?page_id=184

Wargo, Eric. (2015a). "Altered States of Reading (Part 1): VALIS, Vallee, and Vaal." *The Nightshirt*. http://thenightshirt.com/?p=3329

Wargo, Eric. (2015b). "*Don't Look Now*: Witches, Weird Sisters, and the Eroticism of ESP." *The Nightshirt*. http://thenightshirt.com/?p=2491

Wargo, Eric. (2015c). "Feeding the Psi God: Precognitive Dreaming, Memory, and Ritual." *The Nightshirt*. http://thenightshirt.com/?p=2791

Wargo, Eric. (2015d). "The Great Work of Immortality: Astral Travel, Dreams, and Alchemy." *The Nightshirt*. http://thenightshirt.com/?p=2857

Wargo, Eric. (2015e). "Quantum Psychoanalysis: Interpreting Precognitive Dreams." *The Nightshirt*. http://thenightshirt.com/?p=3483

Wargo, Eric. (2016a). "The Phil Dick Circuit and the Future of Precognitive Technology." *The Nightshirt*. http://thenightshirt.com/?p=3519

Wargo, Eric. (2016b). "Psi's Big Guns: Sleep Paralysis and Astral Time Travel." *The Nightshirt*. http://thenightshirt.com/?p=3773

Wargo, Eric. (2016c). "Stories Latent in the Landscape: Spirits, Time Slips, and 'Super-Psi'." *The Nightshirt*. http://thenightshirt.com/?p=3874

Wargo, Eric. (2017). "Master Minkowski's Wild Ducks (Zen and the Glass Block Universe)." *The Nightshirt*. http://thenightshirt.com/?p=4046

Weber, Max. (1962). *Basic Concepts in Sociology*. London: Peter Owen.

Wegner, Daniel. (2002). *The Illusion of Conscious Will.* Cambridge, MA: The MIT Press.

Wendt, Alexander. (2015). *Quantum Mind and Social Science.* Cambridge, UK: Cambridge University Press.

White, Christopher G. (2018). *Other Worlds.* Cambridge, MA: Harvard University Press.

White, Jonathan W. (2017). *Midnight in America.* Chapel Hill, NC: The University of North Carolina Press.

Wilson, Maer. (2016). *The Other Side of Philip K. Dick.* Middletown, DE: Author.

Winnicott, D. W. (1971). *Playing and Reality.* London: Routledge.

Winson, Jonathan. (1986). *Brain & Psyche.* New York: Vintage.

Wiseman, Richard. (2010). *Paranormality.* Author.

Wolchover, Natalie. (2014). "A New Physics Theory of Life." *Quanta.* https://www.quantamagazine.org/a-new-thermodynamics-theory-of-the-origin-of-life-20140122/

Wolf, Fred Alan. (1989). "On the Quantum Physical Theory of Subjective Antedating." *Journal of Theoretical Biology* 136:13-19.

Wolf, Fred Alan. (1998). "The Timing of Conscious Experience: A Causality-Violating, Two-Valued, Transactional Interpretation of Subjective Antedating and Spatial-Temporal Projection." *Journal of Scientific Exploration* 12:511-542.

Wolf, Stewart. (1993). *Brain, Mind, and Medicine.* Piscataway, NJ: Transaction Publishers.

Wotiz, John H.; Rudofsky, Susanna. (1993). "Herr Professor Doktor Kekulé: Why Dreams?" In J.H. Wotiz (ed.), *The Kekule Riddle.* Clearwater, FL: Cache River Press.

Yates, Frances A. (1996[1966]). *The Art of Memory.* London: Pimlico.

Žižek, Slavoj. (1989). *The Sublime Object of Ideology.* London: Verso.

Žižek, Slavoj. (2006a). "Freud Lives!" *London Review of Books* 28(10):32.

Žižek, Slavoj. (2006b). *The Parallax View.* Cambridge, MA: The MIT Press.

Žižek, Slavoj. (2013). *Less than Nothing.* London: Verso.

Žižek, Slavoj. (2014). *Event*. Brooklyn, NY: Melville House.

Zurek, Woiciech Hubert. (2009, March 29). "Quantum Darwinism." *arXiv*. arXiv:0903.5082v1

Zyga, Lisa. (2010, July 21). "Time Travel Theory Avoids Grandfather Paradox." *Phys.org*. https://phys.org/news/2010-07-theory-grandfather-paradox.html

Zyga, Lisa. (2011, March 1). "Time Travel Experiment Demonstrates How To Avoid the Grandfather Paradox (Update)." *Phys.org*. https://phys.org/news/2011-03-grandfather-paradox.html

Zyga, Lisa. (2015, June 25). "Physicists Find Quantum Coherence and Quantum Entanglement Are Two Sides of the Same Coin." *Phys.org*. https://phys.org/news/2015-06-physicists-quantum-coherence-entanglement-sides.html

Aaronson, Scott, 143
Abbott, Edward A., 102, 148
Abel Rudolf (KGB spy), 88
Aberfan disaster, 32-35, 197
Adams, Douglas, 140
Adams, James Carmalt (brother-in-law of Kurt Vonnegut), 64-65, 78
afterwardsness (*Nachträglichkeit*), 238
Aharonov, Yakir, 127-28, 129, 131, 134, 322
"A. Lincoln, Simulacrum" (Dick), 298-301
American Society for Psychical Research (ASPR), 21, 58
"Appointment at Samarra, An" (Maugham), 358n20
Anzieu, Didier, 225, 229
archetypes (*see also* collective unconscious; Jung, Carl), 27, 92, 257, 259-62, 264-65, 268, 273, 275, 276, 308, 313, 319, 320, 333, 341
Arnold, Kyle, 302, 303, 304, 308, 314
Arrival (Villeneuve) (*see also* "Story of Your Life"), 123, 171, 317-19, 329
Asimov, Isaac, 2, 4, 9, 141, 164, 331
association (mental) (*see also* free association), 35, 113-14, 118, 160, 178, 193, 203, 210-13, 238, 261, 262-63, 313-14, 319, 342, 372n20, 372-73n29
Attia, Eli (architect), 27

Bach, Richard, 86
Back to the Future (Zemeckis), 102
Ballard, Robert, 288
Barad, Karen, 135-36, 323, 361n4
Barbary Shore (Mailer), 87-88, 89-90, 301
Barker, John, 32
Bayard, Pierre, 392n33
Baynes, Helton Godwin ("Peter"), 270-71, 381n58
Becker, Ernest, 247
Beitman, Bernard D., 265, 268, 333
Bell, John, 130
Bem, Daryl, 4-5, 6, 82-84, 164, 170, 187, 217, 273, 392n28
Bennett, Charles, 142
Bergson, Henri, 13, 36, 90, 150, 159, 390-91n4,
Beyond the Pleasure Principle (Freud), 226, 239, 240, 248, 375-76n13

biases, cognitive (*see also* hindsight bias), 9, 24-25, 29, 32, 33, 34, 37, 42, 84, 89, 197, 235, 261-62, 325, 331, 342-43, 354-55n18

Bierman, Dick, 81

bilking (*see also* grandfather paradox), 104, 145

Bishop, Morris, 100

black holes, 61, 313

Black, Mr. (Ian Stevenson case), 21-22

block universe (*see also* Minkowski, Hermann), 56, 61, 102, 108, 119, 130, 133, 137, 144, 154, 170, 171, 198, 231, 280, 289, 308, 309, 312, 318, 323, 334, 342, 360n56, 362n32, 390-91n4, 391n5

Bloom, Harold, 314,

Bohr, Niels, 124-127, 134-135, 209, 391n6

Bradbury, Ray, 104-05, 177, 358n12

Braude, Stephen, 106-07, 109, 111, 348n41

Breakfast of Champions (Vonnegut), 65

bricolage (Levi-Strauss), 123

Brukner, Časlav, 137

Buonomano, Dean, 116, 367n70

Bush, Claudia, 304-11, 339,

butterfly effect, 105-06, 109, 125, 341, 358n15

Caidin, Martin, 86

Carpenter, James (*see also* "first sight"), 84-85, 90-91, 188

Carington, Whately, 67-68, 73, 74-76, 353n33

Carroll, Lewis, 15, 63, 83

Carter, Howard, 317, 322

Carter, Rev. Ernest (Ian Stevenson case), 21

Caruth, Cathy, 377n29

castration (psychoanalytic construct), 180, 195-97, 199, 251, 291-92, 313, 338, 339-40, 289-390n51

Chalmers, David, 161

Changed in a Flash (Krohn & Kripal), 41, 329-31, 392n29

chaos theory, 105-06, 151, 341,

Chiang, Ted, 121, 132, 317, 318,

Chiribella, Giulio, 137

Civil War, U.S., 31-32, 288, 298, 384n13

Civilization and Its Discontents (Freud), 187, 230-31

clairvoyance (*see also* remote viewing), 50, 58, 66-67, 69-72, 82, 85, 109, 193, 198, 199

Clarke, Arthur C., 295

Clemens, Henry, 241-44

Clemens, Samuel, *see* Twain, Mark

closed timelike curve (*see also* self-fulfilling prophecy, time loop), 119, 143, 198, 363n55

Close Encounters (Spielberg), 310

Cochran, Jacqueline (pilot), 86

coincidence, meaningful (*see also* synchronicity), 20, 24, 27-30, 37, 39, 64, 95, 185, 257-68, 276, 281, 286, 287, 292, 296, 299-301, 308, 313, 333, 383n69

Coleridge, Samuel Taylor, 332, 338, 339

collective unconscious (Jung), 90,

261-65, 272, 273, 276, 308, 320, 324, 333
conditioning, 80, 82, 113, 164, 366n52
consciousness; and quantum biology, 155-57, 159-61, 168; as explanatory framework for psi phenomena, 57-58, 61, 72, 76, 84-85, 90-92, 112, 126, 136, 150, 158-61, 332, 359n32; relationship to brain of (*see also* materialism), 57, 84, 90-91, 158-61, 168-69
Copenhagen Interpretation, 3-4, 125-126, 133, 144, 321-22,
Costa de Beauregard, Olivier, 130, 144, 170
countertransference (*see also* transference), 256, 268-71, 381-82n58,
Cramer, John G., 128-29, 168, 322, 343
Crick, Francis, 151, 210
cryptomnesia, 187, 249, 261, 264-65, 273, 301, 374-75n54, 377n34

Darwin, Charles, 163, 207, 224
Davies, Paul, 151
Dean, James, 234-36, 241, 248, 251
decoherence, 126
"Deep Thought" (Adams), 140
De Moura, Vicente, 257, 258, 268, 271, 274, 275, 378n7, 382n61
Derrida, Jacques, 238, 369n39
Dick, Anne R., 302, 386-87n9, 387n10
Dick, Jane, 293, 301-03, 309,

312, 313, 339, 341, 388n22
Dick, Philip K., 12, 13, 87, 90, 97, 129, 157, 177, 593, 295-315, 318, 327, 330, 331, 332, 339, 340, 341, 342, 354n2, 370n43, 385-390; "2-3-74" experience of, 303-304, 309-11, 327, 388n26; correspondence with Claudia Bush of, *see* Bush, Claudia; Oedipal feelings and, 301-03, 313; precognitive dreams of, 304-11
Dick, Tessa B., 303, 305, 308, 311, 370n43, 387n11, 389n42, 389n46
Di Corpo, Ulisse, 150-51, 313
différance (Derrida), 238
Disneyland, 298-99, 301, 387n10
dissipative structures (Prigogine), 149
Dobyns, York H., 119, 360n56, 362n32
Doctor Who, 103, 363n1
Dossey, Larry, 219, 224, 348n37, 376-77n25
double-slit experiment, 123-25, 128, 132, 134, 135, 321, 361n4, 363n48
Douglas, Mary, 175-76
dreaming (see also dreams, pre-cognitive/premonitory; Freud, Sigmund): mnemonic theory of, 34-35, 113, 211-17, 231, 342; neuroscience theories of, 209-13, 231, 341; wish-fulfillment theory of, *see* Freud, Sigmund
"Dreams and Occultism" (Freud), 190-94

dreams, precognitive/premonitory, 7-9, 30-42, 45-49, 60-62, 69, 72, 92, 94, 99-101, 107, 107-14, 117-18, 171, 178, 180-85, 188, 190-91, 214, 218-32, 241-44, 256-57, 266, 268, 273-75, 335-44, 347n34, 347-48n35, 393; about the *Titanic*, 20-22; in Jule Eisenbud's work, 194, 195-98, 215-17; of J. W. Dunne, *see* Dunne, J. W.; of Elizabeth Krohn, *see* Krohn, Elizabeth; of Philip K. Dick, *see* Dick, Philip K.

Drem, Scotland, 44, 86

Dr. Jekyll and Mr. Hyde (Stevenson), 54-55

Dunkirk, evacuation of, 43-44

Dunne, Brenda, 70

"Dunne dreams," *see* dreams, precognitive/premonitory

Dunne, J. W. (John William), 41, 43-63, 72, 74, 90, 94, 99, 111, 112, 114, 117, 149, 163, 178, 180, 183, 193, 198, 203, 214-15, 217, 221, 222, 244, 258, 273, 276, 298, 305, 307, 330, 336-37, 341, 344; and dream of Lieutenant B.'s crash, 59-60, 117; and dream of Mont Pelée eruption, 51-52, 58, 218-20; dream theory of, compared to Freud's, 183, 215-17; Serialism theory of, 49, 55, 57, 72, 99, 112, 183

Echeverria, Fernando, 118

effect size, 67, 71

Ehrenwald, Jan, 280

Einstein, Albert, 4, 36, 55-56, 102-03, 122, 126-27, 130, 133, 134, 135, 207, 253, 290, 322, 390-91n4

Einstein-Podolsky-Rosen (EPR) experiment, 122-23, 129-30

Eisenbud, Jule, 23, 175, 194, 195-99, 215-17, 277, 280, 285, 289, 290, 293, 301, 359n30, 381n48, 383n70, 384-85

Eliot, T. S., 100, 344,

Emerson, Ralph Waldo, 343

"endochronometer" (Asimov), *see* thiotimoline

endosymbiosis (Margulis), 156-57

England, Jeremy, 364n6

enjoyment, *see jouissance*

entanglement (quantum), 57, 71, 122-23, 126, 129-30, 132, 135, 136, 139-40, 142, 143-44, 152, 153, 156, 160, 161, 164, 168, 170, 236, 263, 323, 361n4, 362-63n47

entropy (*see also* Thermodynamics, Second Law of), 101-02, 127, 149, 364n6; and Edwin May precognition theory, 244-45, 376-77n25; and the sublime, 245-46

Epper, Ignaz (artist), 259

Esalen, 85, 327, 329, 330

ESP (extrasensory perception), 6, 24, 66-77, 80-92, 108, 112-14, 122, 128, 129, 141, 144, 201, 260, 262, 280, 349n55, 352-57

eukaryotes, 156-57

Everett, Hugh, 109

Exegesis (Dick), 97, 304, 305,

308, 309, 314, 315

Experiment with Time, An (Dunne), 41, 46, 49, 50, 57, 99-100, 183, 198, 214-15, 217, 336-37, 344

"experimental metaphysics" (*see also* Barad, Karen), 135-136, 323, 343

"Experiments on the Paranormal Cognition of Drawings" (Carington), 74-76

extrasensory perception, *see* ESP

Falk, Ruma, 261

Fantappiè, Luigi (*see also* syntropy), 150

fate, 94, 175, 178, 179, 180, 194, 201-03, 243, 268, 280-83, 285-86, 289-90, 292-93, 323, 331,

feedback (role in ESP experiments and precognition of), 69, 72, 74, 75-76, 193, 353, 360n37

"Feeling the Future" (Bem), 4-5, 82-84, 92, 273

Feinberg, Gerald, 72-73, 112, 129, 163

Fermat's principle of least time, 132, 318, 321

Ferrari, Diane C., 71, 76

Feynman, Richard, 127, 128, 321, 322, 342, 391n10

file-drawer effect (*see also* selection bias), 25, 34, 37, 71, 86, 265, 336

"First in Our Family, The," *see* "A. Lincoln Simulacrum"

"first sight" (Carpenter), 85, 91, 157, 188

Fisher, Matthew, 366n55

Fitzgerald, F. Scott, 36

Flatland (Abbott), 102

Fleming, Graham, 152,

Fliess, Wilhelm, 205, 206, 223, 224, 225, 227, 320, 371

Florensky, Pavel, 369n25

Flournoy, Theodore, 187, 249

Forrester, John, 238, 371n4

Forsyth, David (Freud student), 191-93

fort-da game (*see also Beyond the Pleasure Principle*), 239, 248, 313

Francis, Henry W. (Ian Stevenson case), 21

"Frau B." (Freud patient), 181-82, 183, 268

free association, 204-06, 212, 336, 339

free will, 10, 108-09, 137, 279-80, 362n32

"free won't" (Ramachandran), 167, 325

Freud, Anna, 189, 226-27, 229

Freud, Sigmund, 12, 13, 62, 103, 109, 113, 118, 167, 172, 173, 178-94, 200, 203-13, 217, 219, 220, 221, 222, 249, 256, 259, 260, 263, 265, 267, 268, 269, 270, 271, 277, 279, 280, 288-89, 301, 303, 320, 321, 332, 335, 338, 367-71, 374-77, 379n21; and "death drive" (*see also* trauma), 236-39, 246, 247-48, 375-76n13, 377n29; archaeological metaphors of, 230-32, 276; cancer and treatment of, 223-27; Irma dream of, 203-07, 222-30, 289, 311,

320, 340, 371n6; medallion episode of, 179-80, 227, 230, 280; seduction theory of, 237; wish-fulfillment theory of, 181, 182-84, 188, 190, 200, 206-09, 212-13, 216-17, 223, 227-29, 275, 371n6
Freud, Sophie, 225-26, 229, 239
Friedrich, Caspar David, 246
frustrated spontaneous emission (physics phenomenon), 131-32
Futility (Robertson), 23-27, 281-285, 287, 288-90
future detector, 141-145, 153-55, future-influencing-present effect (*see also* Priestley, J. B.), 92-95, 116, 193, 249, 268, 357n59

Gardner, Martin, 24-27, 33, 38, 182, 187, 289, 299, 349n55
"Gathering No Moss" (Robertson), 285, 384n9
Geertz, Clifford, 331
Gladstone, Gerald, 45-49, 60-62, 220-22, 337, 373-74
Gleick, James, 102-105, 113, 321, 358n15
Gnosticism, 314, 339
Goddard, Victor, 43-49, 60-62, 86, 220-22, 337, 350, 373-74
Gödel, Kurt, 160
Golem, 168
Graff, Dale E., 215, 377n26
grandfather paradox (*see also* bilking), 61, 104, 119, 143, 177, 195-98
Gravity's Rainbow (Pynchon), 79-80, 273, 354n2, 356n43
Guinness, Alec, 233-36, 241, 248-51

Guite, Malcolm, 332
Gurney, Edmund, 236, 260

Halperin, David, 242-43
Hameroff, Stuart, 155-56, 160
Hammerschlag, Anna (*see also* Freud, Sigmund, Irma dream of), 203, 205, 223, 225, 226, 229
Hammid, Hella, 69
Hannah, Jack W., 23-24, 349n55
Hansen, George, 367n2, 385n20
Hebbian learning, 162, 211
Heisenberg, Werner, 125-26, 127, 131, 135
Henderson, Mrs. (Ian Stevenson case), 22, 117
Herbert, Frank, 157, 327, 371n1
Herbert, Nick, xi, 361n3, 370-71n48
hermeneutic circle, 372-73n29
"Herr P." (Freud case), 191-95, 276, 277, 324
Hidden Channels of the Mind (Rhine), 108
Hill, Betty (UFO abductee), 310
hindsight bias, 9, 24-25, 29-30, 89, 90, 94, 197-198, 288, 289, 325
Hinton, Charles Howard, 148-49, 157, 160, 161, 170
Hitchhiker's Guide to the Galaxy (Adams), 140
Hobson, J. Allan, 210, 213, 241
Honorton, Charles, 69, 71, 76, 215
Howell, John, 131, 134, 141; beam-amplification experiment of, 3, 4, 131, 134, 135, 141, 162

Hubbard, L. Ron, 314-15
hypercube, *see* tesseract
hypnagogic/hypnopompic states, 20-21, 85, 116, 311

Inchbald, Guy, 350-51n22
indeterminacy, quantum, 126, 127, 209, 238,
information: as distinguished from meaning, 91-92, 138-40; as equivalent to causation, 138-40; classical theory of (Shannon), 139; quantum theory of (*see also* quantum computation),137, 144, 149
Interpretation of Dreams, The (Freud), 173, 180, 183-85, 188, 200, 205-09, 223-29
Interstellar (Nolan), 103
Irma dream, *see* Freud, Sigmund

Jahn, Robert, 70
Jakobshavn ice-fjord, 17-18, 345n1
Jones, Ernest, 180, 189, 226, 230
Jones, Eryl Mai (Aberfan victim), 32, 33
jouissance, 239-40, 244-45, 247-48
Jung, Carl, 13, 62, 64, 65, 78, 90, 91, 92, 95, 110, 159, 185, 189, 220, 224, 255-77, 304, 320, 324, 327, 330, 332, 337, 338, 364n10, 370n43, 375n13, 378-83
Jurassic Park (Crichton), 358n15
Jurassic Park (Spielberg), 26, 112, 153

Kaiser, David, 139
Kammerer, Paul, 150, 364n10
Kant, Immanuel, 245-46, 269
Kekulé von Stradonitz, Friedrich August, 201, 207, 228, 374n52
Klinkhammer, Gunnar, 118
Koch, Christof, 158
Korzybski, Alfred, 157
Kozyrev, Nicolai, 297
Krenz, Claudia, *see* Bush, Claudia
Kripal, Jeffrey J., xi, 8, 17, 41, 86, 108, 110, 114, 118, 283, 312, 326, 326-33, 345n11, 357n52, 392n21,n29
Krippner, Stanley, 69, 215
Krohn, Elizabeth, 40-41, 107, 219, 243, 326, 328-31
Kubrick, Stanley, 27, 100-01, 110, 347n23
Kundalini, 272, 275, 381n49, 382n63

Lacan, Jacques, 195, 239-41, 247-48, 313, 324-25, 330, 335, 365n36, 376n14, 377n29
Laplanche, Jean, 238
law of large numbers, 24, 25, 33, 34, 37, 41, 68, 235, 336
L'Engle, Madeleine, 147, 363n1
Levi-Strauss, Claude, 123
Lewis, C. S., 100
Libet, Benjamin, 166-68, 187, 325
Lincoln, animatronic (*see also* Disneyland), 298-99, 301, 387, n10
"Little Gidding" (Eliot), 344
Llewellyn, Sue, 211-13

Lloyd, Seth, 138, 142-143,

364n19

Lolita (Nabokov), 100-01, 110

Loftus, Elizabeth, 30, 115, 237

long-term depression (synaptic plasticity), 162, 211

long-term potentiation (synaptic plasticity), 162-63, 211

Lorenz, Edward, 105, 149, 151, 358n15

Luckhurst, Roger, 351n37

Luke, Gospel of, 121-22, 249-51

Macbeth (Shakespeare), 202-03, 363n1

Mailer, Norman, 87-90, 301, 312

Man & Time (Priestley), 37, 93-95

Mandell, David, 31, 41, 107, 347-48n35

many worlds interpretation (Everett), 109

Margulis, Lynn, 156

Marwaha, Sonali Bhatt, 73, 74, 76, 81, 92,

materialism (see also consciousness), 36, 72, 90-91, 150, 158-59, 165, 169, 266, 333, 364n13; transcendental, 365n36

Maugham, W. Somerset, 358n20

May, Edwin, 73, 74, 76, 244-45, 356n46, 357n53, 359n31, 366n49

McDougall, William, 66

McMoneagle, Joseph, 76-77

meaning; as focus of precognitive phenomena, 11, 13, 31-32, 36-37, 42, 89, 90-92, 95, 151, 235, 276, 323, 325, 331-334; arrival of, 11-12, 95, 273, 318-320, 324; as distinguished from information, 11, 91-92, 119, 138-40, 152-54, 163-64; as something transpersonal (*see also* archetypes; collective unconscious), 90-91, 264-265, 273, 333; cultural, 91, 149, 209, 331-33; individual/subjective nature of, 28, 35-37, 39, 159, 213, 261-62, 342-344; materialistic challenge to (*see also* materialism), 65, 90, 15; inaccessibility to science of, 178, 209, 213, 342-43

mechanism (*see also* materialism), 3, 65

Meeting the Universe Halfway (Barad), 135

memory; distortion/revision of (*see also* hindsight bias), 9, 24-25, 26-27, 30-31, 32, 52-53, 62, 89, 94, 114, 116-17, 179, 188, 243, 249, 325; precognition as a form of, 36, 42, 57, 59, 72-75, 111-18, 162-65, 188-89, 319; processes/neurobiology of, 111-16, 160-62, 163, 203, 210-213, 231, 313; role of dreams in consolidation of, *see* dreaming; super-abilities of, *see* cryptomnesia

Meninsky, Bernard, 249-51

microtubules, 155-57, 160, 162-63

Middleton, J. Connon (Ian Stevenson case), 20, 22, 42

Millenium Hilton, 27-28, 379n25

Minkowski, Hermann (*see also*

block universe), 56, 61, 102, 108, 119, 130, 133, 144, 154, 171, 289, 312, 318, 333, 390-91n4

mixed mediumship, 86

Möbius strip, 324-25

Moffett, Annie (*see also* Twain, Mark), 242-43

Mont Pelée eruption, *see* Dunne, J. W.

Morgan, Rev. Charles (Ian Stevenson case), 20-21

morphic resonance (*see also* Sheldrake, Rupert), 150, 163

Moss, Robert, 224

Moss, Thelma (screenwriter), 234

Mossbridge, Julia, 81, 392n28

"Mr. Foresight" (Freud case), *see* "Herr P."

"Mrs. Fields" (baked goods brand), 310

Murphy, Michael, 85, 327

Mutants and Mystics (Kripal), 283, 312, 327, 329n29

Myers, Frederic W. H., 58, 65, 84, 90, 114, 159, 190, 236, 260, 333

Nabokov, Vladimir, 100-101, 110, 113, 117, 217

neurons, 113, 155, 157-58, 160-66, 211, 214

New Era of Thought, A (Hinton), 148, 157

Newton, Isaac, 3, 4, 124

New York Times, The, 20, 26, 87, 88, 89, 100, 285, 288, 289, 294, 308

Nietzsche, Friedrich, 65, 309

Night My Number Came Up, The (*see also* Goddard, Victor), 222

9/11 attacks, 27-31, 34, 51, 106, 244, 246, 247, 287, 336, 347n34, 377n31, 379n25

Noll, Richard, 264-65, 273, 381-82n58

nonlocality (*see also* entanglement), 57, 90, 144, 263, 323, 333

Norns, 202

Novikov, Igor (*see also* self-consistency principle), 118-119, 143, 198, 370-71n48

Oedipal feelings/Oedipus complex, 175, 179, 194-97, 199, 200, 216, 237, 265, 280, 290, 293, 301-03, 383n66

Oedipus the King (Sophocles), 176-78, 179, 180, 230, 291-92, 392n33

O'Neill, J. (Morgan Robertson friend), 293

"On Synchronicity" (Jung), 260, 382n60

Owens, Lance, 382n58

Paquette, Andrew, 215, 347n34, 348n44, 372-73n29

panpsychism, 90, 159

Paranormal Foreknowledge (Eisenbud), 23-24, 175, 194, 195-96, 198-99, 215-17, 280, 384n3

participatory universe (Wheeler), 126, 343

Pauli, Wolfgang, 151, 260, 370-71n48

Peake, Anthony, 33-34, 296, 297, 301, 332

Penrose, Roger, 160

Phallus, the (Lacanian construct), *see* castration

Phantasms of the Living (Gurney, Myers, & Podmore), 236, 260, 274, 383n69

Podmore, Frank, 236, 260

Podolsky, Boris, 122, 129

Pong (video game), 143

Popper, Karl, 186, 208, 364n13, 368n22

post-selection, 119, 131, 141, 142, 151, 152, 153, 154, 163-64, 169, 197, 198, 202, 366n57

Potter, Clara Cook (Ian Stevenson case), 21, 117, 346n7

Pratchett, Terry, 202

precognition (*see also* premonitions; presentiment; time loop); and sexuality, 88, 95, 176, 193-96, 280, 291-92, 354, 370n43, 381n48; as basis of creativity, 13, 89, 91, 168, 277, 312; as focused on survival, 88, 114, 118-19, 217, 241, 243-44, 248, 330, 334; as linked to neurosis, 13, 195, 232, 277, 294, 324-25; as orientation toward rewards, 10-11, 41, 88-89, 95, 101, 114, 118-19, 165, 193, 217, 236, 241, 243, 266, 268, 272-73, 275, 277, 289-90, 330, 334, 356n45, 366n52; as umbrella term, 6; hermeneutic approach to, 91-92, 325-326, 331-334; experimental evidence for, 67-71, 81-84; theories of, 71-73, 84-85

predictive processing, 167-68, 189

premonitions (*see also* Aberfan disaster; *Titanic*), 6, 9-10, 13, 20, 22-24, 27-32, 34, 37-38, 46, 58, 89, 107-10, 116, 118, 178, 180-81, 219, 222, 223-29, 234-36, 241-44, 248-51, 266, 289, 311, 328, 330, 342, 346n7, 348n37, 377n31, 389n46; guilt associated with, 218-20, 243

"Premonitory Dream Fulfilled, A" (Freud), 180-82

presentiment, 6, 31, 81-90, 93, 95, 151, 164, 168, 187, 272, 273, 301, 333, 354-57

Price, Huw, 129-30, 133, 137, 144, 151, 322

Price, Pat, 69

Priestley, J. B., 37, 38, 92-95, 99, 116, 193, 268, 357n59,

Prigogine, Ilya, 149

primary process, 113, 178

priming, 5, 82-83, 187, 217, 368n16

Princeton Engineering Anomalies Research (PEAR) Laboratory, 70

prophecy (*see also* self-fulfilling prophecy), 6, 10, 22-23, 25, 27, 29, 32-33, 37-38, 41-42, 49, 52, 54, 62, 86, 107, 110, 149, 169, 177-78, 179-80, 197-98, 201-03, 219-21, 224, 229-30, 241, 279, 281-84, 287-89, 290-93, 296, 301, 307-08, 309, 311, 312, 314, 325, 355n25, 359-60n36, 368n22

psi, 71, 73, 77, 80, 86, 90, 109,

110, 126, 169, 277
psychokinesis (PK), 85, 92,
109, 110, 198, 265, 357n53,
359n30, 384n15
*Psychopathology of Everyday Life,
The* (Freud), 185, 368n16
Puthoff, Harold, 69
Pynchon, Thomas, 79-80, 354n2,
356n43, 366n52

Quarles van Ufford, Maggy
(Henriette Madeleine Quarles
van Ufford), 255-59, 260, 263,
266-77, 324, 370n43, 378,
380n38, 381-382
Quarles van Ufford, Mischa, 258,
259, 382n64
quantum biology, 151-57, 159-
62, 164-65
quantum cognition, 160
quantum computation, 138, 140,
143, 144, 151, 152, 153, 155,
157, 160, 165, 168, 169
quantum walk, *see* tunneling,
quantum
quantum Zeno effect, 132
qubits (quantum bits), 143, 144,
153, 155, 156, 366n55

Radin, Dean, 81, 84, 92, 104,
164, 168, 265, 273, 345n6
Ramachandran, V. S., 167, 325
Ramón y Cajal, Santiago, 157-58
randomness (*see also* uncertainty,
quantum), 3-4, 125-29, 131-
32, 133-34, 140, 152, 153,
322-23
Rank, Otto, 368n16, 390n3

"Realities of Practical Psychother-

apy, The" (Jung), 268-73
Reichstein, Adam, 270
Reichstein, Maggy, *see* Quarles
van Ufford, Maggy
Reichstein, Gustawa, 270,
378n14
reinforcement, 5, 82, 113-14,
356n45, 366n52, 376n14
relativity theory (Einstein), 36,
55, 56, 130, 103
remote viewing (*see also* clairvoyance), 69-72, 74, 75, 76, 77,
112, 122, 215, 353n37
retrocausation, 4, 11, 107-10,
119, 129, 130-34, 136, 137,
138, 140, 150-51, 152, 155,
176-77, 197-98, 324, 333,
359n30, 360n56, 384n15
reward circuits, 356n45, 366n52
Rhine Center, 30, 84
Rhine, Joseph Banks, 66-67, 109,
71, 75, 260
Rhine, Louisa E., 66-67, 68, 71,
74, 108, 110, 118, 260
Richards, Michael, 29, 42, 106,
377n31
Richet, Charles, 186, 368n19
Rie, Oskar, 205, 206, 226
Robertson, Morgan, 13, 23-27,
42, 87, 182, 281-94, 296,
299, 301, 307, 308, 309, 342,
384n9; alcohol addiction of,
283, 284-85, 286, 290, 293,
385n17; Oedipal feelings of,
290-92
Rosen, Nathan, 122, 129
Rudnytsky, Peter J., 180

Sacks, Oliver, 154
Sapir-Whorf hypothesis, 322,

354-55n18
Sartre, Jean-Paul, 186
scarab episode (Jung case; *see also*
 Quarles van Ufford, Maggy),
 13, 220, 256-57, 260, 261-68,
 271, 274, 277, 330, 380n38,
 382n61
Schavelzon, José, 223, 374n41
Scholte, H. Steven, 81
Schrödinger, Erwin, 135, 151
Sea of Ice, The (*Wreck of Hope*)
 (Friedrich), 246
selection bias, 24-25, 84, 89, 90,
 235, 265
self-consistency principle, 118-
 119, 143, 198, 370-71n48
self-fulfilling prophecy (*see also*
 closed timelike curve; time
 loop), 11, 61, 119, 177, 257,
"Self-Reliance" (Emerson), 343
Serialism, *see* Dunne, J. W.
Serpent Power, The (Woodroffe),
 272-73, 382n64
Shakespeare, William, 24, 189,
 202, 363n1
Shannon, Claude, 139
Sheehan, Daniel P., 6, 364n20
Sheldrake, Rupert, 84, 150, 163,
 354n16
Shermer, Michael, 39, 349n55
Siegel, Bruce, 215, 336, 369n25,
 372n25
"Sleep Walker, The" (Robertson),
 292-93
Slothrop, Tyrone (Pynchon char-
 acter), 79-80, 88, 273, 354n2
Smith, Edward J. (captain of the
 Titanic), 22
Smith, Paul, 70
Society for Psychical Research

(SPR), 58, 66
Sophocles, 176-177, 179, 180,
 230, 392n33
"A Sound of Thunder" (Bradbury), 104-05, 358n15
source-monitoring/source-moni-
 toring error, 115-16, 171, 319
sphinx, 177, 179, 203, 228, 230,
 291-92, 385n21
Spielrein, Sabina, 375-76n13,
 381-82n58
Spottiswoode, James, 81
Stanford Research Institute (SRI),
 69-70, 73, 75, 76, 86, 355n34
Star Gate (remote viewing program), 69-70, 77, 215, 244
Star Trek (TV series), 104, 105,
 142, 376n23
Star Wars (Lucas), 95, 233, 235,
 236, 249, 250, 251
Stead, W. T., 22-23, 25
Stevenson, Ian, 20
"Story of Your Life" (Chiang),
 121, 132, 317-318, 322
Strieber, Whitley, 328, 329
"Subconscious Finnegan, The"
 (Robertson), 284
sublime, the (aesthetic and philosophical category), 245-46, 288
superposition, quantum, 125,
 143, 152, 160, 208
synapse, 113, 158, 160, 162-65,
 170, 211
synchronicity, 13, 27-28, 64, 78,
 256, 260-64, 271, 299, 300,
 313, 380n30; as misrecognized
 precognition, 275-276, 92,
 110, 185, 257-58
*Synchronicity: An Acausal Con-
 necting Principle* (Jung), 260-

63, 383n69
syntropy, 150-51, 313, 366n57

tachyons, 72, 129
Tar Baby vs. St. Sebastian (Richards), 29, 42, 106
Targ, Russell, 69, 86
Tart, Charles, 263, 380n30
tautology, 61, 119, 177, 257, 275, 325
Taylor, Jon, 163, 359n34
"telechronic battery" (Asimov), *see* thiotimoline
teleology, 6, 121, 151, 170, 318, 322, 323
telepathy, 58, 64, 65-67, 69, 70, 71, 72, 76, 77, 78, 85, 90, 102, 109, 112, 114, 115, 179, 182, 189-94, 198, 199, 230, 236, 260, 351n37, 360n37, 369-70n40
teleportation, quantum, 142-43
tesseract, 147-49, 169, 171, 333
Theosophy/Theosophical Society, 58, 264-65, 272
Theosophical Publishing House, 265, 272
Thermodynamics, Second Law of (*see also* entropy), 127, 137, 149, 176, 364n20
thiotimoline, 1-2, 9, 141, 164, 331
Thorne, Kip, 118
"thought transference" (Freud), *see* telepathy
time binding, 157, 199
time eye (*see also* future detector), 153-55, 165, 364n21
time loop (*see also* closed timelike curve, self-fulfilling prophecy),

11-13, 61-62, 89-90, 91-92, 119, 172, 176-79, 193, 201, 203, 119-222, 228-229, 250, 257, 266, 268, 275-277, 280-81, 289, 312, 318-19, 323-326, 331-334, 337, 339-344
Time Machine, The (Wells), 102-03, 385n21
time slips (*see also* Goddard, Victor), 44, 61, 86, 114, 349-50n3, 360n46
time-symmetric solutions in quantum mechanics, 127-34, 137, 163
time travel, 61, 72, 101-07, 118-19, 129, 131, 143, 177, 197-98, 292, 311, 325, 326, 385n21
Tiresias, 230, 291-93, 340
Titanic, 18-27, 33, 34, 38, 42, 51, 117, 279, 281-85, 287-90, 294, 295, 308, 346n14, 346-47n20, 349n55, 377n31
Tollaksen, Jeff, 134
Tolkien, J. R. R., ix, 100, 257
transactional interpretation (*see also* Cramer, John G.), 128-29, 136, 168, 343
transitional objects, *see fort-da* game
transference (*see also* counter-transference), 192, 256, 268, 270, 275, 277, 305
trauma (psychoanalytic theory of), 226, 232, 236-44, 246, 247, 248, 302, 313, 324, 325, 351n37, 377n31
Tron (Lisberger), 142-43
tunneling, quantum, 151, 152, 160, 364n19

Tutankhamun, 18, 380, 322
Twain, Mark, 241-44, 376n17,
376-77n25
two-state vector formalism (*see
also* Aharonov, Yakir), 128,
131, 136
2001: A Space Odyssey (Kubrick),
27-28

Ubik (Dick), 295, 296-98, 304,
315, 386n6
Ullman, Montague, 69, 215
uncertainty, quantum, 126, 127,
128, 130, 132, 134, 141, 322,
323, 362n32
unconscious, the (in Freud; *see
also* collective unconscious),
109, 118, 172, 177-179, 180,
203, 204, 236, 256, 313,
369-70n40; as compared to the
wavefunction, 208, 321-22;
as consciousness displaced in
time, 13, 168-70, 172, 188-89,
216-17, 243, 276-77, 319-20;
criticisms of construct, 186; extraordinary abilities of (*see also*
cryptomnesia), 167, 184-186,
190, 200, 224; in neuroscience,
167-68, 186, 210, 325; in Victorian psychiatry, 167-68, 179,
184-186, 188
Utts, Jessica, 70, 82, 352n19

VALIS (Dick), 308, 311, 312,
315
Vallee, Jacques, 311, 389n42
Vannini, Antonella, 150-51, 313,
366n57
Vaughan, Alan, 64, 65
von Bertalanffy, Ludwig, 149

Vonnegut, Kurt, 43, 56, 64-65,
78, 354n2
Vonnegut, Jane, 64-65
von Neumann, John, 126, 136;
collapse of the wavefunction by
consciousness, theory of, 126,
136, 367n63

Wagenmakers, Eric-Jan, 6
Walker, Evan Harris, 160
Walther, Philip, 137
wavefunction, 125, 126, 127,
128, 133, 321, 322, 367n63;
collapse of the, 125, 126, 127,
133, 321, 367n63
weak measurement (quantum),
131, 141, 153
Weber, Max, 65, 331
We Can Build You (Dick), *see* "A.
Lincoln Simulacrum"
"weird sisters" (Shakespeare),
202, 363n1
Wells, H. G., 100, 102, 103,
148, 295, 385n21
Wharton, Ken, 130, 131, 137,
144
Wheeler-Feynman absorber
theory, 127, 128
Wheeler, John, 122-23, 125,
126, 127, 128, 134, 138, 296
White, Jonathan W., 31-32,
348n36
White Star Line, 19, 22, 25, 26,
299
Wilkins, Sir George Hubert, 86
Wilcox, Ella Wheeler, 283-84
Winnicott, D. W., 239
Winthrop, William Young, 26
Wiseman, Richard, 32-35, 37,
41, 197, 198, 349n55, 370n47

wish-fulfillment theory of
  dreams, *see* Freud, Sigmund
World Trade Center (*see also*
  9/11), 27-31, 246
wormholes, 61, 103, 118, 119,
  148
*Wreck of the Titan, The, see Futil-
  ity*
Wrinkle in Time, A (L'Engle),
  147, 363n1
wyrd (*see also* fate), 202-03, 221,
  224, 230, 240, 325

X-Men (Lee & Kirby), 327, 330

Youth Without Youth (Eliade),
  329, 330

Zen, 355n35, 391n5
Zener cards, 66, 67, 71
Zhuangzi, 99, 113
Žižek, Slavoj, 209, 247, 288,
  331, 325, 365n36, 371n6